CALCULUS

by Gerald L. Bradley and Karl J. Smith

Differential Equations: Computing and Modeling

by C.H. Edwards, Jr. and David E. Penney

SIMON & SCHUSTER
CUSTOM PUBLISHING

Excerpts taken from:
Calculus
by Gerald L. Bradley and Karl J. Smith
Copyright © 1995 by Prentice-Hall, Inc.
Simon & Schuster Company/A Viacom Company
Upper Saddle River, New Jersey 07458

Differential Equations: Computing and Modeling
by C.H. Edwards, Jr., and David E. Penney
Copyright © 1996 by Prentice-Hall, Inc.

This special edition published in cooperation with
Simon & Schuster Custom Publishing.

Printed in the United States of America

10 9 8 7 6 5 4 3 2

ISBN 0-536-59499-6
BA 97194

SIMON & SCHUSTER CUSTOM PUBLISHING
160 Gould Street/Needham Heights, MA 02194
Simon & Schuster Education Group

Table of Contents

1.5 THE LIMIT OF A FUNCTION

IN THIS SECTION Intuitive notion of limits, limits by graphing, limits by table, limits that do not exist

This section introduces you to the limit of a function, a concept that gives calculus its power and distinguishes it from other areas of mathematics, such as algebra.

Our goal in this section is to give an intuitive introduction to the *limit of a function*. A more rigorous treatment will be given in Section 1.8, and variations of the limit concept will be introduced later in the text.

The development of the limit concept was a major mathematical breakthrough in the history of mathematics, and it is unrealistic for you to expect to understand everything about this concept immediately. Have patience, read the examples carefully, and work as many problems as possible, and eventually, the limit concept will become a useful part of your mathematical toolkit.

■ INTUITIVE NOTION OF A LIMIT

The limit of a function f is a tool for investigating the behavior of $f(x)$ as x gets closer and closer to a particular number c. To visualize this concept we begin with an example.

†Volume 28, 1980, issue 3, p. 2; note the journal problem requests $f(1979)$, which, no doubt, was related to the publication date. We have taken the liberty of updating the requested value.

EXAMPLE 1   Velocity as a limit

A freely falling body experiencing no air resistance falls $s(t) = 16t^2$ feet in t seconds. Express the body's velocity at time $t = 2$ as a limit.

Solution We need to define some sort of "mathematical speedometer" for measuring the *instantaneous velocity* of the body at time $t = 2$. Toward this end, we first compute the *average velocity* $\bar{v}(t)$ of the body between time $t = 2$ and any other time t by the formula

$$\bar{v}(t) = \frac{\text{DISTANCE TRAVELED}}{\text{ELAPSED TIME}} = \frac{s(t) - s(2)}{t - 2}$$

$$= \frac{16t^2 - 16(2)^2}{t - 2} = \frac{16t^2 - 64}{t - 2}$$

As t gets closer and closer to 2, it is reasonable to expect the average velocity $\bar{v}(t)$ to approach the value of the required instantaneous velocity at time $t = 2$.

$$\lim_{t \to 2} \bar{v}(t) = \underbrace{\lim_{t \to 2} \frac{16t^2 - 64}{t - 2}}$$

This is the instantaneous velocity at $t = 2$.

Notice that we cannot find the instantaneous velocity at time $t = 2$ by simply substituting $t = 2$ into the average velocity formula because this would yield the meaningless form 0/0. ▬

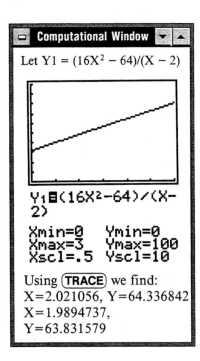

Computational Window

Let Y1 = $(16X^2 - 64)/(X - 2)$

Y1◻(16X²−64)/(X−2)

Xmin=0   Ymin=0
Xmax=3   Ymax=100
Xscl=.5   Yscl=10

Using ⟨TRACE⟩ we find:
X=2.021056, Y=64.336842
X=1.9894737,
Y=63.831579

We now devote the remainder of this section to an intuitive introduction of how we can find the value of limits such as the one that appears in Example 1.

Limit of a Function (Informal Definition)

The notation

$$\lim_{x \to c} f(x) = L$$

is read "the limit of $f(x)$ as x approaches c is L" and means that the functional values $f(x)$ can be made arbitrarily close to L by choosing x sufficiently close to c (but not equal to c).

▨ *What this says*: If $f(x)$ becomes arbitrarily close to a single number L as x approaches c from either side, then we say that L is the limit of $f(x)$ as x approaches c. The limit $\lim_{x \to c} f(x)$ exists if and only if the limiting value from the left equals the limiting value from the right.

This informal definition of limit cannot be used in proofs until we give precise meaning to terms such as "arbitrarily close to L" and "sufficiently close to c." This will be done in Section 1.8. For now, we shall use this informal definition to gain a working knowledge of limits.

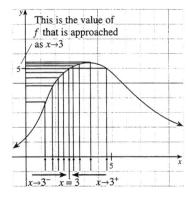

Figure 1.31 Limit as x approaches c

■ LIMITS BY GRAPHING

Figure 1.31 shows the graph of a function f and the number $c = 3$. The arrowheads are used to illustrate possible sequences of numbers along the x-axis, approaching from both the left and the right. As x approaches $c = 3$, $f(x)$ gets closer and closer to 5. We write this as

$$\lim_{x \to 3} f(x) = 5$$

As x approaches 3 from the left we write $x \to 3^-$, and as x approaches 3 from the right we write $x \to 3^+$. We say that the limit at $x = 3$ exists only if the value approached from the left is the same as the value approached from the right.

EXAMPLE 2   Estimating limits by graphing

Given the function f defined by the graph in Figure 1.32, find the following limits by inspection, if they exist:

a. $\lim\limits_{x \to 3^-} f(x)$ **b.** $\lim\limits_{x \to -2^+} f(x)$ **c.** $\lim\limits_{x \to 0} f(x)$

Solution   Take a good look at the given graph; notice the open circles on the graph at $x = 0$ and $x = -2$ and also notice that $f(0) = 5$.

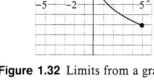

Figure 1.32 Limits from a graph

a. $\lim\limits_{x \to 3^-} f(x)$ is the value that f approaches as x tends toward 3 from the left. From Figure 1.32 we see that this value is -2. We write $\lim\limits_{x \to 3^-} f(x) = -2$.

b. $\lim\limits_{x \to -2^+} f(x)$ is the value that f approaches as x tends toward -2 from the right. We see that this value is 4, so
$$\lim\limits_{x \to -2^+} f(x) = 4$$

c. To find $\lim\limits_{x \to 0} f(x)$ we need to look at both the left and right limits. Look at Figure 1.32 to find
$$\lim\limits_{x \to 0^-} f(x) = 1 \text{ and } \lim\limits_{x \to 0^+} f(x) = 1$$

so $\lim\limits_{x \to 0} f(x)$ exists and $\lim\limits_{x \to 0} f(x) = 1$. Notice here that *the value of the limit as $x \to 0$ is not the same as the value of the function at $x = 0$.* ▬

EXAMPLE 3   Finding the limit from Example 1 by graphing

Find $\lim\limits_{t \to 2} \dfrac{16t^2 - 64}{t - 2}$ by graphing.

Solution

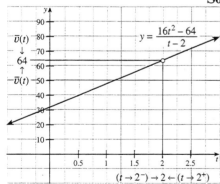

Figure 1.33 $\lim\limits_{t \to 2} \dfrac{16t^2 - 64}{t - 2} = 64$

$$\bar{v}(t) = \frac{16t^2 - 64}{t - 2} = \frac{16(t^2 - 4)}{t - 2} = \frac{16(t - 2)(t + 2)}{t - 2} = 16(t + 2), \quad t \ne 2$$

The graph of $\bar{v}(t)$ is a line with a deleted point, as shown in Figure 1.33. If you have a graphing calculator, compare this with the graph shown on your calculator (see the computational window for Example 1).

The limit can now be seen:
$$\lim\limits_{t \to 2} \bar{v}(t) = 64$$

That is, the instantaneous velocity of the falling body in Example 1 is 64 ft/sec. ▬

Notice from the preceding examples that when we write
$$\lim\limits_{x \to c} f(x) = L$$

⊘ The limit of a function as the independent variable approaches a point does not depend on the value of the function at that point. ⊘

we do not require c itself to be in the domain of f, nor do we require $f(c)$, if it is defined, to be equal to the limit. Functions with the special property that
$$\lim\limits_{x \to c} f(x) = f(c)$$

are said to be **continuous at $x = c$.** This idea is considered in Section 1.7.

■ LIMITS BY TABLE

It is not always convenient (or even possible) to first draw a graph in order to find limits. You can also use a calculator or a computer to construct a table of values for f as $x \to c$.

EXAMPLE 4   Finding a limit with a table

Find $\lim\limits_{t \to 2} \dfrac{16t^2 - 64}{t - 2}$ by using a table.

Solution   You will recognize this limit from Examples 1 and 3. We need to begin by selecting sequences of numbers for $t \to 2^-$ and $t \to 2^+$:

t approaches from the left; $t \to 2^-$. →				←t approaches from the right; $t \to 2^+$.		
t	1.950	1.995	1.999	2	2.001	2.015	2.100
$\bar{v}(t)$	63.200	63.920	63.984	Undefined	64.016	64.240	65.600
$v(t)$ approaches 64 from the left. →				←$v(t)$ approaches 64 from the right.		

That is, the pattern of numbers suggests

$$\lim_{t \to 2} \frac{16t^2 - 64}{t - 2} = 64$$

as we found using a graphical approach in Example 3.   ▬

EXAMPLE 5   Finding limits of trigonometric functions

Evaluate $\lim\limits_{x \to 0} \sin x$ and $\lim\limits_{x \to 0} \cos x$.

Solution   We can evaluate these limits by table or by graph.
By table:

x	1	0.5	0.1	0.01	-0.5	-0.1	-0.01
$\sin x$	0.8415	0.4794	0.0998	0.0099998	-0.4794	-0.0998	-0.0099998
$\cos x$	0.5413	0.8776	0.9950	0.9985	0.8776	0.9950	0.99995

The pattern of numbers in the table suggests that

$$\lim_{x \to 0} \sin x = 0 \quad \text{and} \quad \lim_{x \to 0} \cos x = 1$$ ▬

EXAMPLE 6   Evaluating a trigonometric limit using a table

Evaluate $\lim\limits_{x \to 0} \dfrac{\sin x}{x}$.

Solution $f(x) = \dfrac{\sin x}{x}$ is an even function because

$$f(-x) = \frac{\sin(-x)}{-x} = \frac{-\sin x}{-x} = \frac{\sin x}{x} = f(x)$$

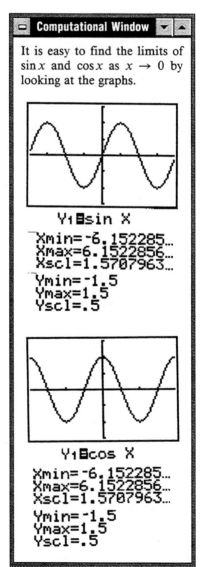

Computational Window ▼ ▲

It is easy to find the limits of $\sin x$ and $\cos x$ as $x \to 0$ by looking at the graphs.

Y₁＝sin X

Xmin=⁻6.152285…
Xmax=6.1522856…
Xscl=1.5707963…
Ymin=⁻1.5
Ymax=1.5
Yscl=.5

Y₁＝cos X

Xmin=⁻6.152285…
Xmax=6.1522856…
Xscl=1.5707963…
Ymin=⁻1.5
Ymax=1.5
Yscl=.5

This means that we only need to find the right-hand limit because the limiting behavior from the left will be the same as that of the right-hand limit. These values are shown in the following table.

x approaches 0 from the right. →				
x	0.1	0.05	0.01	0.001	0
$f(x)$	0.998334	0.999583	0.9999833	0.99999983	undefined
$f(x)$ approaches 1 from below. →				

The table suggests that $\lim_{x \to 0^+} \frac{\sin x}{x} = 1$; therefore, $\lim_{x \to 0} \frac{\sin x}{x} = 1$. We shall consider this limit more completely in Section 2.3.

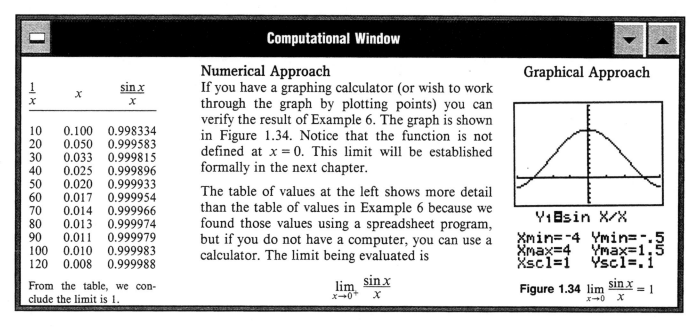

Computational Window

$\frac{1}{x}$	x	$\frac{\sin x}{x}$
10	0.100	0.998334
20	0.050	0.999583
30	0.033	0.999815
40	0.025	0.999896
50	0.020	0.999933
60	0.017	0.999954
70	0.014	0.999966
80	0.013	0.999974
90	0.011	0.999979
100	0.010	0.999983
120	0.008	0.999988

From the table, we conclude the limit is 1.

Numerical Approach

If you have a graphing calculator (or wish to work through the graph by plotting points) you can verify the result of Example 6. The graph is shown in Figure 1.34. Notice that the function is not defined at $x = 0$. This limit will be established formally in the next chapter.

The table of values at the left shows more detail than the table of values in Example 6 because we found those values using a spreadsheet program, but if you do not have a computer, you can use a calculator. The limit being evaluated is

$$\lim_{x \to 0^+} \frac{\sin x}{x}$$

Graphical Approach

Y₁ = sin X/X

Xmin=-4   Ymin=-.5
Xmax=4   Ymax=1.5
Xscl=1   Yscl=.1

Figure 1.34 $\lim_{x \to 0} \frac{\sin x}{x} = 1$

We should note that when we use a table (using either calculator or computer values) we may be misled. All we can say is that if a limit exists, then it can be calculated using a table. That is why when we find a limit from a table we must be cautious about the possibility of erroneous results. For example, if the table method is used with Example 8 (given at the end of this section), an erroneous conclusion is possible.

■ LIMITS THAT DO NOT EXIST

It may happen that a function f does not have a (finite) limit as $x \to c$. When $\lim_{x \to c} f(x)$ fails to exist, we say that $f(x)$ **diverges** as x approaches c. The following examples illustrate how divergence may occur.

EXAMPLE 7   A function that diverges

Evaluate $\lim_{x \to 0} \frac{1}{x^2}$.

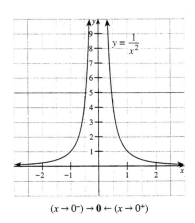

$(x \to 0^-) \to \mathbf{0} \leftarrow (x \to 0^+)$

Figure 1.35 $\lim\limits_{x \to 0} \dfrac{1}{x^2}$ does not exist, and the graph illustrates that f rises without bound.

A Function Diverges to Infinity

⊘ It is important to remember that ∞ is **not** a number, but is merely a symbol denoting unrestricted growth in the magnitude of the function. ⊘

Solution As $x \to 0$, the corresponding functional values of $f(x) = \dfrac{1}{x^2}$ grow arbitrarily large, as indicated in the following table.

	x approaches 0 from the left; $x \to 0^-\longrightarrow$				$\longleftarrow x$ approaches 0 from the right; $x \to 0^+$		
x	-0.1	-0.05	-0.001	0	0.001	0.005	0.01
$f(x) = \dfrac{1}{x^2}$	100	400	1×10^6	undefined	1×10^6	4×10^4	1×10^4

The graph of f is shown in Figure 1.35.

Geometrically, the graph of $y = f(x)$ rises without bound as $x \to 0$. Thus, $\lim\limits_{x \to 0} \dfrac{1}{x^2}$ does not exist, so we say f diverges as $x \to 0$. ∎

A function f that increases or decreases without bound as x approaches c is said to **diverge to infinity** (∞) at c. We indicate this behavior by writing

$$\lim_{x \to c} f(x) = +\infty \qquad \text{if } f \text{ increases without bound and by}$$

$$\lim_{x \to c} f(x) = -\infty \qquad \text{if it decreases without bound.}$$

Using this notation, we can rewrite the answer to Example 7 as

$$\lim_{x \to 0} \frac{1}{x^2} = +\infty$$

EXAMPLE 8   A function that diverges by oscillation

Evaluate $\lim\limits_{x \to 0} \sin\dfrac{1}{x}$.

Solution Note this is not the same as $\lim\limits_{x \to 0} \dfrac{\sin x}{x}$. The values of $f(x) = \sin\dfrac{1}{x}$ oscillate infinitely often between 1 and -1 as x approaches 0. For example, $f(x) = 1$ for $x = 2/\pi, 2/(5\pi), 2/(9\pi), \ldots$ and $f(x) = -1$ for $x = 2/(3\pi), 2/(7\pi), 2/(11\pi), \ldots$. The graph of $f(x)$ is shown in Figure 1.36.

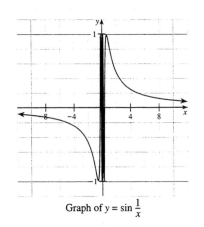

Graph of $y = \sin\dfrac{1}{x}$

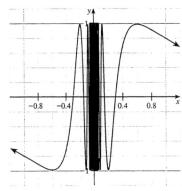

Detail of left hand graph on $[-1, 1]$

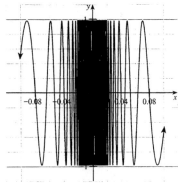

Detail on $[-0.1, 0.1]$

Figure 1.36 $\lim\limits_{x \to 0} \sin\dfrac{1}{x}$ diverges by oscillation.

Because the values of $f(x)$ do not approach a unique number L as $x \to 0$, the limit does not exist. This kind of function limiting behavior is called *divergence by oscillation.*

In the next section, we will introduce some properties of limits that will help us evaluate limits efficiently. In the following problem set remember that the emphasis is on an intuitive understanding of limits, including their evaluation by graphing and by table.

PROBLEM SET 1.5

A *Given the functions defined by the graphs in Figure 1.37, find the limits in Problems 1–12.*

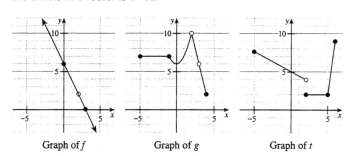

Graph of f Graph of g Graph of t

Figure 1.37 Graphs of the functions f, g, and t

1. $\lim\limits_{x \to 3} f(x)$ **2.** $\lim\limits_{x \to 2} f(x)$ **3.** $\lim\limits_{x \to 0} f(x)$

4. $\lim\limits_{x \to -3} g(x)$ **5.** $\lim\limits_{x \to -1} g(x)$ **6.** $\lim\limits_{x \to 2^+} g(x)$

7. $\lim\limits_{x \to 3^+} g(x)$ **8.** $\lim\limits_{x \to 2^-} t(x)$ **9.** $\lim\limits_{x \to 2^+} t(x)$

10. $\lim\limits_{x \to 2} t(x)$ **11.** $\lim\limits_{x \to 4} t(x)$ **12.** $\lim\limits_{x \to -4} t(x)$

Find the limits by filling in the appropriate values in the tables in Problems 13–15.

13. $\lim\limits_{x \to 5^-} f(x)$, where $f(x) = (4x - 5)$

x	2	3	4	4.5	4.9	4.99
$f(x)$	3					

14. $\lim\limits_{x \to 2^-} g(x)$, where $g(x) = \dfrac{x^3 - 8}{x^2 + 2x + 4}$

x	1	1.5	1.9	1.99	1.999	1.9999
$g(x)$	−1					

15. $\lim\limits_{x \to 2} h(x)$, where $h(x) = \dfrac{3x^2 - 2x - 8}{x - 2}$

x	1	1.9	1.99	1.999	3	2.5	2.1	2.001
$h(x)$	7							

16. Find $\lim\limits_{x \to 0} \dfrac{\tan 2x}{\tan 3x}$ using the following procedure based on the fact that $f(x) = \tan x$ is an odd function:

If $f(x) = \dfrac{\tan 2x}{\tan 3x}$, then

$$f(-x) = \dfrac{\tan(-2x)}{\tan(-3x)} = \dfrac{-\tan 2x}{-\tan 3x} = f(x).$$

Thus, we simply need to check for $x \to 0^+$. Find the limit by completing the following table.

x	1	0.5	0.1	0.01	0.001	0.0001
$f(x)$	15.33					

Describe each illustration in Problems 17–22 using a limit statement.

17. 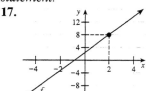   **18.**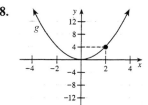

19. 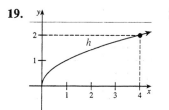   **20.**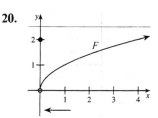

21. 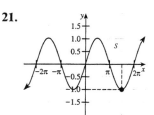   **22.**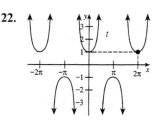

B 23. ■ **What Does This Say?** Explain a process for finding a limit.

Evaluate the limits in Problems 24–58 to two decimal places by graphing or by using a table of values. If the limit does not exist, explain why.

24. $\lim\limits_{x \to 0^+} x^4$ **25.** $\lim\limits_{x \to 0^+} \cos x$

26. $\lim\limits_{x \to 2^-} (x^2 - 4)$ **27.** $\lim\limits_{x \to 3^-} (x^2 - 4)$

28. $\lim\limits_{x \to 1^+} \dfrac{1}{x - 3}$ **29.** $\lim\limits_{x \to -3^+} \dfrac{1}{x - 3}$

30. $\lim\limits_{x \to 3} \dfrac{1}{x - 3}$ **31.** $\lim\limits_{x \to \pi/2} \tan x$

32. $\lim\limits_{x\to 0}\dfrac{\cos x}{x}$

33. $\lim\limits_{x\to \pi}\dfrac{\cos x}{x}$

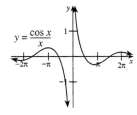

$y = \dfrac{\cos x}{x}$

34. $\lim\limits_{x\to 0.4}|x|\sin\dfrac{1}{x}$

35. $\lim\limits_{x\to 0}|x|\sin\dfrac{1}{x}$

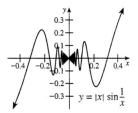

$y = |x|\sin\dfrac{1}{x}$

36. $\lim\limits_{x\to 0}\dfrac{1-\cos x}{x}$

37. $\lim\limits_{x\to \pi}\dfrac{1-\cos x}{x}$

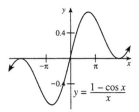

$y = \dfrac{1-\cos x}{x}$

38. $\lim\limits_{x\to 3}\dfrac{x^2+3x-10}{x-2}$ **39.** $\lim\limits_{x\to 3}\dfrac{x^2+3x-10}{x-3}$

40. $\lim\limits_{x\to 1}\dfrac{x^5-1}{x-1}$ **41.** $\lim\limits_{x\to 0}\dfrac{x}{\sin x}$

42. $\lim\limits_{x\to \pi/2}\dfrac{2x-\pi}{\cos x}$ **43.** $\lim\limits_{x\to 1}\dfrac{\sin\frac{\pi}{x}}{x-1}$

44. $\lim\limits_{x\to 9}\dfrac{\sqrt{x}-3}{x-9}$ **45.** $\lim\limits_{x\to 9}\dfrac{\sqrt{x}-3}{x-3}$

46. $\lim\limits_{x\to 2}\dfrac{\sqrt{x+2}-2}{x-2}$ **47.** $\lim\limits_{x\to 1}\dfrac{\sqrt[3]{x}-1}{\sqrt{x}-1}$

48. $\lim\limits_{x\to 3^+}\dfrac{\sqrt{x-3}+x}{3-x}$ **49.** $\lim\limits_{x\to 4^+}\dfrac{\frac{1}{\sqrt{x}}-\frac{1}{2}}{x-4}$

50. $\lim\limits_{x\to 0}\dfrac{\sin 2x}{x}$ **51.** $\lim\limits_{x\to 0}\dfrac{\sin 3x}{x}$

52. $\lim\limits_{x\to 0}\dfrac{1-\frac{1}{x+1}}{x}$ **53.** $\lim\limits_{x\to 1}\dfrac{1-\frac{1}{x}}{x-1}$

54. $\lim\limits_{x\to 0}(1+x)^{1/x}$ **55.** $\lim\limits_{x\to 1}(1+x)^{1/x}$

56. $\lim\limits_{x\to 0}\left(x^2-\dfrac{2^x}{2,000}\right)$ **57.** $\lim\limits_{x\to 0}\dfrac{\tan x-x}{x^2}$

58. $\lim\limits_{x\to 0}\cos\dfrac{1}{x}$

59. A ball is thrown directly upward from the edge of a cliff and travels in such a way that t seconds later, its height above the ground at the base of the cliff is

$$s(t) = -16t^2 + 40t + 24 \text{ ft}$$

a. Compute the limit

$$v(t) = \lim\limits_{x\to t}\dfrac{s(x)-s(t)}{x-t}$$

to find the instantaneous velocity of the ball at time t.

b. What is the ball's initial velocity?

c. When does the ball hit the ground, and what is its impact velocity?

d. When does the ball have velocity 0? What physical interpretation should be given to this time?

60. Tom and Sue are driving along a straight, level road in a car whose speedometer needle is broken but which has a trip odometer that can measure the distance traveled from an arbitrary starting point in tenths of a mile. At 2:50 P.M., Tom says he would like to know how fast they are traveling at 3:00 P.M., so Sue takes down the odometer readings listed in the table below, makes a few calculations, and announces the desired velocity. What is her result?

time t	2:50	2:55	2:59	3:00	3:01	3:03	3:06
odometer reading	33.9	38.2	41.5	42.4	43.2	44.9	47.4

Computational Window

In Problems 61–64, estimate the limits by plotting points or by using tables.

61. $\lim\limits_{x\to 13}\dfrac{x^3-9x^2-45x-91}{x-13}$

62. $\lim\limits_{x\to 13}\dfrac{x^3-9x^2-39x-86}{x-13}$

63. $\lim\limits_{x\to 13}\dfrac{x^4-26x^3+178x^2-234x+1,521}{x-13}$

64. $\lim\limits_{x\to 0}(\sin x)^x$

65. The tabular approach is a convenient device for discussing limits informally, but if it is not used very carefully, it can be misleading. For example, for $x \neq 0$, let

$$f(x) = \sin\dfrac{1}{x}$$

a. Construct a table showing the values of $f(x)$ for $x = \dfrac{-2}{\pi}, \dfrac{-2}{9\pi}, \dfrac{-2}{13\pi}, \dfrac{2}{19\pi}, \dfrac{2}{7\pi}, \dfrac{2}{3\pi}$. Based on this table, what would you say about $\lim\limits_{x\to 0} f(x)$?

b. Construct a second table, this time showing the values of $f(x)$ for $x = \dfrac{-1}{2\pi}, \dfrac{-1}{11\pi}, \dfrac{-1}{20\pi}, \dfrac{1}{50\pi}, \dfrac{1}{30\pi}, \dfrac{1}{5\pi}$.

c. What conclusions can you make about $\lim\limits_{x\to 0} f(x)$?

1.6 PROPERTIES OF LIMITS

IN THIS SECTION Computations with limits, using algebra to find limits, limits of piecewise-defined functions

It is important to be able to find limits easily and efficiently, but the methods of graphing and table construction of the previous section are not always easy or efficient. In this section we state some limit rules and then show how to use these rules along with algebra to evaluate limits.

■ COMPUTATIONS WITH LIMITS

Here is a list of properties that can be used to evaluate a variety of limits.

Basic Properties and Rules for Limits

For any real number c, suppose the functions f and g both have limits at $x = c$.

Constant rule
$$\lim_{x \to c} k = k \text{ for any constant } k$$

Limit of x rule
$$\lim_{x \to c} x = c$$

Multiple rule
$$\lim_{x \to c} [sf(x)] = s \lim_{x \to c} f(x) \text{ for any constant } s$$
The limit of a constant times a function is the constant times the limit of the function.

Sum rule
$$\lim_{x \to c} [f(x) + g(x)] = \lim_{x \to c} f(x) + \lim_{x \to c} g(x)$$
The limit of a sum is the sum of the limits.

Difference rule
$$\lim_{x \to c} [f(x) - g(x)] = \lim_{x \to c} f(x) - \lim_{x \to c} g(x)$$
The limit of a difference is the difference of the limits.

Product rule
$$\lim_{x \to c} [f(x)g(x)] = \left[\lim_{x \to c} f(x)\right]\left[\lim_{x \to c} g(x)\right]$$
The limit of a product is the product of the limits.

Quotient rule
$$\lim_{x \to c} \frac{f(x)}{g(x)} = \frac{\lim_{x \to c} f(x)}{\lim_{x \to c} g(x)} \text{ if } \lim_{x \to c} g(x) \neq 0$$
The limit of a quotient is the quotient of the limits, as long as the limit of the denominator is not zero.

Power rule
$$\lim_{x \to c} \left[f(x)\right]^n = \left[\lim_{x \to c} f(x)\right]^n \qquad n \text{ is a rational number and the limit on the right exists.}$$
The limit of a power is the power of the limit.

Another property that will be especially important to us in our future work is given in the following box.

Squeeze Rule If on some interval about c,

$$g(x) \le f(x) \le h(x) \text{ and } \lim_{x \to c} g(x) = \lim_{x \to c} h(x) = L,$$

then $\lim_{x \to c} f(x) = L$.

> **What this says**: If a function can be squeezed between two functions with equal limits, then that function must also have that same limit.

These limit rules can be used to evaluate a variety of limits. We shall not prove any of these results until Section 1.8, but it is fairly easy graphically to justify the rules for the limit of a constant and the limit of x, as shown in Figure 1.38.

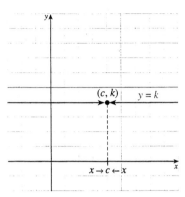

a. Limit of a constant: $\lim_{x \to c} k = k$

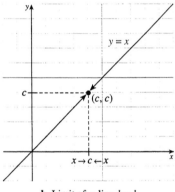

b. Limit of x: $\lim_{x \to c} k = k$

Figure 1.38 Two basic limits

EXAMPLE 1 Finding the limit of a polynomial function

Evaluate $\lim_{x \to 2}(2x^5 - 9x^3 + 3x^2 - 11)$.

Solution $\lim_{x \to 2}(2x^5 - 9x^3 + 3x^2 - 11) = \lim_{x \to 2}(2x^5) - \lim_{x \to 2}(9x^3) + \lim_{x \to 2}(3x^2) - \lim_{x \to 2}(11)$

Sum and difference rules

$= 2[\lim_{x \to 2} x^5] - 9[\lim_{x \to 2} x^3] + 3[\lim_{x \to 2} x^2] - 11$

Multiple and constant rules

$= 2 [\lim_{x \to 2} x]^5 - 9[\lim_{x \to 2} x]^3 + 3[\lim_{x \to 2} x]^2 - 11$

Power rule

$= 2(2)^5 - 9(2)^3 + 3(2)^2 - 11 = -7$

Limit of x rule

COMMENT: If you consider Example 1 carefully, it is easy to see that if f is any polynomial, then the limit at $x = c$ can be found by substituting $x = c$ into the formula for $f(x)$.

Limit of a Polynomial Function If P is a polynomial function, then

$$\lim_{x \to c} P(x) = P(c)$$

EXAMPLE 2 Finding the limit of a rational function

Evaluate $\lim_{z \to -1} \dfrac{z^3 - 3z + 7}{5z^2 + 9z + 6}$.

Solution $\lim_{z \to -1} \dfrac{z^3 - 3z + 7}{5z^2 + 9z + 6} = \dfrac{\lim_{z \to -1} (z^3 - 3z + 7)}{\lim_{z \to -1} (5z^2 + 9z + 6)}$ *Quotient rule*

$= \dfrac{(-1)^3 - 3(-1) + 7}{5(-1)^2 + 9(-1) + 6}$

$= \dfrac{9}{2}$ *Both numerator and denominator are polynomial functions.*

⊘ You must be careful about when you write the word "limit" and when you do not; pay particular attention to this when looking at the examples in this section. ⊘

Notice that if the denominator of the rational function is not zero, the limit can be found by substitution.

Limit of a Rational Function

If Q is a rational function defined by $Q(x) = \dfrac{P(x)}{D(x)}$, then

$$\lim_{x \to c} Q(x) = \frac{P(c)}{D(c)}$$

provided $D(c) \neq 0$.

EXAMPLE 3   Finding the limit of a power (or root) function

Evaluate $\lim\limits_{x \to -2} \sqrt[3]{x^2 - 3x - 2}$.

Solution
$$\lim_{x \to -2} \sqrt[3]{x^2 - 3x - 2} = \lim_{x \to -2} (x^2 - 3x - 2)^{1/3}$$

$$= \left[\lim_{x \to -2} (x^2 - 3x - 2) \right]^{1/3} \quad \textit{Power rule}$$

$$= [(-2)^2 - 3(-2) - 2]^{1/3} = 8^{1/3} = 2 \qquad \blacksquare$$

Once again, for values of the function for which $f(c)$ is defined, the limit can be found by substitution.

In the last section we found that $\lim\limits_{x \to 0} \sin x = 0$ and $\lim\limits_{x \to 0} \cos x = 1$ using a table. In the following example we use this information, along with the properties of limits to find other trigonometric limits.

EXAMPLE 4   Finding trigonometric limits algebraically

Given that $\lim\limits_{x \to 0} \sin x = 0$ and $\lim\limits_{x \to 0} \cos x = 1$, evaluate:

a. $\lim\limits_{x \to 0} \sin^2 x$ **b.** $\lim\limits_{x \to 0} (1 - \cos x)$

Solution   **a.** $\lim\limits_{x \to 0} \sin^2 x = \left[\lim\limits_{x \to 0} \sin x \right]^2$ *Power rule*

$$= 0^2 \qquad\qquad \lim_{x \to 0} \sin x = 0$$

$$= 0$$

b. $\lim\limits_{x \to 0} (1 - \cos x) = \lim\limits_{x \to 0} 1 - \lim\limits_{x \to 0} \cos x$ *Difference rule*

$$= 1 - 1 \qquad\qquad \textit{Constant rule and}$$
$$\qquad\qquad\qquad\qquad \lim_{x \to 0} \cos x = 1$$
$$= 0 \qquad\qquad\qquad\qquad\qquad \blacksquare$$

The following theorem states that we can find limits of trigonometric functions by direct substitution, as long as the number that x is approaching is in the domain of the given function. The proof of the theorem makes use of the limit formulas $\lim\limits_{x \to 0} \sin x = 0$ and $\lim\limits_{x \to 0} \cos x = 1$.

▣ Computational Window ▼ ▲

It is easy to find the limits of $\sin^2 x$ and $1 - \cos x$ as $x \to 0$ by looking at the graphs.

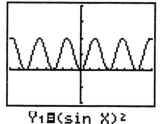

Y₁☰(sin X)²

Xmin=-8 Ymin=-1
Xmax=8   Ymax=2
Xscl=1   Yscl=.5

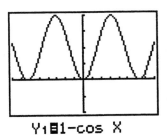

Y₁☰1-cos X

Xmin=-8 Ymin=-1
Xmax=8   Ymax=2
Xscl=1   Yscl=.5

THEOREM 1.3 Limits of trigonometric functions

If c is any number in the domain of the given trigonometric function, then

$$\lim_{x \to c} \cos x = \cos c \qquad \lim_{x \to c} \sec x = \sec c$$

$$\lim_{x \to c} \sin x = \sin c \qquad \lim_{x \to c} \csc x = \csc c$$

$$\lim_{x \to c} \tan x = \tan c \qquad \lim_{x \to c} \cot x = \cot c$$

Proof: We shall show that $\lim_{x \to c} \sin x = \sin c$. The other five limit formulas may be proved in a similar fashion (see Problems 71–72). Let $h = x - c$. Then $x = h + c$, and as $h \to 0$, $x \to c$. Thus,

$$\lim_{x \to c} \sin x = \lim_{h \to 0} \sin(h + c)$$

Using the trigonometric identity $\sin(A + B) = \sin A \cos B + \cos A \sin B$ and the limit formulas for sums and products, we find that

$$\begin{aligned}
\lim_{x \to c} \sin x &= \lim_{h \to 0} \sin(h + c) \\
&= \lim_{h \to 0} [\sin h \cos c + \cos h \sin c] \\
&= \lim_{h \to 0} \sin h \cdot \lim_{h \to 0} \cos c + \lim_{h \to 0} \cos h \cdot \lim_{h \to 0} \sin c \\
&= 0 \cdot \cos c + 1 \cdot \sin c \quad \begin{array}{l} \lim_{h \to 0} \sin h = 0 \ and \\ \lim_{h \to 0} \cos h = 1 \end{array} \\
&= \sin c
\end{aligned}$$

Note that $\sin c$ and $\cos c$ do not change as $h \to 0$ because these are constants with respect to h. ■

■ USING ALGEBRA TO FIND LIMITS

Sometimes the limit of $f(x)$ as $x \to c$ *cannot* be evaluated by direct substitution. In such a case, we look for another function that agrees with f for all values of x *except at the troublesome value* $x = c$. We illustrate with some examples.

EXAMPLE 5 Evaluating a limit using fraction reduction

Evaluate $\lim_{x \to 2} \dfrac{x^2 + x - 6}{x - 2}$.

Solution If you try substitution on this limit, you will obtain:

$$\lim_{x \to 2} \frac{x^2 + x - 6}{x - 2} \quad \begin{array}{l} \nwarrow \text{If } x = 2, \text{ then } x^2 + x - 6 = 0 \\ \swarrow \text{If } x = 2, \text{ then } x - 2 = 0 \end{array}$$

The form 0/0 is called an **indeterminate form** because the form does not help us determine the limit of the expression. In other words, we cannot evaluate a limit for which direct substitution yields 0/0.

If the expression is a rational expression, the next step is to simplify the function by factoring and simplifying to see if the reduced form is a polynomial.

$$\lim_{x \to 2} \frac{x^2 + x - 6}{x - 2} = \lim_{x \to 2} \frac{(x + 3)(x - 2)}{x - 2} = \lim_{x \to 2} (x + 3)$$

This simplification is valid only if $x \neq 2$. Now complete the evaluation of the

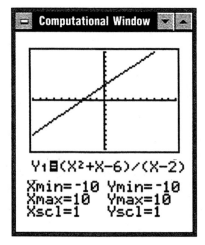

Computational Window

Y₁=(X²+X-6)/(X-2)
Xmin=-10 Ymin=-10
Xmax=10   Ymax=10
Xscl=1   Yscl=1

reduced function by direct substitution. This is not a problem, because $\lim\limits_{x \to 2}$ is concerned with values *as x approaches 2,* not the value where $x = 2$.

$$\lim_{x \to 2} \frac{x^2 + x - 6}{x - 2} = \lim_{x \to 2} (x + 3) = 5$$

Another algebraic technique for finding limits is to rationalize either the numerator or the denominator to obtain an algebraic form that is not indeterminate.

EXAMPLE 6   Evaluating a limit by rationalizing

Evaluate $\lim\limits_{x \to 4} \dfrac{\sqrt{x} - 2}{x - 4}$.

⊘ This method will work only if the resulting numerator allows the fraction to be simplified. ⊘

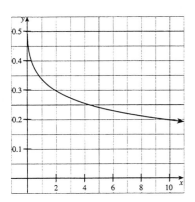

This was Problem 36 of the previous section.

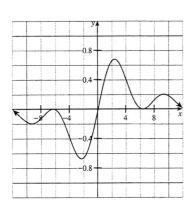

Solution   Once again, notice that both the numerator and denominator of this rational expression are 0 when $x = 4$, so that we cannot evaluate the limit by direct substitution. Instead, we multiply by 1, its form chosen so that the numerator is rationalized.

$$\lim_{x \to 4} \frac{\sqrt{x} - 2}{x - 4} = \lim_{x \to 4} \frac{\sqrt{x} - 2}{x - 4} \cdot \frac{\sqrt{x} + 2}{\sqrt{x} + 2} \quad \textit{Multiply by 1.}$$

$$= \lim_{x \to 4} \frac{x - 4}{(x - 4)(\sqrt{x} + 2)}$$

$$= \lim_{x \to 4} \frac{1}{\sqrt{x} + 2}$$

$$= \frac{1}{\sqrt{4} + 2} = \frac{1}{4}$$

EXAMPLE 7   Evaluating a trigonometric function by multiplying by the conjugate

Evaluate $\lim\limits_{x \to 0} \dfrac{1 - \cos x}{x}$.

Solution   Both the numerator and the denominator of this quotient are 0 when $x = 0$. However, if we multiply both the numerator and denominator of $f(x)$ by $1 + \cos x$ (the conjugate), we can rewrite the quotient $\dfrac{1 - \cos x}{x}$ in a form in which its limit can be found.

$$\lim_{x \to 0} \frac{1 - \cos x}{x} = \lim_{x \to 0} \left(\frac{1 - \cos x}{x} \cdot \frac{1 + \cos x}{1 + \cos x} \right)$$

$$= \lim_{x \to 0} \frac{1 - \cos^2 x}{x(1 + \cos x)}$$

$$= \lim_{x \to 0} \frac{\sin^2 x}{x(1 + \cos x)} \qquad 1 - \cos^2 x = \sin^2 x$$

$$= \lim_{x \to 0} \left[\left(\frac{\sin x}{x} \right) \left(\frac{\sin x}{1 + \cos x} \right) \right]$$

$$= \lim_{x \to 0} \left(\frac{\sin x}{x} \right) \lim_{x \to 0} \left(\frac{\sin x}{1 + \cos x} \right) \qquad \textit{Remember } \lim_{x \to 0} \frac{\sin x}{x} = 1 \textit{ and}$$

$$= 1 \cdot 0 \qquad\qquad\qquad\qquad \textit{evaluate the other limit by direct}$$
$$\qquad\qquad\qquad\qquad\qquad \textit{substitution of } \sin 0 = 0 \textit{ and}$$
$$= 0 \qquad\qquad\qquad\qquad\quad \cos 0 = 1.$$

■ LIMITS OF PIECEWISE-DEFINED FUNCTIONS

In Section 1.4 we defined a *piecewise-defined function*. To evaluate

$$\lim_{x \to c} f(x)$$

where the domain of f is divided into pieces, we first look to see if c is a critical value separating two of the pieces. If so, we need to consider one-sided limits, as illustrated by the following examples.

It is easy to see that the left- and right-hand limits are not the same.

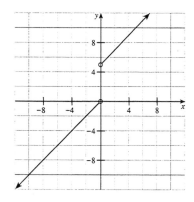

EXAMPLE 8   Limit of a piecewise-defined function

Find $\lim_{x \to 0} f(x)$ where $f(x) = \begin{cases} x + 5 & \text{if } x > 0 \\ x & \text{if } x < 0 \end{cases}$

Solution   Notice that $f(0)$ is not defined, and that it is necessary to consider left- and right-hand limits.

$$\lim_{x \to 0^-} f(x) = \lim_{x \to 0^-} x \qquad f(x) = x \text{ to the left of } 0.$$
$$= 0$$

$$\lim_{x \to 0^+} f(x) = \lim_{x \to 0^+} (x + 5) \quad f(x) = x + 5 \text{ to the right of } 0.$$
$$= 5$$

Because the left- and right-hand limits are not the same, we conclude that $\lim_{x \to 0} f(x)$ does not exist.   ■

EXAMPLE 9   Limit of a piecewise-defined function

Find $\lim_{x \to 0} g(x)$ where $g(x) = \begin{cases} x + 1 & \text{if } x > 0 \\ x^2 + 1 & \text{if } x < 0 \end{cases}$

$$\lim_{x \to 0^-} g(x) = \lim_{x \to 0^-} (x^2 + 1) = 1$$
$$\lim_{x \to 0^+} g(x) = \lim_{x \to 0^+} (x + 1) = 1$$

Compare this graph with the graph in Example 8.

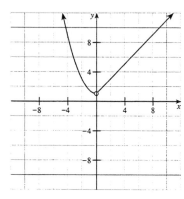

Because the left- and right-hand limits are equal, we conclude that $\lim_{x \to 0} g(x) = 1$.   ■

PROBLEM SET 1.6

Ⓐ *In Problems 1–30, evaluate each limit.*

1. $\lim_{x \to -2} (x^2 + 3x - 7)$

2. $\lim_{t \to 0} (t^3 - 5t^2 + 4)$

3. $\lim_{x \to 3} (x + 5)(2x - 7)$

4. $\lim_{x \to 4} \left(\frac{1}{x} + \frac{3}{x - 5} \right)$

5. $\lim_{x \to 1} \frac{z^2 + z - 3}{z + 1}$

6. $\lim_{x \to 3} \frac{x^2 + 3x - 10}{3x^2 + 5x - 7}$

7. $\lim_{x \to \pi/3} \sec x$

8. $\lim_{x \to \pi/4} \frac{1 + \tan x}{\csc x + 2}$

9. $\lim_{x \to 1/3} \frac{x \sin \pi x}{1 + \cos \pi x}$

10. $\lim_{x \to 6} \frac{\tan(\pi/x)}{x - 1}$

11. $\lim_{u \to -2} \frac{4 - u^2}{2 + u}$

12. $\lim_{x \to 2} \frac{x^2 - 4x + 4}{x^2 - x - 2}$

13. $\lim_{x \to 1} \frac{\frac{1}{x} - 1}{x - 1}$

14. $\lim_{x \to 0} \frac{(x + 1)^2 - 1}{x}$

15. $\lim_{x \to 1} \left(\frac{x^2 - 3x + 2}{x^2 + x - 2} \right)^2$

16. $\lim_{x \to 3} \sqrt{\frac{x^2 - 2x - 3}{x - 3}}$

17. $\lim_{x \to 1} \frac{\sqrt{x} - 1}{x - 1}$

18. $\lim_{y \to 2} \frac{\sqrt{y + 2} - 2}{y - 2}$

19. $\lim_{x \to 0} \frac{1 - \sin x}{\cos^2 x}$

20. $\lim_{x \to 0} \frac{1 - 2 \cos x}{\sqrt{3} - 2\sin x}$

21. $\lim_{x \to 0} \frac{\sin 2x}{x}$

22. $\lim_{x \to 0} \frac{\sin 3x}{2x}$

23. $\lim_{x \to 0} \frac{\tan x}{x}$

24. $\lim_{x \to 0} \frac{\sin^2 x}{x^2}$

25. $\lim_{x \to 0} \frac{\frac{1}{x + 3} - \frac{1}{3}}{x}$

26. $\lim_{x \to 3} \frac{\frac{1}{x} - \frac{1}{3}}{x - 3}$

27. $\lim_{x \to 0} \frac{\sec x - 1}{x \sec x}$

28. $\lim_{x \to \pi/4} \frac{1 - \tan x}{\sin x - \cos x}$

29. $\lim_{x \to 0} \frac{\tan^2 x}{x}$

30. $\lim_{x \to \pi} \frac{\tan x}{1 + \sec x}$

B 31. ■ **What Does This Say?**   How do you find the limit of a polynomial function?

32. ■ **What Does This Say?**   How do you find the limit of a rational function?

33. ■ **What Does This Say?**   How do you find $\lim\limits_{x \to 0} \dfrac{\sin ax}{x}$?

In Problems 34–41, compute the one-sided limit.

34. $\lim\limits_{x \to 2^-} (x^2 - 2x)$

35. $\lim\limits_{x \to 1^+} \dfrac{\sqrt{x-1} + x}{1 - 2x}$

36. $\lim\limits_{x \to 0^-} \dfrac{|x|}{x}$

37. $\lim\limits_{x \to 0^+} \dfrac{|x|}{x}$

38. $\lim\limits_{x \to 2^-} f(x)$ where $f(x) = \begin{cases} 3 - 2x & \text{if } x \le 2 \\ x^2 - 5 & \text{if } x > 2 \end{cases}$

39. $\lim\limits_{x \to 2^+} f(x)$ where $f(x) = \begin{cases} 3 - 2x & \text{if } x \le 2 \\ x^2 - 5 & \text{if } x > 2 \end{cases}$

40. $\lim\limits_{s \to 1^-} g(s)$ where $g(s) = \begin{cases} \dfrac{s^2 - s}{s - 1} & \text{if } s < 1 \\ \sqrt{1 - s} & \text{if } s \ge 1 \end{cases}$

41. $\lim\limits_{s \to 1^+} g(s)$ where $g(s) = \begin{cases} \dfrac{s^2 - s}{s - 1} & \text{if } s < 1 \\ \sqrt{1 - s} & \text{if } s \ge 1 \end{cases}$

■ **What Does This Say?**   *In Problems 42–49, explain why the given limit does not exist.*

42. $\lim\limits_{x \to 1} \dfrac{1}{x - 1}$

43. $\lim\limits_{x \to 2^+} \dfrac{1}{\sqrt{x - 2}}$

44. $\lim\limits_{t \to 2} \dfrac{t^2 - 4}{t^2 - 4t + 4}$

45. $\lim\limits_{x \to 0} \dfrac{|x|}{x}$

46. $\lim\limits_{x \to 1} f(x)$ where $f(x) = \begin{cases} 2 & \text{if } x \ge 1 \\ -5 & \text{if } x < 1 \end{cases}$

47. $\lim\limits_{t \to -1} g(t)$ where $g(t) = \begin{cases} 2t + 1 & \text{if } t \ge -1 \\ 5t^2 & \text{if } t < -1 \end{cases}$

48. $\lim\limits_{x \to \pi/2} \tan x$

49. $\lim\limits_{x \to 1} \csc \pi x$

We can use algebra, graphs, or tables to find limits. Find the limits in Problems 50–53.

50. $\lim\limits_{x \to 3} \dfrac{x^2 - 9}{x - 3}$

51. $\lim\limits_{x \to 0} \dfrac{x - \sin x}{x^3}$

52. $\lim\limits_{x \to 1} \dfrac{x^5 - 1}{x - 1}$

53. $\lim\limits_{x \to 1} \dfrac{\sqrt{x} - 1}{x - 1}$

In Problems 54–59, either evaluate the limit or explain why it does not exist.

54. $\lim\limits_{x \to 1} \dfrac{\frac{1}{x} - 1}{\sqrt{x} - 1}$

55. $\lim\limits_{x \to 0} \left(\dfrac{1}{x} - \dfrac{1}{x^2} \right)$

56. $\lim\limits_{x \to 5} f(x)$ where $f(x) = \begin{cases} x + 3 & \text{if } x \ne 5 \\ 4 & \text{if } x = 5 \end{cases}$

57. $\lim\limits_{t \to 2} g(t)$ where $g(t) = \begin{cases} t^2 & \text{if } -1 \le t < 2 \\ 3t - 2 & \text{if } t \ge 2 \end{cases}$

58. $\lim\limits_{x \to 2} f(x)$ where $f(x) = \begin{cases} 2(x + 1) & \text{if } x < 3 \\ 4 & \text{if } x = 3 \\ x^2 - 1 & \text{if } x > 3 \end{cases}$

59. $\lim\limits_{x \to 3} f(x)$ where $f(x) = \begin{cases} 2(x + 1) & \text{if } x < 3 \\ 4 & \text{if } x = 3 \\ x^2 - 1 & \text{if } x > 3 \end{cases}$

60. THINK TANK PROBLEM   Evaluate
$$\lim_{x \to 0} \left[x^2 - \frac{\cos x}{1{,}000{,}000{,}000} \right]$$

Explain why a calculator solution might lead you to an incorrect conclusion about the limit.

In the next chapter we will formally define the quantity
$$\frac{\Delta f}{\Delta x} = \frac{f(x + \Delta x) - f(x)}{\Delta x}$$

*to be the **difference quotient** of a function f. The number Δx is an arbitrary number (usually assumed to be very small). In each of Problems 61–64, first find $\Delta f / \Delta x$; then compute**
$$\lim_{\Delta x \to 0} \frac{\Delta f}{\Delta x}$$

61. $f(x) = 3x - 5$

62. $f(x) = x^2$

63. $f(x) = \dfrac{3}{x}$

64. $f(x) = \sqrt{x}$

Verify the limit statements in Problems 65–66. You may use $\lim\limits_{u \to 0} \dfrac{\sin u}{u} = 1$ *and* $\lim\limits_{u \to 0} \dfrac{u}{\sin u} = 1$ *without proof.*

65. $\lim\limits_{x \to 0} \dfrac{\sin ax}{\sin bx} = \dfrac{a}{b}$ for constants a, b, with $b \ne 0$

66. $\lim\limits_{x \to 0} \dfrac{\tan ax}{\tan bx} = \dfrac{a}{b}$ for constants a, b, with $b \ne 0$

C 67. Let $f(x) = \dfrac{1}{x^2}$ with $x \ne 0$, and let L be any fixed positive integer. Show that
$$f(x) > 100L \quad \text{if} \quad |x| < \frac{1}{10\sqrt{L}}$$

What does this imply about $\lim\limits_{x \to 0} f(x)$?

68. THINK TANK PROBLEM   Give an example for which neither $\lim\limits_{x \to c} f(x)$ nor $\lim\limits_{x \to c} g(x)$ exists, but $\lim\limits_{x \to c} [f(x) + g(x)]$ does exist.

69. THINK TANK PROBLEM   It is not necessarily true that $\lim\limits_{x \to c} f(x)$ and $\lim\limits_{x \to c} g(x)$ exist whenever $\lim\limits_{x \to c} [f(x) \cdot g(x)]$ or $\lim\limits_{x \to c} \dfrac{f(x)}{g(x)}$ exists.

a. Find functions f and g such that $\lim\limits_{x \to c} [f(x) \cdot g(x)]$ exists and $\lim\limits_{x \to c} g(x) = 0$, but $\lim\limits_{x \to c} f(x)$ does not exist.

b. Find functions f and g such that $\lim\limits_{x \to 0} \dfrac{f(x)}{g(x)}$ exists, but neither $\lim\limits_{x \to 0} f(x)$ nor $\lim\limits_{x \to 0} g(x)$ exists.

70. Use the sum rule to show that if $\lim\limits_{x \to c} [f(x) + g(x)]$ and $\lim\limits_{x \to c} f(x)$ both exist, then so does $\lim\limits_{x \to c} g(x)$.

71. Show that $\lim\limits_{x \to x_0} \cos x = \cos x_0$.

Hint: You will need to use the trigonometric identity $\cos(A + B) = \cos A \cos B - \sin A \sin B$.

72. Show that $\lim\limits_{x \to x_0} \tan x = \tan x_0$ whenever $\cos x_0 \ne 0$.

*This kind of limit will be used to define an idea called a derivative in Section 2.1.

2.4 RATES OF CHANGE: RECTILINEAR MOTION

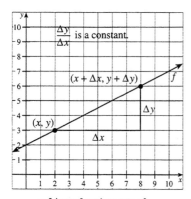

a. Linear function: rate of change $\Delta y/\Delta x$ is constant.

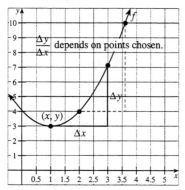

b. Nonlinear function: rate of change $\Delta y/\Delta x$ depends on chosen points.

Figure 2.13 Rate of change is measured by the slope of a tangent line.

Ø The formula for Δy is important. Note the change in y in Figure 2.14. Ø

IN THIS SECTION Rate of change (geometric interpretation), average and instantaneous rate of change, rectilinear motion (physics application), falling body problem.

The derivative can be interpreted as a rate of change, which leads to a wide variety of applications. Viewed as rates of change, derivatives may represent such quantities as the speed of a moving object, the rate at which a population grows, a manufacturer's marginal cost, the rate of inflation, or the rate at which natural resources are being depleted.

■ RATE OF CHANGE—GEOMETRIC INTERPRETATION

Let us begin by thinking of rate of change in geometric terms. Intuitively, a **rate of change** means how fast one variable changes with respect to another variable.

The rate of change of a linear function $f(x) = ax + b$ with respect to its independent variable x is measured by the steepness or slope of its straight-line graph, as shown in Figure 2.13a. For the graph of a linear function, the slope or rate of change is constant. However, if the function under consideration is not linear, its rate of change varies from point to point, as shown in Figure 2.13b. Because the slope of the tangent is given by the derivative of the function, the preceding geometric observations suggest that the rate of change of a function is measured by its derivative. This connection will be made more precise in the following discussion.

■ AVERAGE AND INSTANTANEOUS RATE OF CHANGE

Suppose that y is a function of x, say, $y = f(x)$. Corresponding to a change from x to $x + \Delta x$, the variable y changes from $f(x)$ to $f(x + \Delta x)$. Thus the change in y is $\Delta y = f(x + \Delta x) - f(x)$, and then the **average rate of change of y with respect to x** is

$$\text{AVERAGE RATE OF CHANGE} = \frac{\text{change in } y}{\text{change in } x} = \frac{\Delta y}{\Delta x} = \frac{f(x + \Delta x) - f(x)}{\Delta x}$$

As the interval over which we are averaging becomes shorter (that is, as $\Delta x \to 0$), the average rate of change approaches what we would intuitively call the

*See, for example, "Fallacies, Flaws, and Flimflam," *The College Mathematics Journal*, Vol. 23, No. 3, May 1992 and Vol. 24, No. 4, September 1993.

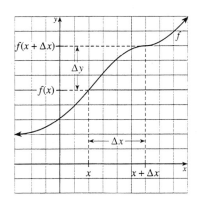

Figure 2.14 A change in Δy corresponding to a change Δx

instantaneous rate of change of y with respect to x, and the difference quotient approaches the derivative $f'(x)$, or $\dfrac{dy}{dx}$. Thus, we have

$$\begin{array}{c}\text{INSTANTANEOUS} \\ \text{RATE OF CHANGE}\end{array} = \lim_{\Delta x \to 0} \frac{\Delta y}{\Delta x} = \lim_{\Delta x \to 0} \frac{f(x + \Delta x) - f(x)}{\Delta x} = f'(x)$$

To summarize:

Instantaneous Rate of Change

If $y = f(x)$, the **instantaneous rate of change** of y with respect to x, is given by the derivative of f:

$$\text{INSTANTANEOUS RATE OF CHANGE OF } y = f'(x) = \frac{dy}{dx}$$

EXAMPLE 1 Instantaneous rate of change

Find the rate at which the function $y = x^2 \sin x$ is changing with respect to x when $x = \pi$.

Solution For any x, the instantaneous rate of change is the derivative,

$$\frac{dy}{dx} = 2x \sin x + x^2 \cos x$$

Thus, the rate when $x = \pi$ is

$$\frac{dy}{dx}\bigg|_{x=\pi} = 2\pi \sin \pi + \pi^2 \cos \pi = 2\pi(0) + \pi^2(-1) = -\pi^2$$

The negative sign indicates that when $x = \pi$, the function is *decreasing* at the rate of $\pi^2 \approx 9.9$ units of y for each one-unit increase in x. ▬

Let us consider an example comparing the average rate of change and the instantaneous rate of change.

EXAMPLE 2 Comparison between average rate and instantaneous rate of change

Let $f(x) = x^2 - 4x + 7$.

a. Find the instantaneous rate of change of f at $x = 3$.

b. Find the average rate of change of f with respect to x between $x = 3$ and 5.

Solution

a. The instantaneous rate of change of the function with respect to x is the derivative of the function; that is,

$$f'(x) = 2x - 4$$

The instantaneous rate of change of f at $x = 3$ is

$$f'(3) = 2(3) - 4 = 2$$

The tangent line at $x = 3$ has slope 2, as shown in Figure 2.15.

b. The (average) rate of change from $x = 3$ to $x = 5$ is found by dividing the change in f by the change in x. That is, the change in f from $x = 3$ to $x = 5$ is

$$f(5) - f(3) = [5^2 - 4(5) + 7] - [3^2 - 4(3) + 7] = 8$$

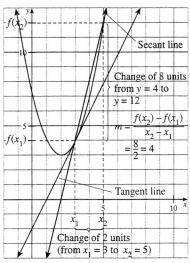

Figure 2.15 Comparison of instantaneous and average rates of change from x_1 to x_2

The average rate of change is

$$\frac{f(5) - f(3)}{5 - 3} = \frac{8}{2} = 4.$$

The slope of the secant line is 4, as shown in Figure 2.14. ▬▬

■ AN APPLICATION TO PHYSICS—RECTILINEAR MOTION

Rectilinear motion is motion along a straight line. For example, the up and down motion of a yo-yo may be regarded as rectilinear, as may the motion of a rocket early in its flight.

When studying rectilinear motion, we may assume that the object is moving along a coordinate line. The position or **displacement** of the object from the origin in relation to the line is a function of time t and is often expressed as $s(t)$. The rate of change of the displacement with respect to time is the object's **velocity** $v(t)$, and the rate of change of the velocity with respect to t is its **acceleration** $a(t)$. Interpreting these rates as derivatives, we see that

$$\text{Velocity is } v(t) = \frac{ds}{dt}.$$

$$\textit{Acceleration is } a(t) = \frac{dv}{dt} = \frac{d^2s}{dt^2}.$$

If $v(t) > 0$, we say that the object is *advancing* and if $v(t) < 0$, the object is *retreating*. If $v(t) = 0$, the object is neither advancing nor retreating, and we say it is *stationary*. The object is *accelerating* when $a(t) > 0$ and is *decelerating* when $a(t) < 0$. The significance of the acceleration is that it gives the rate at which the velocity is changing. These ideas are summarized in the following box.

Rectilinear Motion

An object that moves along a straight line with *displacement* $s(t)$ has *velocity* $v(t) = \frac{ds}{dt}$ and *acceleration* $a(t) = \frac{dv}{dt} = \frac{d^2s}{dt^2}$ when these derivatives exist. The **speed** of the object is $|v(t)|$.

⊘ Rectilinear motion involves *displacement*, *velocity*, and *acceleration*. Sometimes there is confusion between the words speed and velocity. Because speed is the absolute value of the velocity, it indicates how fast an object is moving, whereas velocity indicates both speed and direction (relative to a given coordinate system). ⊘

NOTATIONAL COMMENT: If distance is measured in meters and time in seconds, velocity is measured in meters per second (m/s) and acceleration in meters per second per second (m/s/s). The notation m/s/s is awkward, so m/s² is more commonly used. Similarly, if distance is measured in feet, velocity is measured in feet per second (ft/s) and acceleration in feet per second per second (ft/s²).

When you are riding in a car, moving along a straight road, you do not feel the velocity, but you do feel the acceleration. That is, you feel *changes* in the velocity.

EXAMPLE 3   The position, velocity, and acceleration of a moving object

Assume that the displacement at time t of an object moving along a line is given by

$$s(t) = 3t^3 - 40.5t^2 + 162t$$

for t on [0, 8]. Find the position, velocity, and acceleration.

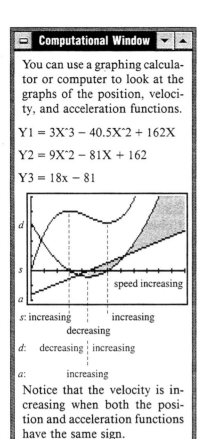

Solution   The position at time t is given by the function s. The starting position is found at time $t = 0$, so

$$s(0) = 0 \qquad \textit{The object starts at the origin.}$$

The velocity is determined by finding the derivative of the position function.

$$v(t) = s'(t) = 9t^2 - 81t + 162 \qquad \begin{array}{l}\textit{The starting velocity is}\\ \textit{162, which is found by}\\ \textit{evaluating } v(0).\end{array}$$
$$= 9(t^2 - 9t + 18)$$
$$= 9(t - 3)(t - 6)$$

When $t = 3$ and when $t = 6$, v the velocity is 0, which means the *object is stationary* at those times. Furthermore,

$v(t) > 0$	on $[0, 3)$	*Object is advancing.*
$v(t) < 0$	on $(3, 6)$	*Object is retreating.*
$v(t) > 0$	on $(6, 8]$	*Object is advancing.*

$$a(t) = s''(t) = v'(t) = 18t - 81 = 18(t - 4.5)$$

We see that

$a(t) < 0$	on $[0, 4.5)$	*Velocity is decreasing; that is, the object is decelerating.*
$a(t) = 0$	at $t = 4.5$	*Velocity is not changing.*
$a(t) > 0$	on $(4.5, 8]$	*Velocity is increasing; that is, the object is accelerating.*

The table (computational window) shown in the margin gives values for s, v, and a. We use these values to plot a few points, as shown in Figure 2.16. The actual path of the object is back and forth on the axis and the figure is for clarification only.

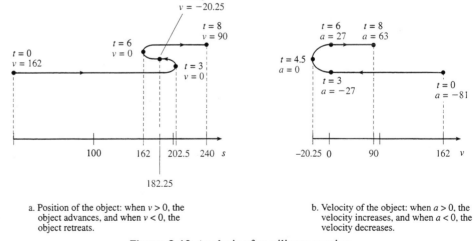

a. Position of the object: when $v > 0$, the object advances, and when $v < 0$, the object retreats.

b. Velocity of the object: when $a > 0$, the velocity increases, and when $a < 0$, the velocity decreases.

Figure 2.16 Analysis of rectilinear motion

Recall that the *speed* of the particle is the absolute value of its velocity. The speed decreases from 162 to 0 between $t = 0$ and $t = 3$, and it increases from 0 to 20.25 as the velocity becomes negative between $t = 3$ and $t = 4.5$. Then, for $4.5 < t < 6$, the particle slows down again, from 20.25 to 0, after which it speeds up.   ■

A common mistake is to think that a particle moving on a straight line speeds up when its acceleration is positive and slows down when the acceleration is negative, but this is not quite correct. Instead, the following is generally true:

- The speed *increases* (particle speeds up) when the velocity and acceleration have the same signs.
- The speed *decreases* (particle slows down) when the velocity and acceleration have opposite signs.

■ FALLING BODY PROBLEM

As a second example of rectilinear motion, we shall consider a *falling body problem*. In such a problem, it is assumed that an object is projected (that is, thrown, fired, dropped, etc.) vertically in such a way that the only acceleration acting on the object is the constant downward acceleration g due to gravity, which on the earth near sea level is approximately 32 ft/s² or 9.8 m/s². At time t, the height of the object is given by the following formula:

Formula for the Height of an Object

$$h(t) = -\tfrac{1}{2}gt^2 + v_0 t + s_0$$

v_0 *is the initial velocity.*

$\{s_0$ *is the initial height.*

g *is the acceleration due to gravity.*

where s_0 and v_0 are the object's initial height and velocity, respectively. We shall derive this formula in Chapter 4.

EXAMPLE 4   Position, velocity, and acceleration of a falling object

Suppose a person standing at the top of the Tower of Pisa (176 ft high) throws a ball directly upward with an initial speed of 96 ft/s.

a. Find the ball's height, its velocity, and acceleration at time t.

b. When does the ball hit the ground, and what is its impact velocity?

c. How far does the ball travel during its flight?

Solution   First, draw a picture such as the one shown in Figure 2.17 to help you understand the problem.

a. Substitute the known values into the height of an object formula:

$$v_0 = 96 \text{ ft/s: } Initial\ velocity$$

$$h(t) = -\tfrac{1}{2}(32)t^2 + 96t + 176 \leftarrow h_0 = 176 \text{ ft: } Height\ of\ tower$$

$$g = 32 \text{ ft/s}^2\text{: } Constant\ downward\ gravitational\ acceleration$$

$$h(t) = -16t^2 + 96t + 176 \qquad \textit{This is the displacement, or position, function. It gives the height of the ball.}$$

The velocity at time t is the derivative:

$$v(t) = \frac{dh}{dt} = -32t + 96$$

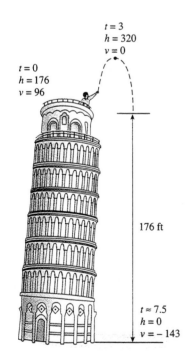

$t = 3$
$h = 320$
$v = 0$

$t = 0$
$h = 176$
$v = 96$

176 ft

$t \approx 7.5$
$h = 0$
$v = -143$

Figure 2.17 The motion of a ball thrown upward from the Tower of Pisa

The acceleration is the derivative of the velocity function:

$$a(t) = \frac{dv}{dt} = \frac{d^2h}{dt^2} = -32$$

This means that the velocity of the ball is always decreasing at the rate of 32 ft/s².

b. The ball hits the ground when $h(t) = 0$. Solve the equation

$$-16t^2 + 96t + 176 = 0$$

to find that this occurs when $t \approx -1.47$ ($t = 3 - 2\sqrt{5}$) and $t \approx 7.47$ ($t = 3 + 2\sqrt{5}$). Disregarding the negative value we see that impact occurs at $t = 3 + 2\sqrt{5}$ sec. The impact velocity is

$$v(3 + 2\sqrt{5}) = -32(3 + 2\sqrt{5}) + 96 \approx -143 \text{ ft/s}$$

The negative sign here means the ball is coming down at the moment of impact.

c. The ball travels upward for some time and then falls downward to the ground, as shown in Figure 2.17. We need to find the distance it travels upward plus the distance it falls to the ground. The turning point at the top (the highest point) occurs when the velocity is zero. Solve the equation

$$-32t + 96 = 0$$

to find that this occurs when $t = 3$. For $t < 3$, the velocity is positive and the ball is rising, and for $t > 3$, the ball is falling. It follows that the ball is at the highest point when $t = 3$. The ball starts at $h(0) = 176$ ft and rises to a maximum height when $t = 3$:

$$h(3) = -16(3)^2 + 96(3) + 176 = 320$$

Thus, the total distance traveled is

$$\underbrace{(320 - 176)}_{\substack{\uparrow \\ \text{Initial height}}} + \underbrace{320}_{\text{Downward distance}} = 464$$

$$\overbrace{}^{\text{Upward distance}}$$

The total distance traveled is 464 ft.   ▬

PROBLEM SET 2.4

Ⓐ *For each function f given in Problems 1–14, find the rate of change with respect to x at $x = x_0$.*

1. $f(x) = x^2 - 3x + 5$ when $x_0 = 2$

2. $f(x) = 14 + x - x^2$ when $x_0 = 1$

3. $f(x) = -2x^2 + x + 4$ for $x_0 = 1$

4. $f(x) = \dfrac{-2}{x + 1}$ for $x_0 = 1$

5. $f(x) = \dfrac{2x - 1}{3x + 5}$ when $x_0 = -1$

6. $f(x) = (x^2 + 2)(x + \sqrt{x})$ when $x_0 = 4$

7. $f(x) = x \cos x$ when $x_0 = \pi$

8. $f(x) = (x + 1) \sin x$ when $x_0 = \frac{\pi}{2}$

9. $f(x) = x + \dfrac{3}{2 - 4x}$ when $x_0 = 0$

10. $f(x) = \dfrac{1}{x + 1} - \dfrac{1}{x - 1}$ when $x_0 = 3$

11. $f(x) = \sin x \cos x$ when $x_0 = \frac{\pi}{2}$

12. $f(x) = \dfrac{x^2}{x^2 + 1}$ when $x_0 = 1$

13. $f(x) = \left(x - \dfrac{2}{x}\right)^2$ when $x_0 = 1$

14. $f(x) = \sin^2 x$ when $x_0 = \frac{\pi}{4}$

Give both exact and approximate values.

The function s(t) in Problems 15–22 gives the displacement of an object moving along a line. In each case:

a. *Find the velocity at time t.*

b. *Find the acceleration at time t.*

c. *Describe the motion of the object; that is, tell where is it advancing and where it is retreating. Compute the total distance traveled by the object during the indicated time interval.*

d. *Tell where the object is accelerating and where it is decelerating.*

 For a review of solving equations see Sections 2.5, 2.6, and 3.7 of the Student Mathematics Handbook.

15. $s(t) = t^2 - 2t + 6$ on $[0, 2]$

16. $s(t) = 3t^2 + 2t - 5$ on $[0, 1]$

17. $s(t) = t^3 - 9t^2 + 15t + 25$ on $[0, 6]$

18. $s(t) = t^4 - 4t^3 + 8t$ on $[0, 4]$

19. $s(t) = \dfrac{2t + 1}{t^2}$ for $1 \le t \le 3$

20. $s(t) = \dfrac{t^2 + 1}{t^2}$ for $1 \le t \le 2$

21. $s(t) = 3 \cos t$ for $0 \le t \le 2\pi$

22. $s(t) = 1 + \sec t$ for $0 \le t \le \frac{\pi}{4}$

 23. It is estimated that x years from now, $0 \le x \le 10$, the average SAT mathematics score of the incoming students at a certain eastern liberal arts college will be

$$f(x) = -6x + 582$$

a. Derive an expression for the rate at which the average SAT score will be changing with respect to time x years from now.

b. What is the significance of the fact that the expression in part **a** is a negative constant?

24. A particle moving on the x-axis has displacement

$$x(t) = 2t^3 + 3t^2 - 36t + 40$$

after an elapsed time of t seconds.

a. Find the velocity of the particle at time t.

b. Find the acceleration at time t.

c. What is the total distance traveled by the particle during the first 3 sec?

25. An object moving on the x-axis has displacement

$$x(t) = t^3 - 9t^2 + 24t + 20$$

after t seconds. What is the total distance traveled by the object during the first 8 sec?

26. A car has velocity

$$v(t) = \frac{90t}{3t + 12}$$

ft/s after t seconds of motion. What is its acceleration (to the nearest hundredth ft/s^2) after 10 sec?

27. An object moves along a straight line so that after t minutes, its distance from its starting point (in meters) is

$$s(t) = 10t + \frac{5}{t + 1}$$

a. At what speed (to the nearest tenth m/min) is the object moving at the end of 4 min?

b. How far (to the nearest tenth m) does the object actually travel during the 5th minute?

28. A bucket containing 5 gal of water has a leak. After t seconds, there are

$$Q(t) = 5\left(1 - \frac{t}{25}\right)^2$$

gallons of water in the bucket.

a. At what rate (to the nearest hundredth gal) is water leaking from the bucket after 2 sec?

b. How long does it take for all the water to leak out of the bucket?

c. At what rate is the water leaking when the last drop leaks out?

29. A person standing at the edge of a cliff throws a rock directly upward. It is observed that 2 sec later the rock is at its maximum height (in feet) and that 5 sec after that, it hits the ground at the base of the cliff.

a. What is the initial velocity of the rock?

b. How high is the cliff?

c. What is the velocity of the rock at time t?

d. With what velocity does the rock hit the ground?

30. A projectile is shot upward from the earth with an initial velocity of 320 ft/s.

a. What is its velocity after 5 sec?

b. What is its acceleration after 3 sec?

31. A rock is dropped from a height of 90 ft. One second later another rock is dropped from height H. What is H (to the nearest foot) if the two rocks hit the ground at the same time?

32. A ball is thrown vertically upward from the ground with an initial velocity of 160 ft/s.

a. When will the ball hit the ground?

b. With what speed will the ball hit the ground?

c. When will the ball reach its maximum height?

d. What is the speed of the ball as it hits the ground?

33. An object is dropped (initial velocity $v_0 = 0$) from the top of a building and falls 3 seconds before hitting the pavement below. Find the height of the building in feet.

34. An astronaut standing at the edge of a cliff on the moon throws a rock directly upward and observes that it passes her on the way down exactly 4 sec later. Three seconds after that, the rock hits the ground at the base of the cliff. Use this information to determine the initial velocity v_0 and the height of the cliff. *Note*: $g = 5.5$ ft/s^2 on the moon.

35. Answer the questions in Problem 34 assuming the astronaut is on Mars, where $g = 12$ ft/s^2.

36. A car is traveling at 88 ft/s (60 mph) when the driver applies the brakes to avoid hitting a child. After t seconds, the car is $s(t) = 88t - 8t^2$ feet from the point where the brakes were first applied. How long does it take for the car to come to a stop, and how far does it travel before stopping?

37. It is estimated that t years from now, the circulation of a local newspaper will be

$$C(t) = 100t^2 + 400t + 5,000$$

a. Find an expression for the rate at which the circulation will be changing with respect to time t years from now.

b. At what rate will the circulation be changing with respect to time 5 years from now?

c. By how much will the circulation actually change during the 6th year?

38. An efficiency study of the morning shift at a certain factory indicates that an average worker who arrives on the job at 8:00 A.M. will have assembled

$$f(x) = -\tfrac{1}{3}x^3 + \tfrac{1}{2}x^2 + 50x$$

units x hours later.

a. Find a formula for the rate at which the worker will be assembling the units after x hours.

b. At what rate will the worker be assembling units at 9:00 A.M.?

c. How many units will the worker actually assemble between 9:00 A.M. and 10:00 A.M.?

39. An environmental study of a suburban community suggests that t years from now, the average level of carbon monoxide in the air will be $q(t) = 0.05t^2 + 0.1t + 3.4$ parts per million.

a. At what rate will the carbon monoxide level be changing with respect to time one year from now?

b. By how much will the carbon monoxide level change in the first year?

c. By how much will the carbon monoxide level change over the next (second) year?

40. According to *Newton's law of universal gravitation*, if an object of mass M is separated by a distance r from a second object of mass m, then the two objects are attracted to one another by a force that acts along the line joining them and has magnitude

$$F = \frac{GmM}{r^2}$$

where G is a positive constant. Show the rate of change of F with respect to r is inversely proportional to r^3.

41. The population of a bacterial colony is approximately $P(t) = P_0 + 61t + 3t^2$ thousand t hours after observation begins, where P_0 is the initial population. Find the rate at which the colony is growing after 5 hours.

If $y = f(x)$, the percentage rate of change of y with respect to x is defined by the expression

$$\frac{f'(x)}{f(x)} \cdot 100$$

Use this definition in Problems 42–47.

42. The gross domestic product (GDP) of a country was $g(t) = t^2 + 5t + 106$ billion dollars t years after 1990.

a. At what rate was the GDP changing in 1992?

b. At what percentage rate was the GDP changing in 1992?

43. It is projected that x months from now, the population of a certain town will be $P(x) = 2x + 4x^{3/2} + 5,000$.

a. At what rate will the population be changing with respect to time 9 months from now?

b. At what percentage rate will the population be changing with respect to time 9 months from now?

44. Assume that your starting salary is $30,000 and you get a raise of $3,000 each year.

a. Express the percentage rate of change of your salary as a function of time and draw the graph.

b. At what percentage rate will your salary be increasing after one year?

c. What will happen to the percentage rate of change of your salary in the long run?

45. The gross domestic product (GDP) of a certain country is growing at a constant rate. In 1990 the GDP was 125 billion dollars, and in 1992 it was 155 billion dollars. At what percentage rate will the GDP be growing in 1995?

46. If y is a linear function of x, what will happen to the percentage rate of change of y with respect to x as x increases without bound?

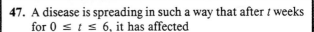

Computational Window

47. A disease is spreading in such a way that after t weeks for $0 \le t \le 6$, it has affected

$$N(t) = 5 - t^2(t - 6)$$

hundred people. Health officials declare that this disease will reach epidemic proportions when the percentage rate of increase of $N(t)$ at the start of a particular week is at least 30% per week. The epidemic designation level is dropped when the percentage rate falls below this level.

a. Find the percentage rate of change of $N(t)$ at time t.

b. Between what weeks is the disease at the epidemic level?

48. An object attached to a helical spring is pulled down from its equilibrium position and then released, as shown in Figure 2.18.

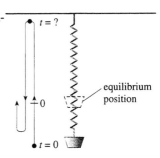

Figure 2.18 Helical spring

Suppose that t seconds later, its displacement (in centimeters measured in relation to the equilibrium position) is given by

$$s(t) = 7 \cos t$$

a. Find the velocity and acceleration of the object at time t.

b. Find the length of time required for one complete oscillation. This is called the *period* of the motion.

c. What is the distance between the highest point reached by the object and the lowest point? Half of this distance is called the *amplitude* of the motion.

49. Two cars leave a town at the same time and travel at constant speeds along straight roads that meet at an angle of 60° in the town. If one car travels twice as fast as the other and the distance between them increases at the rate of 45 mi/hr, how fast is the slower car traveling?

50. SPY PROBLEM   Our friend the spy, who escaped from the diamond smugglers in Problem 39 of Chapter 1 Supplementary Problems, is on a secret mission in space. An encounter with an enemy agent leaves him with a mild concussion that causes him to forget where he is. Fortunately, he remembers the formula for the height of a projectile,

$$h(t) = -\frac{1}{2} gt^2 + v_0 t + s_0$$

and the values of g for various heavenly bodies. Therefore, to deduce his whereabouts, he throws a rock directly upward (from ground level) and notes that it reaches a maximum height of 37.5 ft and hits the ground 5 sec after leaving his hand. Where is he? *Note*: You will need to know that g is 32 ft/s² on earth, 5.5 ft/s² on the moon, 12 ft/s² on Mars, and 28 ft/s² on Venus.

C 51. Find the rate of change of the volume of a cube with respect to the length of one of its edges. How is this rate related to the surface area of the cube?

52. Show that the rate of change of the volume of a sphere with respect to its radius is equal to its surface area.

53. Van der Waal's equation states that a gas that occupies a volume V at temperature T (Kelvin) exerts pressure P, where

$$\left(P + \frac{A}{V^2}\right)(V - B) = kT$$

and A, B, and k are physical constants. Find the rate of change of pressure with respect to volume, assuming fixed temperature.

54. According to Debye's formula in physical chemistry, the orientation polarization P of a gas satisfies

$$P = \frac{4}{3}\pi N\left(\frac{\mu^2}{3kT}\right)$$

where μ, k, and N are constants and T is the temperature of the gas. Find the rate of change of P with respect to T.

3.5 INFINITE LIMITS AND ASYMPTOTES

IN THIS SECTION Asymptotes, limits involving infinity, graphs with asymptotes

In order to complete our discussion of curve sketching we need to introduce two concepts, asymptotes and limits involving infinity.

■ ASYMPTOTES

Recall from Chapter 1 that $\lim_{x \to c} f(x)$ does not exist when $f(x)$ increases or decreases without bound as x approaches c. This is one kind of *limit involving infinity*, and a

*"The Mechanics of Bird Migration," Ibis III, pp. 525–556.

goal of this section is to examine such limits and to see how they may be used in curve sketching.

As a preview of the ideas we plan to explore, let us examine the graph shown in Figure 3.40.

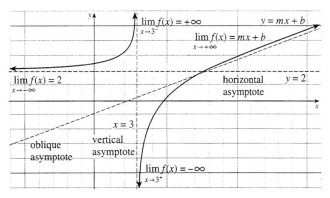

Figure 3.40 A typical graph with asymptotes

Suppose the graph shown in Figure 3.40 is the graph of a function we will call f. Notice that as x approaches 3 from either side, the corresponding functional values of f get large without bound (in absolute value), and the graph of f approaches the vertical line $x = 3$. This approach is through positive values ("up") as x approaches 3^- (from the left) and through negative values ("down") as x approaches 3^+ (from the right). We indicate the behavior of f for x near 3 by writing*

$$\lim_{x \to 3^-} f(x) = +\infty \quad \text{and} \quad \lim_{x \to 3^+} f(x) = -\infty$$

and we describe the corresponding geometric behavior by saying that the line $x = 3$ is a **vertical asymptote** of the graph of f.

Note also that as x increases without bound (that is, as x moves toward the right on the x-axis), the graph of f follows the line $y = mx + b$. For this reason, the line $y = mx + b$ (where $m \neq 0$) is called an **oblique** (or **slant**) **asymptote.**

At the other end of the x-axis (as x decreases without bound), the graph approaches the line $y = 2$. We write

$$\lim_{x \to -\infty} f(x) = 2$$

and say that the line $y = 2$ is a **horizontal asymptote** of the graph.

More specifically, an **asymptote** is a line having the property that the distance from a point P on the curve to the line approaches zero as the distance from P to the origin increases without bound, and P is *on a suitable part of the curve.* This last phrase (in italics) is best illustrated by considering Figure 3.41, where L is an asymptote for the function f.

Consider P and d, the distance from P to the line L, as shown in Figure 3.41a. Now, the distance from P to the origin can increase in two ways, depending on whether P moves along the curve in direction 1 or direction 2. In direction 1, the distance d increases without bound, but in direction 2 the distance d approaches zero. Thus, if you consider the portion of the curve in the shaded region of Figure 3.41b, you see that the distance decreases as P moves along the curve in a certain direction.

There are three types of asymptotes that occur frequently enough when sketching curves to merit our consideration: *vertical, horizontal,* and *oblique*

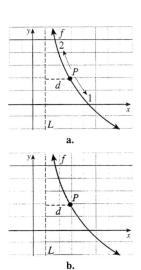

Figure 3.41 An asymptote to a curve

*Many books simply write ∞ to mean $+\infty$. For now, we use $+\infty$ to remind you that $+\infty$ is not the same as $-\infty$.

(*slant*) *asymptotes*. An example of each is shown in Figure 3.42. A graph may pass through a horizontal or oblique (slant) asymptote.

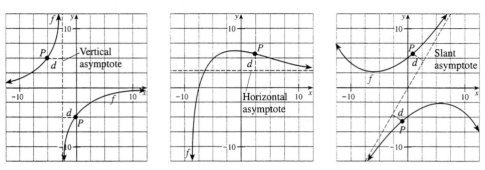

Figure 3.42 Asymptotes

We will define the concepts formally later in this section, and we will also examine examples of graphs with asymptotes. However, we first need to discuss limits involving infinity.

■ LIMITS INVOLVING INFINITY

If the functional values of f get closer and closer to the number L as x increases without bound, we say that $f(x)$ *approaches L as x approaches infinity* and we write $\lim_{x \to +\infty} f(x) = L$. If $f(x)$ approaches L as x decreases without bound, we write $\lim_{x \to -\infty} f(x) = L$. These concepts may be defined formally as follows:

Limits to Infinity   The limit statement $\lim_{x \to +\infty} f(x) = L$ means that for any number $\varepsilon > 0$, there exists a number N_1 such that

$$|f(x) - L| < \varepsilon \quad \text{whenever} \quad x > N_1$$

for x in the domain of f. Similarly, $\lim_{x \to -\infty} f(x) = M$ means that for any $\varepsilon > 0$, there exists a number N_2 such that

$$|f(x) - M| < \varepsilon \quad \text{whenever} \quad x < N_2$$

This definition can be illustrated graphically, as shown in Figure 3.43.

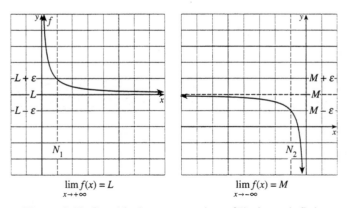

$$\lim_{x \to +\infty} f(x) = L \qquad\qquad \lim_{x \to -\infty} f(x) = M$$

Figure 3.43 Graphical representation of limits to infinity

With this formal definition, we can show that all the rules for limits established in Chapter 1 also apply to $\lim_{x \to +\infty} f(x)$ and $\lim_{x \to -\infty} f(x)$. We now state those limit rules for $x \to +\infty$.

Limit Rules

If $\lim_{x \to +\infty} f(x)$ exists, then for constants a and b:

Power rule: $\lim_{x \to +\infty} [f(x)]^n = \left[\lim_{x \to +\infty} f(x)\right]^n$

Linearity rule: $\lim_{x \to +\infty} [af(x) + bg(x)] = a \lim_{x \to +\infty} f(x) + b \lim_{x \to +\infty} g(x)$

Product rule: $\lim_{x \to +\infty} [f(x)g(x)] = \left[\lim_{x \to +\infty} f(x)\right]\left[\lim_{x \to +\infty} g(x)\right]$

Quotient rule: $\lim_{x \to +\infty} \dfrac{f(x)}{g(x)} = \dfrac{\lim_{x \to +\infty} f(x)}{\lim_{x \to +\infty} g(x)}$ if $\lim_{x \to +\infty} g(x) \neq 0$

The same results hold for $\lim_{x \to -\infty} f(x)$, if it exists.

The following theorem will allow us to evaluate certain limits to infinity with ease.

THEOREM 3.8 Limits to infinity

If n is a positive rational number, and A is any nonzero real number, then

$$\lim_{x \to +\infty} \frac{A}{x^n} = 0$$

Furthermore, if x^n is defined when $x < 0$, then

$$\lim_{x \to -\infty} \frac{A}{x^n} = 0$$

Proof: We begin by proving that $\lim_{x \to +\infty} \frac{1}{x} = 0$. For $\varepsilon > 0$, let $N = \frac{1}{\varepsilon}$. Then for $x > N$ we have

$$x > N = \frac{1}{\varepsilon} \quad \text{so that} \quad \frac{1}{x} < \varepsilon$$

This means that $\left|\frac{1}{x} - 0\right| < \varepsilon$ so that from the definition of limit we have $\lim_{x \to +\infty} \frac{1}{x} = 0$. Now let n be a rational number—say, $n = \frac{p}{q}$. Then

$$\lim_{x \to +\infty} \frac{A}{x^n} = \lim_{x \to +\infty} \frac{A}{x^{p/q}} = A \lim_{x \to +\infty} \left[\frac{1}{\sqrt[q]{x}}\right]^p$$

$$= A \left[\sqrt[q]{\lim_{x \to +\infty} \frac{1}{x}}\right]^p = A\left[\sqrt[q]{0}\right]^p = A \cdot 0 = 0$$

The second part of the proof follows similarly. ∎

Example 1 illustrates how Theorem 3.8 can be used along with the other limit properties to evaluate limits to infinity.

EXAMPLE 1 Evaluating limits to infinity

Evaluate

$$\lim_{x \to +\infty} \sqrt{\frac{3x - 5}{x - 2}} \quad \text{and} \quad \lim_{x \to -\infty} \left(\frac{3x - 5}{x - 2}\right)^3$$

Historical Note

BHASKARACHARYA

The possibility of division by zero is an idea that causes special concern to mathematicians. One of the first recorded observations of division by zero comes from the twelfth-century Hindu mathematician Bhaskaracharya, who made the following observation: "The fraction, whose denominator is zero, is termed an infinite quantity." Bhaskaracharya then went on to give "a very beautiful conception of infinity" that involved his view of God and creation.

From *Mathematics in India in the Middle Ages* by Chandra B. Sharma.

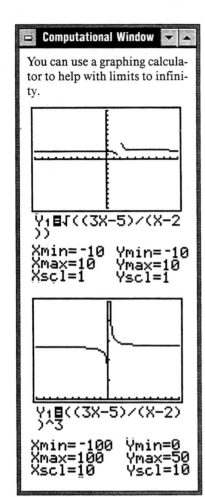

Solution   Notice that for $x \neq 0$,

$$\frac{3x - 5}{x - 2} = \frac{x\left(3 - \frac{5}{x}\right)}{x\left(1 - \frac{2}{x}\right)} = \frac{3 - \frac{5}{x}}{1 - \frac{2}{x}}$$

Also, according to Theorem 3.8, we know that

$$\lim_{x \to +\infty} \frac{5}{x} = \lim_{x \to +\infty} \frac{2}{x} = 0$$

We now find the limits using the quotient rule, the power rule, and Theorem 3.8:

$$\lim_{x \to +\infty} \sqrt{\frac{3x - 5}{x - 2}} = \lim_{x \to +\infty} \left(\frac{3x - 5}{x - 2}\right)^{1/2} = \left(\lim_{x \to +\infty} \frac{3x - 5}{x - 2}\right)^{1/2}$$

$$= \left(\frac{\lim_{x \to +\infty} \left(3 - \frac{5}{x}\right)}{\lim_{x \to +\infty} \left(1 - \frac{2}{x}\right)}\right)^{1/2} = \left(\frac{3 - 0}{1 - 0}\right)^{1/2} = \sqrt{3}$$

Similarly,

$$\lim_{x \to -\infty} \left(\frac{3x - 5}{x - 2}\right)^3 = 3^3 = 27$$

When evaluating a limit of the form

$$\lim_{x \to +\infty} \frac{p(x)}{d(x)} \quad \text{or} \quad \lim_{x \to -\infty} \frac{p(x)}{d(x)}$$

where $p(x)$ and $d(x)$ are polynomials, it is often useful to divide both $p(x)$ and $d(x)$ by the highest power of x that occurs in either. The limit can then be found by applying Theorem 3.8. This process is illustrated by the following examples.

EXAMPLE 2   Evaluating a limit to (positive) infinity

Evaluate $\displaystyle\lim_{x \to +\infty} \frac{3x^3 - 5x + 9}{5x^3 + 2x^2 - 7}$.

Solution   We may assume $x \neq 0$, because we are interested only in very large values of x. Dividing both the numerator and denominator of the given expressions by x^3, we find

$$\frac{3x^3 - 5x + 9}{5x^3 + 2x^2 - 7} = \frac{3x^3 - 5x + 9}{5x^3 + 2x^2 - 7} \cdot \frac{\frac{1}{x^3}}{\frac{1}{x^3}} = \frac{3 - \frac{5}{x^2} + \frac{9}{x^3}}{5 + \frac{2}{x} - \frac{7}{x^3}}$$

Thus,

$$\lim_{x \to +\infty} \frac{3x^3 - 5x + 9}{5x^3 + 2x^2 - 7} = \lim_{x \to +\infty} \frac{3 - \frac{5}{x^2} + \frac{9}{x^3}}{5 + \frac{2}{x} - \frac{7}{x^3}}$$

$$= \frac{\lim_{x \to +\infty} \left(3 - \frac{5}{x^2} + \frac{9}{x^3}\right)}{\lim_{x \to +\infty} \left(5 + \frac{2}{x} - \frac{7}{x^3}\right)}$$

$$= \frac{3 - 0 + 0}{5 + 0 - 0} = \frac{3}{5}$$

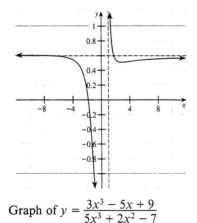

Graph of $y = \dfrac{3x^3 - 5x + 9}{5x^3 + 2x^2 - 7}$

EXAMPLE 3 Evaluating a limit to negative infinity

Evaluate $\lim\limits_{x \to -\infty} \dfrac{95x^3 + 57x + 30}{x^5 - 1{,}000}$.

Solution Dividing the numerator and the denominator by the highest power, x^5, we find that

$$\lim_{x \to -\infty} \frac{95x^3 + 57x + 30}{x^5 - 1{,}000} = \lim_{x \to -\infty} \frac{95x^3 + 57x + 30}{x^5 - 1{,}000} \cdot \frac{\frac{1}{x^5}}{\frac{1}{x^5}}$$

$$= \lim_{x \to -\infty} \frac{\frac{95}{x^2} + \frac{57}{x^4} + \frac{30}{x^5}}{1 - \frac{1{,}000}{x^5}} = \frac{0 + 0 + 0}{1 - 0} = 0$$

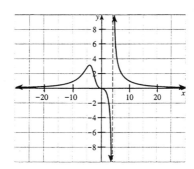

Graph of $y = \dfrac{95x^3 + 57x + 30}{x^5 - 1{,}000}$

EXAMPLE 4 A limit to infinity that does not exist

Evaluate $\lim\limits_{x \to +\infty} \dfrac{3x^2 - 2x}{x - 1}$.

Solution We note that the degree of the numerator is greater than the degree of the denominator. Intuitively, we expect that the limit does not exist because the numerator is growing faster than the denominator. If we divide the numerator by the denominator we find

$$\lim_{x \to +\infty} \frac{3x^2 - 2x}{x - 1} = \lim_{x \to +\infty} \left[(3x + 1) + \frac{1}{x - 1} \right]$$

$$= \lim_{x \to +\infty} (3x + 1) + \lim_{x \to +\infty} \frac{1}{x - 1}$$

$$= +\infty$$

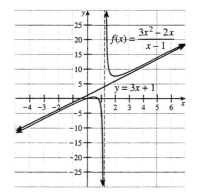

Compare the graphs of $f(x)$ $= \dfrac{3x^2 - 2x}{x - 1}$ and $y = 3x + 1$.

EXAMPLE 5 A limit where technology may fail

Evaluate $\lim\limits_{x \to +\infty} \dfrac{x^{4.359} + 1}{x^{\sqrt{19}}}$.

Solution Consider three similar functions:

$$y_1 = \frac{x^{4.359} + 1}{x^{\sqrt{19}}} \qquad y_2 = \frac{x^{4.359} + 1}{x^{4.36}} \qquad y_3 = \frac{x^{4.359} + 1}{x^{4.359}}$$

If you begin with a calculator (table) or a graph you might obtain a faulty conclusion. Look at the graph of these three functions in Figure 3.44. From the graph you might be led to the *incorrect* conclusion that the limits as $x \to +\infty$ for y_1, y_2, and y_3 are all 1. Let us consider the situation more carefully. We note $\sqrt{19} \approx 4.358898944$.

If we use the approximation $\sqrt{19} \approx 4.36$, we obtain y_2:

$$\lim_{x \to +\infty} \frac{x^{4.359} + 1}{x^{4.36}} = \lim_{x \to +\infty} \left(\frac{1}{x^{0.001}} + \frac{1}{x^{4.36}} \right) = 0 + 0 = 0$$

Let's use a better approximation. With $\sqrt{19} \approx 4.359$, we obtain y_3:

$$\lim_{x \to +\infty} \frac{x^{4.359} + 1}{x^{4.359}} = \lim_{x \to +\infty} \left(1 + \frac{1}{x^{4.359}} \right) = 1$$

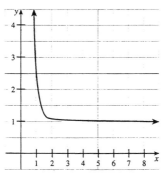

Figure 3.44 Graphs of y_1, y_2, and y_3; with the given scale, the three graphs look the same.

We note that our preliminary conclusion that these limits were the same was incorrect. Let's look at some better graphs (which we might not consider if we relied only on the technology), as shown in Figure 3.45.

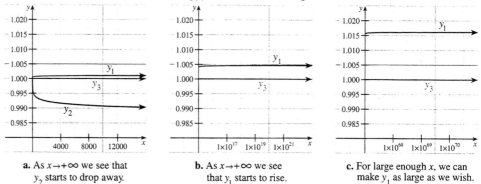

Figure 3.45 Detail of Figure 3.4

a. As $x \to +\infty$ we see that y_2 starts to drop away.

b. As $x \to +\infty$ we see that y_1 starts to rise.

c. For large enough x, we can make y_1 as large as we wish.

Instead of using a numerical approximation (which is what most calculators or computers would use), we confirm what we begin to expect from Figure 3.45c.

$$\lim_{x \to +\infty} \frac{x^{4.359} + 1}{x^{\sqrt{19}}} = \lim_{x \to +\infty} \left(\frac{x^{4.359}}{x^{\sqrt{19}}} + \frac{1}{x^{\sqrt{19}}} \right) = +\infty \quad \textit{Because } \sqrt{19} < 4.359$$

In mathematics, we use the symbol ∞ to describe the situation in Example 5 or whenever it is necessary to indicate either the process of unrestricted growth or the end result of such growth. With this understanding, we can speak of *infinite limits*—that is, limits that increase or decrease without bound. The limit statement $\lim_{x \to c} f(x) = +\infty$ may be defined formally as follows.

Infinite Limit

We write $\lim_{x \to c} f(x) = +\infty$ if for any number $N > 0$ (no matter how large), it is possible to find a number $\delta > 0$ such that $f(x) > N$ whenever $0 < |x - c| < \delta$.

⊘ ▒ **What this does not say**: An infinite limit does not exist in the sense that limits were defined in Chapter 1. The symbolism $\lim_{x \to c} f(x) = +\infty$ *does not mean* that $f(x)$ approaches a *number* $+\infty$ as x approaches c. That is, ∞ is **not a** *number*. Nevertheless, writing $\lim_{x \to c} f(x) = +\infty$ or $\lim_{x \to c} f(x) = -\infty$ conveys more specific information than simply saying "the limit of $f(x)$ as x approaches c does not exist." ⊘

A similar definition holds for the infinite limit statement $\lim_{x \to c} f(x) = -\infty$ (see Problem 62, Problem Set 3.5). For example,

$$\lim_{x \to 5^-} \frac{4}{x - 5} = -\infty \quad \text{and} \quad \lim_{x \to 5^+} \frac{4}{x - 5} = +\infty \quad \text{or} \quad \lim_{x \to -4^-} \frac{-7}{x + 4} = +\infty \quad \text{and} \quad \lim_{x \to -4^+} \frac{-7}{x + 4} = -\infty$$

are infinite limits. The graphs of these functions are shown in Figure 3.46.

Figure 3.46 Graphs showing infinite limits

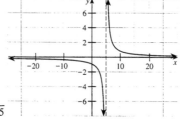

a. Graph of $y = \dfrac{4}{x - 5}$

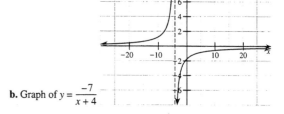

b. Graph of $y = \dfrac{-7}{x + 4}$

EXAMPLE 6   Infinite limit

Find $\lim\limits_{x \to 2^-} \dfrac{3x-5}{x-2}$ and $\lim\limits_{x \to 2^+} \dfrac{3x-5}{x-2}$.

Solution   Notice that $\dfrac{1}{x-2}$ increases without bound as x approaches 2 from the right and $\dfrac{1}{x-2}$ decreases without bound as x approaches 2 from the left. That is,

$$\lim_{x \to 2^+} \frac{1}{x-2} = +\infty \quad \text{and} \quad \lim_{x \to 2^-} \frac{1}{x-2} = -\infty$$

We also have $\lim\limits_{x \to 2} (3x-5) = 1$, and it follows that

$$\lim_{x \to 2^+} \frac{3x-5}{x-2} = +\infty \quad \text{and} \quad \lim_{x \to 2^-} \frac{3x-5}{x-2} = -\infty$$

■ GRAPHS WITH ASYMPTOTES

We shall now show how limits involving infinity can be used along with the curve-sketching techniques developed in the last two sections to sketch graphs with asymptotes. We need the following definitions:

Vertical Asymptote   The line $x = c$ is a **vertical asymptote** of the graph of f if either of the one-sided limits

$$\lim_{x \to c^-} f(x) \quad \text{or} \quad \lim_{x \to c^+} f(x)$$

Horizontal Asymptote   is infinite. The line $y = L$ is a **horizontal asymptote** of the graph of f if

$$\lim_{x \to +\infty} f(x) = L \quad \text{or} \quad \lim_{x \to -\infty} f(x) = L$$

Oblique Asymptote   The line $y = mx + b$ is an **oblique asymptote** of the graph of f if f is a rational function such that the numerator and denominator have no common factors and

$$f(x) = \frac{p(x)}{d(x)} = mx + b + \frac{r}{d(x)}$$

where $\lim\limits_{x \to +\infty} \dfrac{r}{d(x)} = 0$.

EXAMPLE 7   Graphing a rational function using asymptotes

Sketch the graph of $f(x) = \dfrac{3x-5}{x-2}$.

Solution

Vertical Asymptotes. First, make sure the given function is written in simplified form. Because vertical asymptotes for $f(x) = \dfrac{3x-5}{x-2}$ occur at values of x for which f is not defined, we look for values that cause the denominator to be zero; that is, we solve $d(c) = 0$ and then evaluate $\lim\limits_{x \to c^-} f(x)$ and $\lim\limits_{x \to c^+} f(x)$ to ascertain the behavior of the function at $x = c$. For this

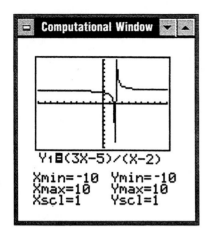

example, $x = 2$ is a value that causes division by zero, so we find

$$\lim_{x \to 2^-} \frac{3x - 5}{x - 2} = -\infty \quad \text{and} \quad \lim_{x \to 2^+} \frac{3x - 5}{x - 2} = +\infty$$

(We found these limits in Example 6.) This means that $x = 2$ is a vertical asymptote and that the graph is moving downward as $x \to 2$ from the left and upward as $x \to 2$ from the right. This information is recorded on the preliminary graph shown in Figure 3.47a by a dashed vertical line with upward ($\uparrow$) and downward ($\downarrow$) arrows.

Horizontal Asymptotes. In order to find the horizontal asymptotes we compute

$$\lim_{x \to +\infty} \frac{3x - 5}{x - 2} = \lim_{x \to +\infty} \frac{3x - 5}{x - 2} \cdot \frac{\frac{1}{x}}{\frac{1}{x}} = \lim_{x \to +\infty} \frac{3 - \frac{5}{x}}{1 - \frac{2}{x}} = \frac{3 - 0}{1 - 0} = 3$$

and

$$\lim_{x \to -\infty} \frac{3x - 5}{x - 2} = 3 \qquad \text{(The steps here are the same as for } x \to +\infty.)$$

This means that $y = 3$ is a horizontal asymptote. This information is recorded on the preliminary graph shown in Figure 3.47a by a dashed horizontal line with outbound arrows ($\leftarrow$, $\rightarrow$).

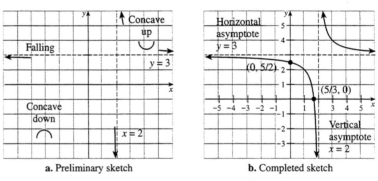

a. Preliminary sketch   **b.** Completed sketch

Figure 3.47 Graph of $f(x) = \dfrac{3x - 5}{x - 2}$

Oblique Asymptotes. This function does not have oblique asymptotes. (Do you see why?)

The preliminary sketch gives us some valuable information about the graph, but it does not present the entire picture. Next, we use calculus to find where the function is increasing and decreasing (first derivative) and where it is concave upward and concave downward (second derivative).

$$f'(x) = \frac{-1}{(x - 2)^2} \quad \text{and} \quad f''(x) = \frac{2}{(x - 2)^3} \qquad \begin{array}{l} \textit{The details for finding} \\ \textit{these derivatives are} \\ \textit{not shown.} \end{array}$$

Neither derivative is ever zero, and both are undefined at $x = 2$. Checking the signs of the first and second derivatives, we find that this curve has no points of inflection (the function is not defined at $x = 2$). This information is added to the preliminary sketch shown in Figure 3.47a. The completed graph is shown in Figure 3.47b.

PROBLEM SET 3.5

Ⓐ *Evaluate the limits in Problems 1–36.*

1. $\lim\limits_{x \to +\infty} \dfrac{2,000}{x + 1}$

2. $\lim\limits_{x \to +\infty} \dfrac{7,000}{\sqrt{x} + 1}$

3. $\lim\limits_{x \to +\infty} \dfrac{3x + 5}{x - 2}$

4. $\lim\limits_{x \to +\infty} \dfrac{x + 2}{3x - 5}$

5. $\lim\limits_{t \to -\infty} \dfrac{5 + t}{7 - t}$

6. $\lim\limits_{s \to -\infty} \dfrac{3s + 4}{7 - 2s}$

7. $\lim\limits_{x \to +\infty} \dfrac{3x^2 - 7x + 5}{-2x^2 + x - 9}$

8. $\lim\limits_{t \to +\infty} \dfrac{9t^5 + 50t^2 + 800}{t^5 - 1,000}$

9. $\lim\limits_{t \to +\infty} \dfrac{17t^5 + 800t^2 + 1,000}{t^6 - 1}$

10. $\lim\limits_{x \to -\infty} \dfrac{100\, x^6 + x^2 - x + 500}{x^7 + 2}$

11. $\lim\limits_{x \to +\infty} \dfrac{8x^3 - 9x + 5}{x^2 + 300x}$

12. $\lim\limits_{x \to +\infty} \dfrac{5,000x^4 + 300x^3 + 1,000}{x^5 + 3}$

13. $\lim\limits_{x \to -\infty} \dfrac{(2x + 5)(x - 3)}{(7x - 2)(4x + 1)}$

14. $\lim\limits_{x \to +\infty} \dfrac{(3x^2 - 10)(x^2 + x)}{(4x^3 - x^2 + 1)(x - 7)}$

15. $\lim\limits_{x \to -\infty} \dfrac{(2x + 1)(x + 5)(x - 3)}{x^4 + 9}$

16. $\lim\limits_{x \to +\infty} \dfrac{x(x + 1)(x + 2)}{x^4 - 4}$

17. $\lim\limits_{t \to +\infty} \left(\dfrac{8t + 1}{7t} - \dfrac{1 - t}{t + 5} \right)$

18. $\lim\limits_{x \to +\infty} \left(\dfrac{x}{x + 1} - \dfrac{2x}{x - 1} \right)$

19. $\lim\limits_{t \to +\infty} \left(\dfrac{8t + 5}{3 - 2t} \right)^3$

20. $\lim\limits_{t \to +\infty} \sqrt{\dfrac{18t^2 + t - 4}{3t + 2t^2}}$

21. $\lim\limits_{x \to +\infty} \dfrac{x}{\sqrt{x^2 + 1,000}}$

22. $\lim\limits_{x \to -\infty} \dfrac{3x}{\sqrt{4x^2 + 10}}$

23. $\lim\limits_{x \to +\infty} \dfrac{x^{5.916} + 1}{x^{\sqrt{35}}}$

24. $\lim\limits_{x \to +\infty} \dfrac{x^{6.083} + 1}{x^{\sqrt{37}}}$

25. $\lim\limits_{x \to +\infty} \dfrac{x^{5.831} + 1}{x^{\sqrt{34}}}$

26. $\lim\limits_{x \to +\infty} \dfrac{x^{5.744} + 1}{x^{\sqrt{33}}}$

27. $\lim\limits_{x \to -2^-} \dfrac{x^2 - 3x + 4}{x + 2}$

28. $\lim\limits_{x \to 1^-} \dfrac{x - 1}{|x^2 - 1|}$

29. $\lim\limits_{x \to 3^+} \dfrac{x^2 - 4x + 3}{x^2 - 6x + 9}$

30. $\lim\limits_{x \to 3^+} \left(\dfrac{1}{x - 7} - \dfrac{1}{x - 3} \right)$

31. $\lim\limits_{x \to 0^+} \dfrac{x^2 - x + 1}{x - \sin x}$

32. $\lim\limits_{x \to \frac{\pi}{4}^+} \dfrac{\sec x}{\tan x - 1}$

33. $\lim\limits_{x \to +\infty} \left(x \sin \dfrac{1}{x} \right)$

34. $\lim\limits_{x \to 0^+} \dfrac{x^2 - x}{x - \sin x}$

35. $\lim\limits_{x \to 0^+} \dfrac{x^2 \csc x}{1 - \cos x}$

36. $\lim\limits_{x \to 0^+} \dfrac{x - \sin x}{\sqrt{\sin x}}$

Find all vertical and horizontal asymptotes of the graphs of the functions given in Problems 37–46. Find where each graph is rising and where it is falling, determine concavity, and locate all critical points and points of inflection. Finally, sketch the graph.

37. $f(x) = \dfrac{3x + 5}{7 - x}$

38. $g(x) = \dfrac{15}{x + 4}$

39. $f(x) = 4 + \dfrac{2x}{x - 3}$

40. $g(x) = x - \dfrac{x}{4 - x}$

41. $h(x) = x^2 + \dfrac{2}{x}$

42. $f(x) = \dfrac{x^2 + 2x - 3}{x + 1}$

43. $f(x) = \dfrac{x^3 + 1}{x^3 - 8}$

44. $f(x) = \dfrac{2x^2 - 5x + 7}{x^2 - 9}$

45. $g(x) = \dfrac{8}{x - 1} + \dfrac{27}{x + 4}$

46. $f(x) = \dfrac{1}{x + 1} + \dfrac{1}{x - 1}$

Sketch the graphs of the piecewise-defined functions in Problems 47–50.

47. $f(x) = \begin{cases} x^2 - 3x & \text{if } x \le 1 \\ \sqrt{x} & \text{if } x > 1 \end{cases}$

48. $f(t) = \begin{cases} \sqrt{t(t - 1)} & \text{if } t > 0 \\ 1 + t^3 & \text{if } t \le 0 \end{cases}$

49. $f(t) = \begin{cases} \cos t - \sin t & \text{if } t \le 0 \\ \cos^2 t & \text{if } t > 0 \end{cases}$

50. $f(x) = \begin{cases} x^2 - 3x & \text{if } x \le 1 \\ \frac{1}{2}(3x - 7) & \text{if } 1 < x < 3 \\ \dfrac{3x - 1}{x + 5} & \text{if } x \ge 3 \end{cases}$

Ⓑ 51. **THINK TANK PROBLEM** Sketch the graph of a function f with all the following properties:

The graph has $y = 1$ and $x = 3$ as asymptotes;

f is increasing for $x < 3$ and $3 < x < 5$ and is decreasing elsewhere;

The graph is concave up for $x < 3$ and for $x > 7$ and concave down for $3 < x < 7$;

$f(0) = 4 = f(5)$ and $f(7) = 2$.

52. **THINK TANK PROBLEM** Sketch a graph of a function g with all of the following properties:

The graph has no inflection points and only one critical point $(1, 1)$;

$\lim\limits_{x \to -\infty} g(x) = \lim\limits_{x \to +\infty} g(x) = 2$; and

$\lim\limits_{x \to -1^+} g(x) = \lim\limits_{x \to 3^-} g(x) = -\infty$;

g is increasing for $x < -1$ and is decreasing only for $-1 < x < 1$.

53. ■ **What Does This Say?** Frank Kornerkutter has put off doing his math homework until the last minute, and he is now trying to evaluate

$$\lim_{x \to 0^+} \left(\dfrac{1}{x^2} - \dfrac{1}{x} \right)$$

At first he is stumped, but suddenly he has an idea: Because

$$\lim_{x \to 0^+} \dfrac{1}{x^2} = +\infty \quad \text{and} \quad \lim_{x \to 0^+} \dfrac{1}{x} = +\infty$$

it must surely be true that the limit in question has the value $+\infty - (+\infty) = 0$. Having thus "solved" his problem he celebrates by taking a nap. Is he right, and if not, what is wrong with his argument?

54. Find constants a and b that guarantee that the graph of the function defined by

$$f(x) = \frac{ax + 5}{3 - bx}$$

will have a vertical asymptote at $x = 5$ and a horizontal asymptote at $y = -3$.

55. JOURNAL PROBLEM: *College Mathematics Journal** by Michael G. Murphy.   Find the oblique asymptote of the curve with equation

$$y = \frac{x^2 + 3x + 7}{x + 2}$$

Solution 1.   By division,

$$\frac{x^2 + 3x + 7}{x + 2} = x + 1 + \frac{5}{x + 2}$$

Because the final term tends to zero as x grows, the asymptote is the line of equation $y = x + 1$.

Solution 2.   Following a procedure frequently used in calculating limits at infinity,

$$\frac{x^2 + 3x + 7}{x + 2} = \frac{x + 3 + \frac{7}{x}}{1 + \frac{2}{x}}$$

For large x, the value is approximately $x + 3$, so the asymptote should be the line of equation $y = x + 3$.

Reconcile these solutions. What is wrong?

56. JOURNAL PROBLEM: *Parabola*†.   Draw a careful sketch of the curve

$$y = \frac{x^2}{x^2 - 1}$$

indicating clearly any vertical or horizontal asymptotes, turning points, or points of inflection.

57. Let

$$P(x) = a_n x^n + a_{n-1} x^{n-1} + \cdots + a_1 x + a_0$$

be a polynomial with $a_n \neq 0$ and let

$$L = \lim_{x \to -\infty} P(x) \quad \text{and} \quad M = \lim_{x \to +\infty} P(x).$$

Fill in the missing entries in the following table:

Sign of a_n	n	L	M
+	even	a.	$+\infty$
+	odd	$-\infty$	b.
−	even	c.	d.
−	odd	e.	$-\infty$

*Volume 22, May 1991, p. 221.

†Volume 20, Issue 1, 1984. A *turning point* is what we have called a relative extrema.

58. A town planning commission estimates that t years from now, the population of the town will be p thousand people given by the formula

$$p(t) = \frac{57t + 8}{3t + 4}$$

a. What is the population of the town? What will it be in 10 years?

b. Sketch the graph of the population function p. What is the "ultimate population" of the town—that is, what is $\lim_{t \to +\infty} p(t)$?

59. a. Show that, in general, the graph of the function

$$f(x) = \frac{ax^2 + bx + c}{rx^2 + sx + t}$$

will have $y = \frac{a}{r}$ as a horizontal asymptote and that when $br \neq as$, the graph will cross this asymptote at the point where

$$x = \frac{at - cr}{br - as}$$

b. What can be said about the case where $br = as$?

c. Sketch the graph of each of the following functions:

$$g(x) = \frac{x^2 - 4x - 5}{2x^2 + x - 10}$$

$$h(x) = \frac{3x^2 - x - 7}{-12x^2 + 4x + 8}$$

Ⓒ 60. Let $f(x) = p(x)/d(x)$ be a rational function, and let c be a number for which $d(c) = 0$ but $p(c) \neq 0$. Explain why $\lim_{x \to c^-} f(x)$ and $\lim_{x \to c^+} f(x)$ must both be infinite. Note that this means $x = c$ is a vertical asymptote of the graph of f.

61. Consider the rational function

$$f(x) = \frac{a_n x^n + a_{n-1} x^{n-1} + \cdots + a_1 x + a_0}{b_m x^m + b_{m-1} x^{m-1} + \cdots + b_1 x + b_0}$$

a. If $m > n$ and $b_m \neq 0$, show that the x-axis is the only horizontal asymptote of the graph of f.

b. If $m = n$, show that the line $y = a_n/b_m$ is the only horizontal asymptote of the graph of f.

c. If $m < n$, is it possible for the graph to have a horizontal asymptote? Explain.

62. ■ **What Does This Say?**   State what you think should be the formal definition of each of the following limit statements:

a. $\lim_{x \to c^+} f(x) = -\infty$ **b.** $\lim_{x \to c^-} f(x) = +\infty$

63. Prove that if

$$\lim_{x \to +\infty} f(x) \quad \text{and} \quad \lim_{x \to +\infty} g(x)$$

both exist, so does

$$\lim_{x \to +\infty} [f(x) + g(x)]$$

and

$$\lim_{x \to +\infty} [f(x) + g(x)] = \lim_{x \to +\infty} f(x) + \lim_{x \to +\infty} g(x)$$

Hint: The key is to show that if

$$|f(x) - L| < \frac{\varepsilon}{2}$$

for $x > N_1$ and

$$|g(x) - M| < \frac{\varepsilon}{2}$$

for $x > N_2$, then

$$|[f(x) + g(x)] - (L + M)| < \varepsilon$$

whenever $x > N$ for some number N. You should also show that N relates to N_1 and N_2.

64. Prove the following limit rule. If $\lim_{x \to c} f(x) = +\infty$ and

$$\lim_{x \to c} g(x) = A \qquad A > 0$$
$$\text{then } \lim_{x \to c} [f(x)g(x)] = +\infty$$

Hint: Notice that because $\lim_{x \to c} g(x) = A$, the function $g(x)$ is near A when x is near c. Therefore, because $\lim_{x \to +\infty} f(x) = +\infty$, the product $f(x)g(x)$ is large if x is near c. Formalize these observations for the proof.

65. Prove the following limit rule. If $\lim_{x \to c} f(x) = +\infty$ and $\lim_{x \to c} g(x) = A$ where $A < 0$, then

$$\lim_{x \to c} \frac{f(x)}{g(x)} = -\infty$$

3.6 SUMMARY OF CURVE SKETCHING

IN THIS SECTION General curve sketching, graphing strategy
In this section we tie together your graphing skills from previous courses as well as the calculus-based curve sketching developed in this chapter.

■ GENERAL CURVE SKETCHING

It is worthwhile to combine the techniques of curve sketching from calculus with those techniques studied in precalculus courses. You may be familiar with **extent** (finding the domain and the range of the function) or **symmetry** (with respect to the x-axis, y-axis, or origin). These features are reviewed in the *Student Mathematics Handbook and Integration Table for CALCULUS*. We now have all the tools we need to describe a general procedure for curve sketching, and this procedure is summarized in Table 3.2 on page 216.

EXAMPLE 1   Sketching a curve with an oblique asymptote

Discuss and sketch the graph of $y = \dfrac{x^2 - x - 2}{x - 3}$.

Solution   Performing the division, we write

$$y = \frac{x^2 - x - 2}{x - 3} = x + 2 + \frac{4}{x - 3}$$

Find the first and second derivatives, along with the critical values for y' and y'':

Derivatives	Critical values
$y' = 1 - 4(x - 3)^{-2}$	$1 - 4(x - 3)^{-2} = 0$
	$1 = 4(x - 3)^{-2}$
	$(x - 3)^2 = 4$
	$x - 3 = \pm 2$
	$x = 5, 1$
$y'' = 8(x - 3)^{-3}$	$8(x - 3)^{-3} = 0$
	No second-order critical values

Computational Window

$Y_1 \boxminus (X^2 - X - 2)/(X - 3)$

Xmin=-10   Ymin=-10
Xmax=10   Ymax=10
Xscl=1   Yscl=1

APPENDIX C   Significant Digits

Throughout this book, various computational windows appear and, in the answers to the problems, you will frequently find approximate (decimal) answers. Sometimes your answer may not exactly agree with the answer found in the back of the book. This does not necessarily mean that your answer is incorrect, particularly if your answer is very close to the given answer.

To use your calculator intelligently and efficiently, you should become familiar with its functions and practice doing problems with the same calculator, whenever possible. Read the computational windows provided throughout this text, and consult the *Owner's Manual* for your particular calculator when you have questions. In addition, there are *Technology Manuals* accompanying this text that are available for TI and HP Graphic Calculators, as well as for MATLAB and for Maple.

■ SIGNIFICANT DIGITS

Applications involving measurements can never be exact. It is particularly important that you pay attention to the accuracy of your measurements when you use a computer or calculator, because using available technology can give you a false sense of security about the accuracy in a particular problem. For example, if you measure a triangle and find that the sides are approximately 1.2 and 3.4 and then find the ratio of $1.2/3.4 \approx 0.35294117$, it appears that the result is more accurate than the original measurements! Some discussion about accuracy and significant digits is necessary.

The digits known to be correct in a number obtained by a measurement are called **significant digits**. The digits 1, 2, 3, 4, 5, 6, 7, 8, and 9 are always significant, whereas the digit 0 may or may not be significant.

1. Zeros that come between two other digits are significant, as in 203 or 10.04.
2. If the zero's only function is to place the decimal point, it is not significant, as in

$$\underbrace{0.00000}_{\text{Placeholders}} 23 \quad \text{or} \quad 23,\underbrace{000}_{\text{Placeholders}}$$

If the decimal does more than fix the decimal point, it is not significant, as in

$$0.0023\underset{\uparrow}{0} \quad \text{or} \quad 23,\underbrace{000}.01$$

$$\text{This digit is significant.} \qquad \text{These are significant.}$$

This second rule can, of course, result in certain ambiguities, such as 23,000 (measured to the *exact* unit). To avoid such confusion, we use scientific notation in this case:

$$2.3 \times 10^4 \text{ has two significant digits}$$

$$2.3000 \times 10^4 \text{ has five significant digits}$$

Numbers that come about by counting are considered to be exact and are correct to any number of significant digits.

When you compute an answer using a calculator, the answer may have 10 or more digits. In the computational windows, we generally show the 10 or 12 digits that result from the numerical calculation, but frequently the number in the answer section will have only 5 or 6 digits in the answer. It seems clear that if the first 3 or 4 nonzero digits of the answer coincide, you probably have the correct method of doing the problem.

However, you might ask why are there discrepancies and how many digits should you use when you write down your final answer? Roughly speaking, the significant digits in a number are the digits that have meaning. In order to clarify the concept, we must for the moment assume that we know the exact answer. We then assume that we have been able to compute an approximation to this exact answer. Usually, we do this by some sort of iterative process, in which the answers are getting closer and close to the exact answer. In such a process, we hope that the number of significant digits in our approximate answer are increasing at each trial. If our approximate answer is, say 6 digits long (some of those digits might even be zero), and the difference between our answer and the exact answer is 4 units or less in the last place, then the first 5 digits are significant.

For example, if the exact answer is 3.14159 and or approximate answer is 3.14162, then our answer has 5 significant digits. Note that saying that our answer is correct to 5 significant digits does not guarantee that all of those 5 digits exactly is correct to 5 significant digits does not guarantee that all of those 5 digits exactly match the first 5 digits of the exact answer. In fact, if an exact answer is 6.001 and our computed answer is 5.997, then our answer has 3 significant digits and not one of them matches the digits in the exact answer. Also note that it may be necessary for an approximation to have more digits that are actually significant for it to have a certain number of significant digits. For example, if the exact answer is 6.003 and our approximation is 5.998, then it has 3 significant digits, but only if we consider the total 4-digit number and do not strip off the last nonsignificant digit.

Again, suppose you know that all digits are significant in the number 3.456; then you know that the exact number is at most 3.4564 or at least 3.4555. Some people may say that the number 3.456 is correct to 3 decimal places. This is the same as saying that it has 4 significant digits.

Why bother with significant digits? If you multiply (or divide) two numbers with the same number of significant digits, then the product will generally be at least twice as long, but will have roughly the same number of significant digits as the original factors. You can then dispense with the unneeded digits. In fact, to keep them would be misleading about the accuracy of the result.

Frequently, we can make an educated guess of the number of significant digits in an answer. For example, if we compute an iterative approximation such as

$$2.3123, 2.3125, 2.3126, 2.31261, 2.31262, \ldots$$

we would generally conclude that the answer is 2.3126 to 5 signficant digits. Of course, we may very well be wrong, and if we went on iterating the answer might end up as 2.4.

■ ROUNDING AND RULES OF COMPUTATION USED IN THIS BOOK

In hand and calculator computations, rounding a number is done to reduce the number of digits displayed and make the number easier to comprehend. In addition, if you suspect that the digit in the last place is not significant, then you might be tempted to round and remove this last digit. This can lead to error. For example, if the computed value is 0.64 and the true value is known to be between 0.61 and 0.67, then the computed value has only 1 significant digit. However, if we round it to 0.6 and the true value is really 0.66, then 0.6 is not correct to even 1 significant digit. In the interest of making the text easier to read, we have used the following rounding procedure.

ROUNDING PROCEDURES   To round off numbers:

1. Increase the last retained digit by 1 if the remainder is greater than or equal to 5; or
2. Retain the last digit unchanged if the remainder is less than 5.

Elaborate rules for computation of approximate data can be developed when needed (in chemistry, for example), but in this text we will use three simple rules:

RULES FOR SIGNIFICANT DIGITS   *Addition-subtraction*: Add or subtract in the usual fashion, and then round off the result so that the last digit retained is in the column farthest to the right in which both given numbers have significant digits.
Multiplication-Division: Multiply or divide in the usual fashion, and then round off the results to the smaller number of significant digits found in either of the given numbers.

Counting numbers: Numbers used to count or whole numbers used as exponents are considered to be correct to any number of significant digits.

ROUNDING RULE

We use the following rounding procedure in problems requiring rounding by involving several steps: *Round only once, at the end. That is, do not work with rounded results, since round-off errors can accumulate.*

■ CALCULATOR EXPERIMENTS

You should be aware that you are much better than your calculator at performing certain computations. For example, almost all calculators will fail to give the correct answer to

$$(10.0 \text{ EE} + 50.0) + 911.0 - (10.0 \text{ EE} + 50.0)$$

Calculators will return the value of 0, while you know at a glance that the answer is 911.0. We must reckon with this poor behavior on the part of calculators, which is called *loss of accuracy due to catastrophic cancellation*. In this case, it is easy to catch the error immediately, but what if the computation is so complicated (or hidden by other computations) that we do not see the error?

First, we want to point out that the order in which you perform computations can be very important. For example, most calculators will correctly conclude that

$$(10.0 \text{ EE} + 50.0) - (10.0 \text{ EE} + 50.0) + 911.0 = 911$$

There are other cases besides catastrophic cancellation where the order in which a computation is performed will substantially affect the result. For example, you may not be able to calculate

$$(10.0 \text{ EE} + 50.0)*(911.0 \text{ EE} + 73.0)/(20.0 \text{ EE} + 60.0)$$

but by rearranging the factors as

$$((10.0 \text{ EE} + 50.0)/(20.0 \text{ EE} + 60.0))*(911.0 \text{ EE} + 73.0)$$

should provide the correct answer of 4.555 EE 65. So, for what do we need to watch? Try not to subtract two numbers that are close to each other in magnitude. If you must, then be aware that you may obtain an inaccurate result. When you have a sequence of multiplications and divisions in a string, try to arrange the factors so that in each partial result up to that point, the intermediate answer stays as close to 1.0 as possible.

Second, since all computations a calculator performs are done with a finite number of digits, it is unable to do exact computations involving nonterminating decimals. This enables us to see how many digits the calculator actually uses when it computes a result. For example,

$$(7.0/17.0)*(17.0) - 7.0$$

should give the result, but on most calculators it does not. The size of the answer gives an indication of how many digits "Accuracy" the calculator uses internally. That is, the calculator may display decimal numbers that have 10 digits, but use 12 digits internally. If the answer to the above computation is something similar to 1.0 EE—12, then the calculator is using 12 digits internally.

■ TRIGONOMETRIC EVALUATIONS

In many problems you will be asked to compute the values of trigonometric functions such as the sine, cosine, or tangent. In calculus, trigonometric arguments are usually assumed to be measured in radians. You must make sure the calculator is in radian mode. If it is in radian mode, then the sine of a small number will almost be equal to that number. For example,

$$\sin(0.00001) = 0.00001 \cdots$$

If not, then you are not using radian mode—make sure you know how to put your calculator in radian mode.

■ GRAPHING BLUNDERS

When you are using the graphing features, you must always be careful to choose reasonable scales for the domain (horizontal scale) and range (vertical scale). If the scale is too large, you may not see important wiggles. if the scale is too small, you may not see important behavior elsewhere in the plane. Of course, knowing the techniques of graphing discussed in Chapter 3 will prevent you from making such blunders. Some calculators may have trouble with curves that jump suddenly at a point. An example of such a curve would be

$$y = \frac{e^x}{x}$$

which jumps at the origin. Try plotting this curve with your calculator using different horizontal and vertical scales, making sure that you understand how your calculator handles such graphs.

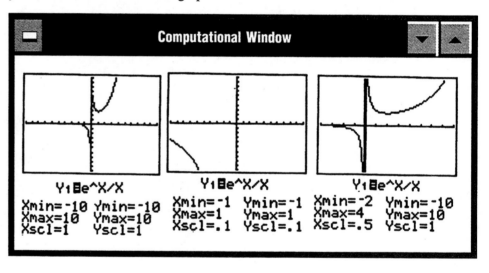

Historical Notes

Historical Note

The numeration system we use evolved over a long period of time. It is often called the *Hindu-Arabic* system because its origins can be traced back to the Hindus in Bactria (now Afghanistan). Later, in A.D. 700, India was invaded by the Arabs, who used and modified the Hindu numeration system and in turn introduced it to Western civilization. The Hindu Brahmagupta stated the rules for operations with positive and negative numbers in the seventh century A.D. There are some indications that the Chinese had some knowledge of negative numbers as early as 200 B.C. On the other hand, the Western mathematician Girolamo Cardan (1501–1576) was calling numbers such as (−1) absurd as late as 1545.

How Global Climate Is Modeled

We find a good example of mathematical modeling by looking at the work being done with weather prediction. In theory, if the correct assumptions could be programmed into a computer, along with appropriate mathematical statements of the ways global climate conditions operate, we would have a model to predict the weather throughout the world. In the global climate model, a system of equations calculates time-dependent changes in wind as well as temperature and moisture changes in the atmosphere and on the land. The model may also predict alterations in the temperature of the ocean's surface. At the National Center for Atmospheric Research, they use a CRAY supercomputer to do this modeling.

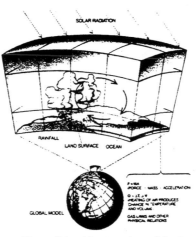

From *Scientific American*, March 1991.

Historical Note
RENÉ DESCARTES (1596–1650)

The Cartesian coordinate system is named in honor of the French mathematician René Descartes. Tradition tells us that he thought of his coordinate system while lying in bed watching a fly crawl around on the ceiling of his bedroom. He noticed that the path of the fly could be described if he knew the relation connecting the fly's distance from each of the walls. This idea of a coordinate system ties together the two great branches of mathematics, algebra and geometry, to form what is known as **analytic geometry.** Plane analytic geometry is that subject devoted primarily to the graphing of equations in two variables and finding the equations of points in the plane.

2

Historical Note

SOPHIE GERMAIN (1776–1831)

Sophie Germain was one of the first women recorded in the history of mathematics as doing original mathematical research. In her time, women were not admitted to first-rate universities and were not, for the most part, taken seriously, so she wrote at first under the pseudonym LeBlanc. Even though Germain's most important research was in number theory, she was awarded the prize of the French Academy for a paper entitled "Memoir on the Vibrations of Elastic Plates." As we progress through this book we will profile many mathematicians in the history of mathematics, and you will notice that most of them are white males. Why? This issue is addressed in the questions at the end of this chapter.

Historical Note

The Navajo are a Native American people who, despite considerable interchange and assimilation with the surrounding dominant culture, maintain a world view that remains vital and distinctive. The Navajo believe in a dynamic universe. Rather than consisting of objects and situations, the universe is made up of processes. Central to our Western mode of thought is the idea that things are separable entities that can be subdivided into smaller discrete units. For us, things that change through time do so by going from one specific state to another specific state. While we believe time to be continuous, we often even break it into discrete units or freeze it and talk about an instant or point in time. Among the Navajo, where the focus is on process, change is ever present; interrelationship and motion are of primary significance. These incorporate and subsume space and time.

From *Ethnomathematics* by Marcia Ascher, pp. 128–129.

Historical Note

KARL WEIERSTRASS
(1815–1897)

The idea of continuity evolved from the notion of a curve "without breaks or jumps" to a rigorous definition given by Karl Weierstrass. Our definition of continuity is a refinement of a definition first given by Bernhard Bolzano (1781–1848). Galileo and Leibniz had thought of continuity in terms of the density of points on a curve, but using today's standards we would say they were in error because the rational numbers have this property, yet do not form a continuous curve. However, this was a difficult concept, which evolved over a long period of time. Another mathematician, J.W.R. Dedekind (1831–1916), took an entirely different approach to conclude that continuity is due to the division of a segment into two parts by a point on the segment. As Dedekind wrote, "By this commonplace remark, the secret of continuity is to be revealed."

From Carl Boyer, *A History of Mathematics* (New York, John Wiley & Sons. Inc., 1968), p. 607.

Historical Note

Historical Note

Historical Note

AUGUSTIN-LOUIS CAUCHY
(1789–1857)

In the nineteenth century, leading mathematicians, including Augustin-Louis Cauchy and Karl Weierstrass (1815–1897) sought to make the concept of limit more precise. The ε-δ definition given in this section is the result of those efforts.

Cauchy is described by the historian Howard Eves not only as a first-rate mathematician with tremendous mathematical productivity, but also as a lawyer, a mountain climber, and a painter.

Cauchy wrote a treatise on integrals in 1814 that was considered a classic, and in 1816 his paper on wave propagation in liquids won a prize from the French Academy. It has been said that with his work the modern era of analysis began. In all, he wrote over 700 papers, which are today considered no less than brilliant.

Isaac Newton (1642–1727) Sir Isaac Newton was one of the greatest mathematicians of all time. He was a genius of the highest order but was often absent-minded. One story about Newton is that when he was a boy, he was sent to cut a hole in the bottom of the barn door for the cats to go in and out. He cut two holes—a large one for the cat and a small one for the kittens. Newton considered himself a theologian rather than a mathematician or a physicist. He spent years searching for clues about the end of the world and the geography of hell. One of Newton's quotations about himself is, "I seem to have been only like a boy playing on the seashore and diverting myself in now and then finding a smoother pebble or prettier shell than ordinary, whilst the great ocean of truth lay all undiscovered before me."

Gottfried Leibniz (1646–1716) At the age of 14, Leibniz attempted to reform Aristotelian logic. He wanted to create a general method of reasoning by calculation. At the age of 20, he applied for his doctorate at the university in Leipzig and was refused (because they said he was too young). He received his doctorate the next year at the University of Altdorf, where he made such a favorable impression that he was offered a professorship, which he declined, saying he had very different things in view. Leibniz went on to invent calculus, but not without a bitter controversy developing between Leibniz and Newton. Most historians agree that the bitterness over who invented calculus materially affected the history of mathematics. J. S. Mill characterized Leibniz by saying, "It would be difficult to name a man more remarkable for the greatness and universality of his intellectual powers than Leibniz."

4

When working with rational forms, we need to be careful about division by zero and the possibility of obtaining an indeterminate form. One of the earliest recorded treatments of indeterminate equations is attributed to the Hindu mathematician Āryabhaṭa (476–550?). He gave rules for approximations of square roots and sums of arithmetic progressions as well as rules for basic algebraic manipulations. One example of his work is the following calculation for π: "Add four to one hundred, multiply by eight and add again sixty-two thousand; the result is the approximate value of the circumference of a circle whose diameter is twenty-thousand." It is remarkable that today, most of us would not attempt such a verification of the approximation 3.1416 without using a calculator. The first Indian satellite was named ARYABHAT in his honor.

MARIA AGNESI (1718–1799)

One of the more famous women in the history of mathematics is Maria Agnesi. She was born in Milan, the first of 21 children. Her first publication, at age 9, was a Latin discourse defending higher education for women. Her most important work is a now-classic calculus textbook published in 1748. Maria Agnesi is also remembered for a curve called the witch of Agnesi. This curve is defined by the equation

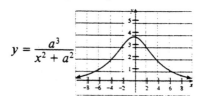

$$y = \frac{a^3}{x^2 + a^2}$$

The curve was named *versoria* by Guido Grandi (1672–1742), but Agnesi confused the word *versoria* with the word *versiera*, which means "devil's grandmother" in Latin. Later, when translated into English, *versiera* was rendered as "witch." The curve has ever since been called the "witch of Agnesi."

GUILLAUME FRANCOIS ANTOINE DE L'HÔPITAL (1661–1704)

The French mathematician Marquis de l'Hôpital published the rule in the late 17th century in what is often regarded as the first calculus text. Actually, the rule was discovered by l'Hôpital's teacher, Johann Bernoulli. Not only did l'Hôpital neglect to cite his sources in his book, but there is also evidence that he paid Bernoulli for his results and for keeping their arrangements for payment confidential. In a letter dated March 17, 1694, he asked Bernoulli "to communicate to me your discoveries . . ."—with the request not to mention them to others—". . . it would not please me if they were made public."

Historical Note

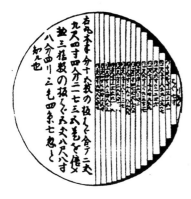

EARLY ASIAN CALCULUS

The mathematician Seki Kōwa (1642–1708) measured the area of a circle using rectangles. This sample was drawn by a student of Kōwa. The Japanese called this process for finding area *yenri*.

Historical Note

GEORG FRIEDRICH BERNHARD RIEMANN (1826–1866)

We meet Riemann in this section in the context of what we call Riemann sums. In his personal life he was frail, bashful, and timid, but in his professional life he was one of the giants in mathematical history. He is known for his work in geometry (for example, Riemannian geometry and Riemann surfaces) and analysis. In his book, *Space Through the Ages*, Cornelius Lanczos said, "Although Riemann's collected papers fill only one single volume of 538 pages, this volume weighs tons if measured intellectually. Every one of his many discoveries was destined to change the course of mathematical science."

Riemann Sum

Historical Note

PIERRE SIMON LAPLACE (1749–1827)

Newton and Leibniz have been credited with the discovery of calculus, but much of its refinement was due to the mathematicians Laplace, Lagrange, and Gauss. Pierre Simon Laplace was a French mathematician who did outstanding work in differential equations, which were introduced in this chapter. He was also known for his work in celestial mechanics, geodesy, and probability. We will meet Lagrange and Gauss in other historical notes, but these three great mathematicians of calculus were contrasted by W. W. Rouse Ball.

The great masters of modern analysis are Lagrange, Laplace, and Gauss, who were contemporaries. It is interesting to note the marked contrast in their styles. Lagrange is perfect both in form and matter: he is careful to explain his procedure, and though his arguments are general they are easy to follow. Laplace on the other hand explains nothing, is indifferent to style, and, if satisfied that his results are correct, is content to leave them either with no proof or with a faulty one. Gauss is exact and elegant as Lagrange, but even more difficult to follow than Laplace, for he removes every trace of the analysis by which he reached his results, and strives to give a proof which while rigorous shall be as concise and synthetical as possible.

A Short Account of the History of Mathematics as quoted in *Mathematical Circles Adieu* by Howard Eves (Boston: Prindle, Weber & Schmidt, Inc., 1977).

"Kinematics of Jogging" by Ralph Boas

Ralph Boas (1912–1992), Professor Emeritus of Mathematics from the Northwestern University, wrote this guest essay. Professor Boas is well known for his papers and professional activities. In addition to his work in real and complex analysis, he wrote many expository articles, such as this guest essay, about teaching or using mathematics.

Nature herself exhibits to us measurable and observable quantities in definite mathematical dependence; the conception of a function is suggested by all the processes of nature where we observe natural phenomena varying according to distance or to time. Nearly all the "known" functions have presented themselves in the attempt to solve geometrical, mechanical, or physical problems.

J. T. Mertz, *A History of European Thought in the Nineteenth Century* (Edinburgh and London, 1903), p. 696.

Some people think that calculus is dull, but it did not seem so three centuries ago, when it was invented. Then, it produced unexpected results; and, now and then, it still does. This essay is about such a result.

You have learned about the intermediate value theorem (see Section 1.6), which tells you, for instance, that if you jog at 8 min per mile, there must be some instant when your speed is exactly $\frac{1}{8}$ mi per minute—assuming, as is only natural in a course in calculus, that your elapsed time is a continuous function of the distance covered. This principle is very intuitive and was recognized before calculus was invented: Galileo was aware of it in 1638 and thought that it had been known to Plato. On the other hand, there is a question with a much less intuitive answer that was noticed only recently (and, as happens more often than mathematicians like to admit, by a physicist). Suppose that you average 8 min/mi, must you cover some one continuous mile (such as a "measured mile" on a highway) in exactly 8 min? The answer is not intuitive at all: It depends on whether or not your total distance was an integral number of miles. More precisely, if you cover an integral number of miles, then you cover exactly one mile in some 8 min. However, if you cover a nonintegral number of miles, there is not necessarily any one continuous mile that you cover in 8 min.

To prove this, let x be the distance (in miles) covered at any point during your trip, and suppose that when you stop you have covered an integral number of n miles. Let $f(x)$ be the time (in minutes) that it took to cover the first x miles; we will suppose that f is a continuous function. If you averaged 8 min/mi, then $f(x) - 8x = 0$ when $x = 0$ and when $x = n$. Now suppose that you never did cover any consecutive mile in 8 min; in mathematical terms,

$$f(x + 1) - f(x) \neq 8$$

Because

$$f(x + 1) - f(x) - 8$$

is continuous and never 0, it must either always be positive, or else always negative; let us suppose the former. Write the corresponding facts for $x = 0$, 1, . . . , n:

$$f(1) - f(0) > 8$$
$$f(2) - f(1) > 8$$
$$\vdots$$
$$f(n) - f(n - 1) > 8$$

If we add these inequalities we obtain

$$f(n) - f(0) > 8n$$

But we started with the assumption that $f(n) = 8n$ and $f(0) = 0$, so assuming that $f(x + 1) - f(x)$ is never 8 leads to a contradiction.

It is somewhat harder to show that only integral values of n will work. Suppose you jog so that your time to cover x miles is

$$J(x) = k \sin^2 \frac{\pi x}{n} + 8x$$

where n is *not* an integer and k is a small number. This is a legitimate assumption, because J is an increasing function (as a time has to be), if k is small enough. To be sure of this, we calculate $J'(x)$—and here we actually have to use some calculus (or have a calculator that will do it for us). We find

$$J'(x) = \frac{k\pi}{n} \sin \frac{2\pi x}{n} + 8$$

If k is small enough $\left(k < \frac{8n}{\pi}\right)$, then $J'(x) > 0$. This shows not only that J increases, but also that

$$J(x + 1) - J(x)$$

cannot be eight. Because $J(x + 1) - J(x)$ is never negative, if you jog so that your time is $J(x)$, you will never even cover a whole mile in less than 8 min.

8

JOHN NAPIER (1550–1617)

Napier was the Isaac Asimov of his day, having envisioned the tank, the machine gun, and the submarine. He also predicted that the end of the world would occur between 1688 and 1700. He is best known today as the inventor of logarithms, which until the advent of the calculator were used extensively with complicated calculations. Today we use the logarithmic function to model many situations. Napier considered mathematics only a diversion from his theological work, on which he felt his reputation would solely depend.

Historical Note

LEONHARD EULER (1707–1783)

Euler's name is attached to almost every branch of mathematics. He was the most prolific writer on the subject of mathematics, and his mathe-

matical textbooks were masterfully written. His writing was not at all slowed down by his total blindness for the last 17 years of his life. He possessed a phenomenal memory, had almost total recall, and could mentally calculate long and complicated problems.

When Euler was 13 he registered at the University of Basel and was introduced to another famous mathematician, John Bernoulli, who was an instructor there at the time. If Bernoulli thought that a student was promising, he would provide, sometimes gratis, private instruction. Here is Euler's own account of this first encounter with Bernoulli:

"I soon found an opportunity to gain introduction to the famous professor John Bernoulli, whose good pleasure it was to advance me further in the mathematical sciences. True, because of his business he flatly refused me private lessons, but he gave me much wiser advice, namely, to get some more difficult mathematical books and work through them with all industry, and wherever I should find some check or difficulties, he gave me free access to him every Saturday afternoon and was so kind as to elucidate all difficulties, which happened with such greatly desired advantage that whenever he had obviated one check for me, because of that ten others disappeared right away, which is certainly the way to make a happy advance in the mathematics sciences."

From *Elements of Algebra* by Leonhard Euler

GUSTAV DIRICHLET (1805–1859)

Gustav Lejune Dirichlet was a professor of mathematics at the University of Berlin and is known because he was instrumental in formulating a rigorous foundation for calculus. He was not known as a good teacher. His nephew wrote that the mathematics instruction he received from Dirichlet was the most dreadful experience of his life. Howard Eves tells of the time Dirichlet was to deliver a lecture on definite integrals, but because of illness he posted the following note:

> Because of illness I cannot
> lecture today
>   Dirichlet

The students then doctored the note to read:

$$\int_{Easter}^{Michaelmas} (\text{Because of illness I cannot lecture today}) \, d(1 \text{ Frdor})$$
>   Dirichlet

Michaelmas and Easter were school holidays, and 1 Frdor (Fredrichsd'or) was the customary honorarium for a semester's worth of lectures.

Historical Note

PIERRE DE FERMAT
(1601–1665)

A lawyer by profession, Fermat liked to do mathematics in his spare time. He wrote well over 3,000 mathematical papers and notes. In Chapter 2 we saw how his work served to inspire Isaac Newton. In addition to his innovative work with tangents, he obtained the first procedure for differentiating polynomials. However, Fermat's real love was in the area of number theory. His most famous problem has come to be known as Fermat's last theorem. He wrote in the margin of a book:

"To divide a cube into two cubes, a fourth power, or in general, any power whatever above the second, into powers of the same denominations, is impossible, and I have assuredly found an admirable proof of this, but the margin is too narrow to contain it."

In 1993, this problem was reported solved, and the proof looks promising, but to date has not been verified.

GROUP RESEARCH PROJECT*

"Ups and Downs"

Mathematics is one of the oldest of the sciences; it is also one of the most active, for its strength is the vigor of perpetual youth.

A. R. Forsyth
Nature 84 (1910): 285

This project is to be done in groups of three or four students. Each group will submit a single written report.

You have been hired by Two Flags to help with the design of their new roller coaster. You are to plan the path design of ups and downs for a straight stretch with horizontal length of 185 ft. One possible design is shown below, and here is the information you will need:

   a. There must be a support every 10 ft.

   b. The descent can be no steeper than 80° at any point (angles refer to the angle that the path makes with a horizontal).

   c. The design must start with a 45° incline.

   d. The amount of material needed for a support is the square of the height of the support. For example, a support that is 20 ft high requires $20^2 = 400$ ft of material.

We also define the **thrill** of the coaster as the sum of the angle of steepest descent in each fall in radians plus the number of tops.

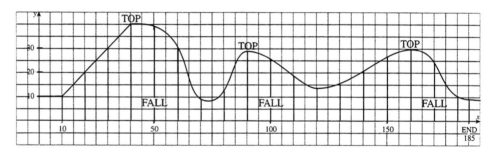

The whole of mathematics consists in the organization of a series of aids to the imagination in the process of reasoning.

A. N. Whitehead
Universal Algebra (Cambridge, 1898), p. 12

Your paper should include, but is not limited to, the following concerns: You should design two roller coaster paths; one should be the most thrilling, and the other should use the least material for supports. Your paper should address where the path is increasing at an increasing rate, and decreasing at a decreasing rate. You should address the safety criteria (a–d listed above) and show the graphs of the path, the slope, and the rate of change of the slope.

*This group project is from Diane Schwartz from Ithaca College, Ithaca, N.Y.

"Wine Barrel Capacity"

This project is to be done in groups of three or four students. Each group will submit a single written report.

A wine barrel has a hole in the middle of its side called a **bung hole.** To determine the volume of wine in the barrel, a **bung rod** is inserted in the hole until it hits the lower seam. Determine how to calibrate such a rod so that it will measure the volume of the wine in the barrel.

You should make the following assumptions:

1. The barrel is cylindrical.

2. The distance from the bung hole to the corner is λ.

3. The ratio of the height to the diameter of the barrel is t. This ratio should be chosen so that for a given λ value, the volume of the barrel is maximal.

Your paper is not limited to the following questions, but it should include these concerns: You should show that the volume of the cylindrical barrel is $V = 2\pi\lambda^3 t(4 + t^2)^{-3/2}$, and you should find the approximate ideal value for t. Johannes Kepler was the first person to show mathematically why coopers were guided in their construction of wine barrels by one rule: *make the staves* (the boards that make up the sides of the barrel) *one and one-half times as long as the diameter.* (This is the approximate t-value.) You should provide dimensions for the barrel as well as for the bung rod.

Johannes Kepler (1571–1630) is usually remembered for his work in astronomy, in particular for his three laws of planetary motion. However, Kepler was also a renowned mathematician and served as court mathematician to the Austrian emperor Matthew I. While at Matthew I's court, Kepler observed with admiration the ability of a young vintner to declare quickly and easily the capacities of a number of different wine casks. He describes how this can be done in his book *The New Stereometry of Wine Barrels, Mostly Austrian.*

bung rod

*The idea for this group research project comes from research done at Iowa State University as part of a National Science Foundation grant. Our thanks to Elgin Johnston of Iowa State University.

"Quality Control"

The calculus is the greatest aid we have to the appreciation of physical truth in the broadest sense of the word.

W. F. Osgood
Bulletin American Mathematical Society.

This project is to be done in groups of three or four students. Each group will submit a single written report.

I own a plant that manufactures disk drives. My problem is to decide how many hours of labor to put into the drive. The minimum labor time required to get a drive is 5 hours, but a 5-hour drive will fail at some point during the warranty period with a probability of 10%. Any extra labor time will reduce this failure probability at an exponential rate: Specifically, each additional hour of labor cuts the failure probability by 40%. A failed disk drive is returned to us for repair, requiring an average of 2 additional hours of labor; in addition it incurs an estimated cost of $200 for handling and damage to the reputation of the product. Suppose that the labor cost is $7 per hour.

Your paper is not limited to the following questions but should include these concerns: How many hours of labor should be put into each machine to minimize my cost per machine? Suppose that hourly labor cost is w dollars instead of $7 per hour; answer the same question. The labor cost w is a parameter, and the optimum labor time depends on w. Exactly what is the nature of this dependence? For what w should we go with the basic 5-hour product, and for what w should this be increased, and by how much?

It is certainly true that all physical phenomena are subject to strictly mathematical conditions, and mathematical processes are unassailable in themselves. The trouble arises from the data employed. Most phenomena are so highly complex that one can never be quite sure that he is dealing with all the factors until the experiment proves it. So that experiment is rather the criterion of mathematical conclusions and must lead the way.

A. E. Dolbear
Matter, Ether, Motion (Boston, 1894), p. 89.

*This problem is from a set of course notes for an introductory calculus course taught by Peter D. Taylor of Queen's University, Kingston, Ontario.

GROUP RESEARCH PROJECT*

"Houdini's Escape"

HARRY HOUDINI (born Ehrich Weiss) (1874–1926)

Mathematics is the gate and key of the sciences. . . . Neglect of mathematics works injury to all knowledge, since he who is ignorant of it cannot know the other sciences or the things of this world. And what is worse, those who are thus ignorant are unable to perceive their own ignorance and so do not seek a remedy.

Roger Bacon
Opus Majus, Part 4, Distinctia Prima, cap. 1

This project is to be done in groups of three or four students. Each group will submit a single written report.

Harry Houdini was a famous escape artist. In this project we relive a trick of his that challenged his mathematical prowess, as well as his skill and bravery. It may challenge these qualities in you as well.

Houdini had his feet shackled to the top of a concrete block which was placed on the bottom of a giant laboratory flask. The cross sectional radius of the flask, measured in feet, was given as a function of height z from the ground by the formula $r(z) = 10z^{-1/2}$, with the bottom of the flask at $z = 1$ ft. The flask was then filled with water at a steady rate of 22π ft^3/min. Houdini's job was to escape the shackles before he was drowned by the rising water in the flask.

Now Houdini knew it would take him exactly 10 minutes to escape the shackles. For dramatic impact, he wanted to time his escape so it was completed precisely at the moment the water level reached the top of his head. Houdini was exactly 6 ft tall. In the design of the apparatus, he was allowed to specify only one thing: the height of the concrete block he stood on.

Your paper is not limited to the following questions but should include these concerns: How high should the block be? (You can neglect Houdini's volume and the volume of the block.) How fast is the water level changing when the flask first starts to fill? How fast is the water level changing at the instant when the water reaches the top of his head? You might also help Houdini with any size flask by generalizing the derivation: Consider a flask with cross-sectional radius $r(z)$ an arbitrary function of z with a constant inflow rate of $dV/dt = A$. Can you find dh/dt as a function of $h(t)$?

It seems to be expected of every pilgrim up the slopes of the mathematical Parnassus, that he will at some point or other of his journey sit down and invent a definite integral or two towards the increase of the common stock.

J. J. Sylvester
Notes to the Meditation on Poncelet's Theorem; Mathematical Papers, Vol. 2, p. 214

*MAA Notes 17 (1991), "Priming the Calculus Pump: Innovations and Resources," by Marcus S. Cohen, Edward D. Gaughan, R. Arthur Knoebel, Douglas S. Kurtz, and David J. Pengelley.

3 Linear Equations of Higher Order

3.1 Introduction: Second-Order Linear Equations

In Chapters 1 and 2 we confined our attention to first-order differential equations. We now turn to equations of higher order $n \geqq 2$, beginning in this chapter with equations that are linear. The general theory of linear differential equations parallels the case of second-order linear equations (the case $n = 2$), which we outline in this initial section.

Recall that a second-order differential equation in the (unknown) function $y(x)$ is one of the form

$$G(x, y, y', y'') = 0. \tag{1}$$

This differential equation is said to be **linear** provided that G is linear in the dependent variable y and its derivatives y' and y''. Thus a linear second-order equation takes the form

> $$A(x)y'' + B(x)y' + C(x)y = F(x). \tag{2}$$

Unless otherwise noted, we will always assume that the (known) coefficient functions $A(x)$, $B(x)$, $C(x)$, and $F(x)$ are continuous on some open interval I (perhaps unbounded) on which we wish to solve this differential equation, but they need not be linear functions. Thus the differential equation

$$e^x y'' + (\cos x)y' + (1 + \sqrt{x})y = \tan^{-1} x$$

is linear because the dependent variable and its derivatives appear linearly, whereas the equations

$$y'' = yy' \qquad \text{and} \qquad y'' + 3(y')^2 + 4y^3 = 0$$

and not linear because products and powers of y or its derivatives appear.

If the function $F(x)$ on the right-hand side of Eq. (2) vanishes identically on I, then we call Eq. (2) a **homogeneous** linear equation; otherwise, it is **nonhomogeneous**. For example, the second-order equation

$$x^2 y'' + 2xy' + 3y = \cos x$$

is nonhomogeneous; its *associated* homogeneous equation is

$$x^2 y'' + 2xy' + 3y = 0.$$

The homogeneous linear equation **associated** with Eq. (2) is

$$A(x)y'' + B(c)y' + C(x)y = 0. \tag{3}$$

In case the differential equation in (2) models a physical system, the nonhomogeneous term $F(x)$ frequently corresponds to some *external* influence on the system.

A Typical Application

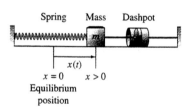

Spring   Mass   Dashpot

$x(t)$

$x = 0$ $x > 0$

Equilibrium
position

FIGURE 3.1.1. A mass-spring-dashpot system

Linear differential equations frequently appear as mathematical models of mechanical systems and electrical circuits. For example, suppose that a mass m is attached both to a spring that exerts on it a force F_S and to a dashpot (shock absorber) that exerts a force F_R on the mass (Fig. 3.1.1). Assume that the restoring force F_S of the spring is proportional to the displacement x (positive to the right, negative to the left) of the mass from equilibrium, and that the dashpot force F_R is proportional to the velocity $v = dx/dt$ of the mass. With the aid of Fig. 3.1.2 we also get the appropriate directions of action of these two forces:

$$F_S = -kx \qquad \text{and} \qquad F_R = -cv \qquad (k, c > 0).$$

The minus signs are correct—F_S is negative when x is positive, F_R is negative when v is positive. Newton's law $F = ma$ now gives

$$mx'' = F_S + F_R; \tag{4}$$

that is,

$$m\frac{d^2x}{dt^2} + c\frac{dx}{dt} + kx = 0. \tag{5}$$

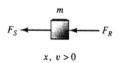

m

$F_S \longleftarrow \quad \longleftarrow F_R$

$x, v > 0$

FIGURE 3.1.2. Directions of the forces acting on m

Thus we have a differential equation in the position function $x(t)$ of the mass m. This homogeneous second-order linear equation governs the *free vibrations* of the mass; we will return to this problem in detail in Section 3.4.

If, in addition to F_S and F_R, the mass m is acted on by an external force $F(t)$—which must then be added to the right-hand side in Eq. (4)—the resulting equation is

$$m\frac{d^2x}{dt^2} + c\frac{dx}{dt} + kx = F(t). \tag{6}$$

This nonhomogeneous linear differential equation governs the *forced vibrations* of the mass under the influence of the external force $F(t)$.

Homogeneous Second-Order Linear Equations

Consider the general second-order linear equation

$$A(x)\, y'' + B(x)\, y' + C(x)\, y = F(x), \tag{7}$$

where the coefficient functions A, B, C, and F are continuous on the open interval I. Here we will assume in addition that $A(x) \neq 0$ at each point of I, so we can divide each term in Eq. (7) by $A(x)$ and write it in the form

$$\blacktriangleright \qquad y'' + p(x)\, y' + q(x)\, y = f(x). \tag{8}$$

We will discuss first the associated homogeneous equation

$$\blacktriangleright \qquad y'' + p(x)\, y' + q(x)\, y = 0. \tag{9}$$

A particularly useful property of this *homogeneous* linear equation is the fact that the sum of any two solutions of (9) is again a solution, as is any constant multiple of a solution. This is the central idea of the following theorem.

▮*HEOREM 1:* Principle of Superposition

Let y_1 and y_2 be two solutions of the homogeneous linear Eq. (9) on the interval I. If c_1 and c_2 are constants, then the linear combination

$$y = c_1 y_1 + c_2 y_2 \tag{10}$$

is also a solution of (9) on I.

Proof: The conclusion follows almost immediately from the *linearity* of the operation of differentiation, which gives

$$y' = c_1 y_1' + c_2 y_2' \qquad \text{and} \qquad y'' = c_1 y_1'' + c_2 y_2'' .$$

Then

$$\begin{aligned}
y'' + py' + qy &= (c_1 y_1 + c_2 y_2)'' + p(c_1 y_1 + c_2 y_2)' + q(c_1 y_1 + c_2 y_2) \\
&= (c_1 y_1'' + c_2 y_2'') + p(c_1 y_1' + c_2 y_2') + q(c_1 y_1 + c_2 y_2) \\
&= c_1 (y_1'' + py_1' + qy_1) + c_2 (y_2'' + py_2' + qy_2) \\
&= c_1 \cdot 0 + c_2 \cdot 0 = 0
\end{aligned}$$

because y_1 and y_2 are solutions. Thus $y = c_1 y_1 + c_2 y_2$ is also a solution. ∎

EXAMPLE 1   We can see by inspection that

$$y_1(x) = \cos x \qquad \text{and} \qquad y_2(x) = \sin x$$

are two solutions of the equation

$$y'' + y = 0.$$

Theorem 1 tells us that any linear combination of these solutions, such as

$$y(x) = 3y_1(x) - 2y_2(x) = 3 \cos x - 2 \sin x$$

is also a solution. We will see later that, conversely, *every* solution of $y'' + y = 0$ is a linear combination of these two particular solutions y_1 and y_2. Thus a general solution of $y'' + y = 0$ is

$$y(x) = c_1 \cos x + c_2 \sin x. \qquad \blacksquare$$

Earlier in this section we gave the linear equation $mx'' + cx' + kx = F(t)$ as a mathematical model of the motion of the mass shown in Fig. 3.1.1. Physical considerations suggest that the motion of the mass should be determined by its initial position and initial velocity. Hence, given any preassigned values of $x(0)$ and $x'(0)$, Eq. (6) ought to have a *unique* solution satisfying these initial conditions. More generally, in order to be a "good" mathematical model of a deterministic physical situation, a differential equation must have unique solutions satisfying any appropriate initial conditions. The following existence and uniqueness theorem (proved in the Appendix) gives us this assurance for the general second-order linear equation.

THEOREM 2: Existence and Uniqueness

Suppose that the functions p, q, and f are continuous on the open interval I containing the point a. Then, given any two numbers b_0 and b_1, the equation

$$y'' + p(x)y' + q(x)y = f(x) \qquad (8)$$

has a unique (that is, one and only one) solution on the entire interval I that satisfies the initial conditions

$$y(a) = b_0, \qquad y'(a) = b_1. \qquad (11)$$

Remark 1: Equation (8) and the conditions in (11) constitute a second-order linear **initial value problem.** Theorem 2 tells us that any such initial value problem has a unique solution on the *whole* interval I where the coefficient functions in (8) are continuous. Recall from Section 1.3 that a *nonlinear* differential equation generally has a unique solution on only a smaller interval.

Remark 2: Whereas a *first-order* differential equation $dy/dx = F(x, y)$ generally admits only a single solution curve $y = y(x)$ passing through a given initial point (a, b), Theorem 2 implies that the *second-order* equation in (8) has infinitely many solution curves passing through the point (a, b_0)—namely, one for each (real number) value of the initial slope $y'(a) = b_1$. That is, instead of there being only one line through (a, b_0) tangent to a solution curve, *every* nonvertical straight line through (a, b_0) is tangent to a solution curve of Eq. (8). Figure 3.1.3 shows a variety of solution curves of the equation

$$y'' + 3y' + 2y = 0,$$

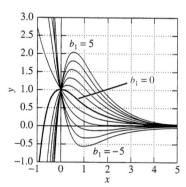

FIGURE 3.1.3. Solution curves of $y'' + 3y' + 2y = 0$ passing through the point (0, 1)

all passing through the point (0, 1). The project material for this section suggests how to construct such a family of solution curves for a given homogeneous second-order linear differential equation.

EXAMPLE 1
Continued We saw in the first part of Example 1 that $y(x) = 3 \cos x - 2 \sin x$ is a solution (on the entire real line) of $y'' + y = 0$. It has the initial values $y(0) = 3$, $y'(0) = -2$. Theorem 2 tells us that this is the *only* solution with these initial values. More generally, the solution

$$y(x) = b_0 \cos x + b_1 \sin x$$

satisfies the *arbitrary* initial conditions $y(0) = b_0, y'(0) = b_1$; this illustrates the *existence* of such a solution, also as guaranteed by Theorem 2. ∎

Example 1 suggests how, given a *homogeneous* second-order linear equation, we might actually find the solution whose existence is assured by Theorem 2. First, we find two "essentially different" solutions y_1 and y_2; second, we attempt to impose on the general solution

$$y = c_1 y_1 + c_2 y_2 \tag{12}$$

the initial conditions $y(a) = b_0, y'(a) = b_1$. That is, we attempt to solve the simultaneous equations

$$c_1 y_1(a) + c_2 y_2(a) = b_0, \qquad c_1 y_1'(a) + c_2 y_2'(a) = b_1 \tag{13}$$

for the coefficients c_1 and c_2.

EXAMPLE 2 Verify that the functions

$$y_1(x) = e^x \qquad \text{and} \qquad y_2(x) = xe^x$$

are solutions of the differential equation

$$y'' - 2y' + y = 0,$$

and then find a solution satisfying the initial conditions $y(0) = 3, y'(0) = 1$.

Solution: The verification is routine; we omit it. We impose the given initial conditions on the general solution

$$y(x) = c_1 e^x + c_2 x e^x,$$

for which

$$y'(x) = (c_1 + c_2)e^x + c_2 x e^x,$$

to obtain the simultaneous equations

$$y(0) = c_1 \qquad = 3,$$
$$y'(0) = c_1 + c_2 = 1.$$

The resulting solution is $c_1 = 3, c_2 = -2$. Hence the solution of the original initial value problem is

$$y(x) = 3e^x - 2xe^x.$$ ∎

In order for the procedure of Example 2 to succeed, the two solutions y_1 and y_2 must have the elusive property that the equations in (13) can always be solved for c_1

and c_2, no matter what the initial conditions b_0 and b_1 might be. The following definition tells precisely how different the two functions y_1 and y_2 must be.

DEFINITION: Linear Independence of Two Functions

Two functions defined on an open interval are said to be **linearly independent** provided that neither is a constant multiple of the other. ■

Two functions are said to be **linearly dependent** on an open interval provided that they are not linearly independent; that is, one of them is a constant multiple of the other. We can always determine whether two given functions f and g are linearly dependent on an interval I by noting at a glance whether either of the two quotients f/g or g/f is a constant on I.

EXAMPLE 3   Thus it is clear that the following pairs of functions are linearly independent on the entire real line:

$$\sin x \quad \text{and} \quad \cos x;$$
$$e^x \quad \text{and} \quad e^{-2x};$$
$$e^x \quad \text{and} \quad xe^x;$$
$$x + 1 \quad \text{and} \quad x^2;$$
$$x \quad \text{and} \quad |x|.$$

But the identically zero function and any other function g are linearly dependent on every interval because $0 = 0 \cdot g(x)$. Also, the functions

$$f(x) = \sin 2x \quad \text{and} \quad g(x) = \sin x \cos x$$

are linearly dependent on any interval because $f(x) = 2g(x)$ for all x (a familiar trigonometric identity). ■

General Solutions

But does the homogeneous equation $y'' + py' + qy = 0$ always have two linearly independent solutions? Theorem 2 says yes! We need only choose y_1 and y_2 so that

$$y_1(a) = 1, \quad y_1'(a) = 0 \quad \text{and} \quad y_2(a) = 0, \quad y_2'(a) = 1.$$

It is then impossible that either $y_1 = ky_2$ or $y_2 = ky_1$ because $k \cdot 0 \neq 1$ for any constant k. Theorem 2 tells us that two such linearly independent solutions *exist;* actually finding them is a crucial matter that we will discuss briefly at the end of this section, and in greater detail beginning in Section 3.3.

We want to show, finally, that given *any* two linearly independent solutions y_1 and y_2 of the homogeneous equation

$$y''(x) + p(x)y'(x) + q(x)y(x) = 0, \tag{9}$$

every solution y of Eq. (9) can be expressed as a linear combination

$$y = c_1 y_1 + c_2 y_2 \tag{12}$$

of y_1 and y_2. This means that the function in (12) is the *general solution* of Eq. (9).

As suggested by the equations in (13), the determination of the constants c_1 and c_2 in (12) depends upon a certain 2×2 determinant of values of y_1, y_2, and their derivatives. Given two functions f and g, the **Wronskian** of f and g is the determinant

$$W = \begin{vmatrix} f & g \\ f' & g' \end{vmatrix} = fg' - f'g.$$

We write either $W(f, g)$ or $W(x)$, depending upon whether we wish to emphasize the two functions or the point x at which their Wronskian is to be evaluated. For example,

$$W(\cos x, \sin x) = \begin{vmatrix} \cos x & \sin x \\ -\sin x & \cos x \end{vmatrix} = \cos^2 x + \sin^2 x = 1$$

and

$$W(e^x, xe^x) = \begin{vmatrix} e^x & xe^x \\ e^x & e^x + xe^x \end{vmatrix} = e^{2x}.$$

These are examples of linearly *independent* pairs of solutions of differential equations (see Examples 1 and 2). Note that in both cases the Wronskian is everywhere *nonzero*.

On the other hand, if the functions f and g are linearly dependent, with $f = kg$ (for example), then

$$W(f, g) = \begin{vmatrix} kg & g \\ kg' & g' \end{vmatrix} = kgg' - kg'g \equiv 0.$$

Thus the Wronskian of two linearly *dependent* functions is identically zero. In Section 3.2 we will prove that, if the two functions y_1 and y_2 are solutions of a homogeneous second-order linear equation, then the strong converse stated in part (b) of Theorem 3 holds.

THEOREM 3: Wronskians of Solutions

Suppose that y_1 and y_2 are two solutions of the homogeneous second-order linear equation (Eq. (9))

$$y'' + p(x)y' + q(x)y = 0$$

on an open interval I on which p and q are continuous.

(a) If y_1 and y_2 are linearly dependent, then $W(y_1, y_2) \equiv 0$ on I;
(b) If y_1 and y_2 are linearly independent, then $W(y_1, y_2) \neq 0$ at each point of I. ∎

Thus, given two solutions of Eq. (9), there are just two possibilities: The Wronskian W is identically zero if the solutions are linearly dependent; the Wronskian is never zero if the solutions are linearly independent. The latter fact is what we need to show that $y = c_1 y_1 + c_2 y_2$ is the general solution of Eq. (9) if y_1 and y_2 are solutions.

THEOREM 4: General Solutions

Let y_1 and y_2 be two linearly independent solutions of the homogeneous equation (Eq. (9))

$$y'' + p(x)y' + q(x)y = 0$$

with p and q continuous on the open interval I. If Y is any solution whatsoever of Eq. (9), then there exist numbers c_1 and c_2 such that

$$Y(x) = c_1 y_1(x) + c_2 y_2(x)$$

for all x in I. ∎

In essence, Theorem 4 tells us that when we have found *two* linearly independent solutions of the homogeneous equation in (9), then we have found *all* of its solutions.

Proof of Theorem 4: Choose a point a of I, and consider the simultaneous equations

$$\begin{aligned} c_1 y_1(a) + c_2 y_2(a) &= Y(a), \\ c_1 y_1'(a) + c_2 y_2'(a) &= Y'(a). \end{aligned} \tag{14}$$

The determinant of the coefficients in this system of linear equations in the unknowns c_1 and c_2 is simply the Wronskian $W(y_1, y_2)$ evaluated at $x = a$. By Theorem 3, this determinant is nonzero, so by elementary algebra it follows that the equations in (14) can be solved for c_1 and c_2. With these values of c_1 and c_2, we define the solution

$$G(x) = c_1 y_1(x) + c_2 y_2(x)$$

of Eq. (9); then

$$G(a) = c_1 y_1(a) + c_2 y_2(a) = Y(a)$$

and

$$G'(a) = c_1 y_1'(a) + c_2 y_2'(a) = Y'(a).$$

Thus the two solutions Y and G have the same initial values at a, as do Y' and G'. By the uniqueness of a solution determined by such initial values (Theorem 2), it follows that Y and G agree on I. Thus we see that

$$Y(x) \equiv G(x) = c_1 y_1(x) + c_2 y_2(x),$$

as desired. ∎

EXAMPLE 4 It is evident that

$$y_1(x) = e^{2x} \qquad \text{and} \qquad y_2(x) = e^{-2x}$$

are linearly independent solutions of

$$y'' - 4y = 0. \tag{15}$$

But $y_3(x) = \cosh 2x$ and $y_4(x) = \sinh 2x$ are also solutions of (15) because

$$\frac{d^2}{dx^2}(\cosh 2x) = \frac{d}{dx}(2 \sinh 2x) = 4 \cosh 2x$$

and, similarly, $(\sinh 2x)'' = 4 \sinh 2x$. It therefore follows from Theorem 4 that the functions $\cosh 2x$ and $\sinh 2x$ can be expressed as linear combinations of $y_1(x) = e^{2x}$ and $y_2(x) = e^{-2x}$. Of course, this is no surprise, because

$$\cosh 2x = \frac{1}{2} e^{2x} + \frac{1}{2} e^{-2x} \quad \text{and} \quad \sinh 2x = \frac{1}{2} e^{2x} - \frac{1}{2} e^{-2x}$$

by the definitions of the hyperbolic cosine and sine. ∎

Linear Second-Order Equations with Constant Coefficients

As an illustration of the general theory introduced in this section, we discuss the homogeneous second-order linear differential equation

$$ay'' + by' + cy = 0 \tag{16}$$

with constant coefficients a, b, and c. We first look for a *single* solution of Eq. (16) and begin with the observation that

$$(e^{rx})' = re^{rx} \quad \text{and} \quad (e^{rx})'' = r^2 e^{rx}, \tag{17}$$

so any derivative of e^{rx} is a constant multiple of e^{rx}. Hence, if we substituted $y = e^{rx}$ in Eq. (16), each term would be a constant multiple of e^{rx}, with the constant coefficients dependent upon r and the coefficients a, b, and c. This suggests that we try to find a value of r so that these multiples of e^{rx} will have sum zero. If we succeed, then $y = e^{rx}$ will be a solution of Eq. (16).

For example, if we substitute $y = e^{rx}$ in the equation

$$y'' - 5y' + 6y = 0,$$

we obtain

$$r^2 e^{rx} - 5re^{rx} + 6e^{rx} = 0.$$

Thus

$$(r^2 - 5r + 6)e^{rx} = 0; \quad (r - 2)(r - 3)e^{rx} = 0.$$

Hence $y = e^{rx}$ will be a solution if either $r = 2$ or $r = 3$. So, in searching for a single solution, we actually have found two solutions: $y_1(x) = e^{2x}$ and $y_2(x) = e^{3x}$.

To carry out this procedure in the general case, we substitute $y = e^{rx}$ in Eq. (16). With the aid of Eq. (17), we find the result to be

$$ar^2 e^{rx} + bre^{rx} + ce^{rx} = 0.$$

Because e^{rx} is never zero, we conclude that $y(x) = e^{rx}$ will satisfy the differential equation in (16) precisely when r is a root of the *algebraic* equation

$$ar^2 + br + c = 0. \tag{18}$$

This quadratic equation is called the **characteristic equation** of the homogeneous linear differential equation

$$ay'' + by' + cy = 0. \tag{16}$$

If Eq. (18) has two *distinct* (unequal) roots, r_1 and r_2, then the corresponding solutions

$y_1(x) = e^{r_1x}$ and $y_2(x) = e^{r_2x}$ of (16) are linearly independent. (Why?) This gives the following result.

▮ *THEOREM 5:* Distinct Real Roots

If the two roots r_1 and r_2 of the characteristic equation in (18) are real and distinct, then

$$y(x) = c_1e^{r_1x} + c_2e^{r_2x} \tag{19}$$

is the general solution of Eq. (16).   ▮

EXAMPLE 5   Find the general solution of

$$2y'' - 7y' + 3y = 0.$$

Solution: We can solve the characteristic equation

$$2r^2 - 7r + 3 = 0$$

by factoring:

$$(2r - 1)(r - 3) = 0.$$

The roots $r_1 = \frac{1}{2}$ and $r_2 = 3$ are real and distinct, so Theorem 5 yields the general solution

$$y(x) = c_1e^{x/2} + c_2e^{3x}.$$

EXAMPLE 6   The differential equation $y'' + 2y' = 0$ has characteristic equation

$$r^2 + 2r = r(r + 2) = 0$$

with distinct real roots $r_1 = 0$ and $r_2 = -2$. Because $e^{0 \cdot x} \equiv 1$, we get the general solution

$$y(x) = c_1 + c_2e^{-2x}.$$ ▮

Remark: Note that Theorem 5 changes a problem involving a differential equation into a problem involving only the solution of an *algebraic* equation.

If the characteristic equation in (18) has equal roots $r_1 = r_2$, we get (at first) only the single solution $y_1(x) = e^{r_1x}$ of Eq. (16). The problem in this case is to produce the "missing" second solution of the differential equation.

A double root $r = r_1$ will occur precisely when the characteristic equation is a constant multiple of the equation

$$(r - r_1)^2 = r^2 - 2r_1r + r_1^2 = 0.$$

Any differential equation with this characteristic equation is equivalent to

$$y'' - 2r_1y' + r_1^2y = 0. \tag{20}$$

But it is easy to verify by direct substitution that $y = xe^{r_1x}$ is a second solution of Eq. (20). It is clear (but you should verify) that

$$y_1(x) = e^{r_1x} \quad \text{and} \quad y_2(x) = xe^{r_1x}$$

are linearly independent functions, so the general solution of the differential equation in (20) is

$$y(x) = c_1 e^{r_1 x} + c_2 x e^{r_1 x}.$$

THEOREM 6: Repeated Roots

If the characteristic equation in (18) has equal (necessarily real) roots $r_1 = r_2$, then

$$y(x) = (c_1 + c_2 x)\, e^{r_1 x} \tag{21}$$

is the general solution of Eq. (16). ■

EXAMPLE 7 To solve the initial value problem

$$y'' + 2y' + y = 0;$$
$$y(0) = 5, \quad y'(0) = -3,$$

we note first that the characteristic equation

$$r^2 + 2r + 1 = (r + 1)^2 = 0$$

has equal roots $r_1 = r_2 = -1$. Hence the general solution provided by Theorem 6 is

$$y(x) = c_1 e^{-x} + c_2 x e^{-x}.$$

Differentiation yields

$$y'(x) = -c_1 e^{-x} + c_2 e^{-x} - c_2 x e^{-x},$$

so the initial conditions yield the equations

$$y(0) = \quad c_1 \qquad = 5,$$
$$y'(0) = -c_1 + c_2 = -3,$$

which imply that $c_1 = 5$ and $c_2 = 2$. Thus the desired particular solution of the initial value problem is

$$y(x) = 5e^{-x} + 2x e^{-x}. \qquad ■$$

The characteristic equation in (18) may have either real or complex roots. The case of complex roots will be discussed in Section 3.3.

3.1 Problems

In Problems 1 through 16, a homogeneous second-order linear differential equation, two functions y_1 and y_2, and a pair of initial conditions are given. First verify that y_1 and y_2 are solutions of the differential equation. Then find a particular solution of the form $y = c_1 y_1 + c_2 y_2$ that satisfies the given initial conditions.

1. $y'' - y = 0$; $\quad y_1 = e^x$, $\quad y_2 = e^{-x}$; $\quad y(0) = 0$,
$\quad y'(0) = 5$

2. $y'' - 9y = 0$; $\quad y_1 = e^{3x}$, $\quad y_2 = e^{-3x}$; $\quad y(0) = -1$,
$\quad y'(0) = 15$

3. $y'' + 4y = 0$; $\quad y_1 = \cos 2x$, $\quad y_2 = \sin 2x$; $\quad y(0) = 3$,
$\quad y'(0) = 8$

4. $y'' + 25y = 0$; $\quad y_1 = \cos 5x$, $\quad y_2 = \sin 5x$;
$\quad y(0) = 10$, $\quad y'(0) = -10$

5. $y'' - 3y' + 2y = 0$; $\quad y_1 = e^x$, $\quad y_2 = e^{2x}$; $\quad y(0) = 1$,
$\quad y'(0) = 0$

6. $y'' + y' - 6y = 0$; $\quad y_1 = e^{2x}$, $y_2 = e^{-3x}$; $\quad y(0) = 7$,
$\quad y'(0) = -1$

7. $y'' + y' = 0$; $\quad y_1 = 1$, $\quad y_2 = e^{-x}$; $\quad y(0) = -2$,
$\quad y'(0) = 8$

8. $y'' - 3y' = 0$; $\quad y_1 = 1$, $\quad y_2 = e^{3x}$; $\quad y(0) = 4$,
$\quad y'(0) = -2$

9. $y'' + 2y' + y = 0$; $\quad y_1 = e^{-x}$, $y_2 = xe^{-x}$; $\quad y(0) = 2$,
$\quad y'(0) = -1$

10. $y'' - 10y' + 25y = 0$; $\quad y_1 = e^{5x}$, $y_2 = xe^{5x}$; $\quad y(0) = 3$,
$\quad y'(0) = 13$

11. $y'' - 2y' + 2y = 0$; $\quad y_1 = e^x \cos x$, $y_2 = e^x \sin x$;
$\quad y(0) = 0$, $\quad y'(0) = 5$

12. $y'' + 6y' + 13y = 0$; $\quad y_1 = e^{-3x} \cos 2x$,
$\quad y_2 = e^{-3x} \sin 2x$; $\quad y(0) = 2$, $\quad y'(0) = 0$

13. $x^2 y'' - 2xy' + 2y = 0$; $\quad y_1 = x$, $\quad y_2 = x^2$;
$\quad y(1) = 3$, $\quad y'(1) = 1$

14. $x^2 y'' + 2xy' - 6y = 0$; $\quad y_1 = x^2$, $\quad y_2 = x^{-3}$;
$\quad y(2) = 10$, $\quad y'(2) = 15$

15. $x^2 y'' - xy' + y = 0$; $\quad y_1 = x$, $\quad y_2 = x \ln x$; $\quad y(1) = 7$,
$\quad y'(1) = 2$

16. $x^2 y'' + xy' + y = 0$; $\quad y_1 = \cos(\ln x)$, $\quad y_2 = \sin(\ln x)$;
$\quad y(1) = 2$, $\quad y'(1) = 3$

The following three problems illustrate the fact that the superposition principle does not generally hold for nonlinear equations.

17. Show that $y = 1/x$ is a solution of $y' + y^2 = 0$, but that if $c \neq 0$ and $c \neq 1$, then $y = c/x$ is not a solution.

18. Show that $y = x^3$ is a solution of $yy'' = 6x^4$, but that if $c^2 \neq 1$, then $y = cx^3$ is not a solution.

19. Show that $y_1 = 1$ and $y_2 = x^{1/2}$ are solutions of $yy'' + (y')^2 = 0$, but that their sum $y = y_1 + y_2$ is not a solution.

Determine whether the pairs of functions in Problems 20 through 26 are linearly independent or linearly dependent on the real line.

20. $f(x) = \pi$, $\quad g(x) = \cos^2 x + \sin^2 x$

21. $f(x) = x^3$, $\quad g(x) = x^2|x|$

22. $f(x) = 1 + x$, $\quad g(x) = 1 + |x|$

23. $f(x) = xe^x$, $\quad g(x) = |x|e^x$

24. $f(x) = \sin^2 x$, $\quad g(x) = 1 - \cos 2x$

25. $f(x) = e^x \sin x$, $\quad g(x) = e^x \cos x$

26. $f(x) = 2\cos x + 3\sin x$, $\quad g(x) = 3\cos x - 2\sin x$

27. Let y_p be a particular solution of the nonhomogeneous equation $y'' + py' + qy = f(x)$ and let y_c be a solution of its associated homogeneous equation. Show that $y = y_c + y_p$ is a solution of the given nonhomogeneous equation.

28. With $y_p = 1$ and $y_c = c_1 \cos x + c_2 \sin x$ in the notation of Problem 27, find a solution of $y'' + y = 1$ satisfying the initial conditions $y(0) = -1 = y'(0)$.

29. Show that $y_1 = x^2$ and $y_2 = x^3$ are two different solutions of $x^2 y'' - 4xy' + 6y = 0$, both satisfying the initial conditions $y(0) = 0 = y'(0)$. Explain why these facts do not contradict Theorem 2 (with respect to the guaranteed uniqueness).

30. (a) Show that $y_1 = x^3$ and $y_2 = |x^3|$ are linearly independent solutions on the real line of the equation $x^2 y'' - 3xy' + 3y = 0$. (b) Verify that $W(y_1, y_2)$ is identically zero. Why do these facts not contradict Theorem 3?

31. Show that $y_1 = \sin x^2$ and $y_2 = \cos x^2$ are linearly independent functions, but that their Wronskian vanishes at $x = 0$. Why does this imply that there is *no* differential equation of the form $y'' + p(x)y' + q(x)y = 0$, with both p and q continuous everywhere, having both y_1 and y_2 as solutions?

32. Let y_1 and y_2 be two solutions of $A(x)y'' + B(x)y' + C(x)y = 0$ on an open interval I where A, B, and C are continuous and $A(x)$ is never zero. (a) Let $W = W(y_1, y_2)$. Show that

$$A(x)\frac{dW}{dx} = y_1(Ay_2'') - y_2(Ay_1'').$$

Then substitute for Ay_2'' and Ay_1'' from the original differential equation to show that

$$A(x)\frac{dW}{dx} = -B(x)W(x).$$

(b) Solve this first-order equation to deduce **Abel's formula**

$$W(x) = K \exp\left(-\int \frac{B(x)}{A(x)}\,dx\right),$$

where K is a constant. (c) Why does Abel's formula imply that the Wronskian $W(y_1, y_2)$ is either zero everywhere or nonzero everywhere (as stated in Theorem 3)?

Apply Theorems 5 and 6 to find general solutions of the differential equations given in Problems 33 through 42.

33. $y'' - 3y' + 2y = 0$ $\qquad$ **34.** $y'' + 2y' - 15y = 0$

35. $y'' + 5y' = 0$ $\qquad$ **36.** $2y'' + 3y' = 0$

37. $2y'' - y' - y = 0$ $\qquad$ **38.** $4y'' + 8y' + 3y = 0$

39. $4y'' + 4y' + y = 0$ $\qquad$ **40.** $9y'' - 12y' + 4y = 0$

41. $6y'' - 7y' - 20y = 0$ $\qquad$ **42.** $35y'' - y' - 12y = 0$

3.1 Computing Project

If a graphics calculator or a computer graphing program is available, you can construct for yourself a picture like Fig. 3.1.3, illustrating a family of solution curves of the differential equation

$$y'' + 3y' + 2y = 0 \tag{1}$$

passing through the (same) point $(0, 1)$. Proceed as follows:

- First show that the general solution of Eq. (1) is

$$y(x) = c_1 e^{-x} + c_2 e^{-2x}. \tag{2}$$

- Then show that the general solution of Eq. (1) satisfying the initial conditions $y(0) = 1, y'(0) = b$ is

$$y(x) = (2 + b)e^{-x} - (1 + b)e^{-2x}. \tag{3}$$

The MATLAB loop

```
x = -1 : 0.025 : 5,
for b = -5 : 1 : 5
    y = (2 + b)*exp(-x) - (1 + b)*exp(-2*x);
    plot(x,y)
    end
```

was used to generate Fig. 3.1.3.

After reproducing Fig. 3.1.3 in such a way, construct for each of the following second-order differential equations a variety of typical solution curves passing through the point $(0, 1)$.

1. $y'' - y = 0$
2. $y'' - 3y' + 2y = 0$
3. $2y'' + 3y' + y = 0$
4. $y'' + y = 0$ (see Example 1)
5. $y'' + 2y' + 2y = 0$, which has general solution
   $y(x) = e^{-x}(c_1 \cos x + c_2 \sin x)$.

3.2 General Solutions of Linear Equations

Only in very special cases can an nth-order differential equation of the general form $G(x, y, y', y'', \ldots y^{(n)}) = 0$ be solved exactly and explicitly. But we now show that our discussion in Section 3.1 of second-order linear equations generalizes in a very natural way to the general ***n*th-order linear** differential equation of the form

$$P_0(x)y^{(n)} + P_1(x)y^{(n-1)} + \cdots + P_{n-1}(x)y' + P_n(x)y = F(x). \tag{1}$$

Unless otherwise noted, we will always assume that the coefficient functions $P_i(x)$ and $F(x)$ are continuous on some open interval I (perhaps unbounded) where we wish to solve the equation. Under the additional assumption that $P_0(x) \neq 0$ at each point of I, we can divide each term in Eq. (1) by $P_0(x)$ to obtain an equation with leading coefficient 1, of the form

▶ $$y^{(n)} + p_1(x)y^{(n-1)} + \cdots + p_{n-1}(x)y' + p_n(x)y = f(x). \tag{2}$$

The **homogeneous** linear equation **associated** with Eq. (2) is

▶ $$y^{(n)} + p_1(x)y^{(n-1)} + \cdots + p_{n-1}(x)y' + p_n(x)y = 0. \tag{3}$$

Just as in the second-order case, a *homogeneous* nth-order linear differential equation has the valuable property that any superposition, or *linear combination,* of solutions of the equation is again a solution. The proof of the following theorem is essentially the same — a routine verification — as that of Theorem 1 of Section 3.1.

THEOREM 1: Principle of Superposition

Let $y_1, y_2, \ldots, y_n$ be n solutions of the homogeneous linear equation in (3) on the interval I. If $c_1, c_2, \ldots, c_n$ are constants, then the linear combination

$$y = c_1 y_1 + c_2 y_2 + \cdots + c_n y_n \tag{4}$$

is also a solution of Eq. (3) on I.   ■

EXAMPLE 1   It is easy to verify that the three functions

$$y_1(x) = e^{3x}, \quad y_2(x) = \cos 2x, \quad \text{and} \quad y_3(x) = \sin 2x$$

are all solutions of the homogeneous third-order equation

$$y^{(3)} - 3y'' + 4y' - 12y = 0$$

on the entire real line. Theorem 1 tells us that any linear combination of these solutions, such as

$$y(x) = 7y_1(x) + 3y_2(x) - 2y_3(x) = 7e^{3x} + 3\cos 2x - 2\sin 2x,$$

is also a solution on the entire real line. We will see that, conversely, every solution of the differential equation of this example is a linear combination of the three particular solutions y_1, y_2, and y_3. Thus its general solution has the form

$$y(x) = c_1 e^{3x} + c_2 \cos 2x + c_3 \sin 2x.$$ ■

Existence and Uniqueness of Solutions

We saw in Section 3.1 that a particular solution of a *second-order* linear differential equation is determined by *two* initial conditions. Similarly, a particular solution of an nth-order linear differential equation is determined by n initial conditions. The following theorem, proved in the Appendix, is the natural generalization of Theorem 2 of Section 3.1.

THEOREM 2: Existence and Uniqueness

Suppose that the functions $p_1, p_2, \ldots, p_n$, and f are continuous on the open interval I containing the point a. Then, given n numbers $b_0, b_1, b_2, \ldots b_{n-1}$, the nth-order linear equation (Eq. (2))

$$y^{(n)} + p_1(x)y^{(n-1)} + \cdots + p_{n-1}(x)y' + p_n(x)y = f(x)$$

has a unique (that is, one and only one) solution on the entire interval I that satisfies the n initial conditions

$$y(a) = b_0, \qquad y'(a) = b_1, \qquad \ldots, \qquad y^{(n-1)}(a) = b_{n-1}. \tag{5}$$

∎

Equation (2) and the conditions in (5) constitute an nth-order **initial value problem.** Theorem 2 tells us that any such initial value problem has a unique solution on the *whole* interval I where the coefficient functions in (2) are continuous. It tells us nothing, however, about how to find this solution. In Section 3.3 we will see how to construct explicit solutions of initial value problems in the *constant* coefficient case that occurs often in applications.

EXAMPLE 1
Continued

We saw earlier that

$$y(x) = 7e^{3x} + 3\cos 2x - 2\sin 2x$$

is a solution of

$$y^{(3)} - 3y'' + 4y' - 12y = 0$$

on the real line. The solution has the initial values $y(0) = 10$, $y'(0) = 17$, and $y''(0) = 51$. Theorem 2 assures us that this is the *only* solution with these initial values. ∎

Note that Theorem 2 implies that the *trivial* solution $y(x) \equiv 0$ is the only solution of the *homogeneous* equation

$$y^{(n)} + p_1(x)y^{(n-1)} + \cdots + p_{n-1}(x)y' + p_n(x)y = 0 \tag{3}$$

that satisfies the *trivial* initial conditions

$$y(a) = y'(a) = \cdots = y^{(n-1)}(a) = 0.$$

EXAMPLE 2

It is easy to verify that

$$y_1(x) = x^2 \qquad \text{and} \qquad y_2(x) = x^3$$

are two different solutions of

$$x^2y'' - 4xy' + 6y = 0,$$

and that both satisfy the initial conditions $y(0) = y'(0) = 0$. Why does this not contradict the uniqueness part of Theorem 2? It is because the leading coefficient in this differential equation vanishes at $x = 0$, so this equation cannot be written in the form of Eq. (3) with coefficient functions *continuous* on an open interval containing the point $x = 0$. ∎

Linearly Independent Solutions

On the basis of our knowledge of general solutions of second-order linear equations, we anticipate that a general solution of the *homogeneous* nth-order linear equation

$$y^{(n)} + p_1(x)y^{(n-1)} + \cdots + p_{n-1}(x)y' + p_n(x)y = 0 \qquad (3)$$

will be a linear combination

$$y = c_1 y_1 + c_2 y_2 + \cdots + c_n y_n, \qquad (4)$$

where $y_1, y_2, \ldots, y_n$ are particular solutions of Eq. (3). But these n particular solutions must be "sufficiently independent" that we can always choose the coefficients $c_1, c_2, \ldots, c_n$ in (4) to satisfy arbitrary initial conditions of the form in (5). The question is this: What should be meant by *independence* of three or more functions?

Recall that *two* functions f_1 and f_2 are linearly *dependent* if one is a constant multiple of the other; that is, if either $f_1 = kf_2$ or $f_2 = kf_1$ for some constant k. If we write these equations as

$$(1)f_1 + (-k)f_2 = 0 \qquad \text{or} \qquad (k)f_1 + (-1)f_2 = 0,$$

we see that the linear dependence of f_1 and f_2 implies that these exist two constants c_1 and c_2 *not both zero* such that

$$c_1 f_1 + c_2 f_2 = 0. \qquad (6)$$

Conversely, if c_1 and c_2 are not both zero, then Eq. (6) certainly implies that f_1 and f_2 are linearly dependent.

By analogy with Eq. (6), we say that n functions $f_1, f_2, \ldots, f_n$ are *linearly dependent* provided that some *nontrivial* linear combination

$$c_1 f_1 + c_2 f_2 + \cdots + c_n f_n$$

of them vanishes identically; "nontrivial" means that *not all* of the coefficients $c_1, c_2, \ldots, c_n$ are zero (although some of them may be zero).

DEFINITION: Linear Dependence of Functions

The n functions $f_1, f_2, \ldots, f_n$ are said to be **linearly dependent** on the interval I provided that there exist constants $c_1, c_2, \ldots, c_n$ not all zero such that

$$c_1 f_1 + c_2 f_2 + \cdots + c_n f_n = 0 \qquad (7)$$

on I; that is,

$$c_1 f_1(x) + c_2 f_2(x) + \cdots + c_n f_n(x) = 0$$

for all x in I.   ∎

If not all the coefficients in (7) are zero, then clearly we can solve for at least one of the functions as a linear combination of the others, and conversely. Thus the functions $f_1, f_2, \ldots, f_n$ are linearly dependent if and only if at least one of them is a linear combination of the others.

EXAMPLE 3   The functions

$$f_1(x) = \sin 2x, \quad f_2(x) = \sin x \cos x, \quad \text{and} \quad f_3(x) = e^x$$

are linearly dependent on the real line because

$$(1)f_1 + (-2)f_2 + (0)f_3 = 0$$

(by the familiar trigonometric identity $\sin 2x = 2 \sin x \cos x$). ∎

The n functions $f_1, f_2, \ldots, f_n$ are called **linearly independent** on the interval I provided that they are not linearly dependent there. Equivalently, they are linearly independent on I provided that the identity

$$c_1 f_1 + c_2 f_2 + \cdots + c_n f_n = 0 \tag{7}$$

holds on I only in the trivial case

$$c_1 = c_2 = \cdots = c_n = 0;$$

that is, *no* nontrivial linear combination of these functions vanishes on I. Put yet another way, the functions $f_1, f_2, \ldots, f_n$ are linearly independent if no one of them is a linear combination of the others. (Why?)

Sometimes one can show that n given functions are linearly dependent by finding, as in Example 3, nontrivial values of the coefficients so that Eq. (7) holds. But in order to show that n given functions are linearly independent, we must prove that nontrivial values of the coefficients *cannot* be found, and this is seldom easy to do in any direct or obvious manner.

Fortunately, in the case of n solutions of a homogeneous nth-order linear equation, there is a tool that makes the determination of their linear dependence or independence a routine matter. This tool is the Wronskian determinant, which we introduced (for the case $n = 2$) in Section 3.1. Suppose that the n functions $f_1, f_2, \ldots, f_n$ are each $n - 1$ times differentiable. Then their Wronskian is the $n \times n$ determinant

$$\blacktriangleright \qquad W = \begin{vmatrix} f_1 & f_2 & \cdots & f_n \\ f_1' & f_2' & \cdots & f_n' \\ \vdots & \vdots & & \vdots \\ f_1^{(n-1)} & f_2^{(n-1)} & \cdots & f_n^{(n-1)} \end{vmatrix}. \tag{8}$$

We write $W(f_1, f_2, \ldots, f_n)$ or $W(x)$, depending upon whether we wish to emphasize the functions or the point x at which their Wronskian is to be evaluated. The Wronskian is named after the Polish mathematician J. M. H. Wronski (1778–1853).

We saw in Section 3.1 that the Wronskian of two linearly dependent functions vanishes identically. More generally, *the Wronskian of n linearly dependent functions $f_1, f_2, \ldots, f_n$ is identically zero.* To prove this, assume that Eq. (7) holds on the interval I for some choice of the constants $c_1, c_2, \ldots, c_n$ not all zero. We then differentiate this equation $n - 1$ times in succession, obtaining the n equations

$$
\begin{aligned}
c_1 f_1(x) + c_2 f_2(x) &+ \cdots + & c_n f_n(x) &= 0, \\
c_1 f_1'(x) + c_2 f_2'(x) &+ \cdots + & c_n f_n'(x) &= 0, \\
&\ \ \vdots & & \\
c_1 f_1^{(n-1)}(x) + c_2 f_2^{(n-1)}(x) &+ \cdots + & c_n f_n^{(n-1)}(x) &= 0,
\end{aligned}
\tag{9}
$$

which hold for all x in I. We recall from linear algebra that a system of n linear *homogeneous* equations in n unknowns has a nontrivial solution if and only if the determinant of coefficients vanishes. In Eq. (9) the unknowns are the constants $c_1, c_2, \ldots, c_n$ and the determinant of coefficients is simply the Wronskian $W(f_1, f_2, \ldots, f_n)$ evaluated at the typical point x of I. Because we know that the c_i are not all zero, it follows that $W(x) \equiv 0$, as we wanted to prove.

Therefore, to show that the functions $f_1, f_2, \ldots, f_n$ are *linearly independent* on the interval I, it suffices to show that their Wronskian is nonzero at just one point of I.

EXAMPLE 4 Show that the functions $y_1(x) = e^{3x}$, $y_2(x) = \cos 2x$, and $y_3(x) = \sin 2x$ (of Example 1) are linearly independent.

Solution: Their Wronskian is

$$
W = \begin{vmatrix} e^{3x} & \cos 2x & \sin 2x \\ 3e^{3x} & -2\sin 2x & 2\cos 2x \\ 9e^{3x} & -4\cos 2x & -4\sin 2x \end{vmatrix}
$$

$$
= e^{3x}\begin{vmatrix} -2\sin 2x & 2\cos 2x \\ -4\cos 2x & -4\sin 2x \end{vmatrix} - 3e^{3x}\begin{vmatrix} \cos 2x & \sin 2x \\ -4\cos 2x & -4\sin 2x \end{vmatrix}
$$

$$
+ 9e^{3x}\begin{vmatrix} \cos 2x & \sin 2x \\ -\sin 2x & 2\cos 2x \end{vmatrix} = 26e^{3x} \neq 0.
$$

Because $W \neq 0$ everywhere, it follows that y_1, y_2, and y_3 are linearly independent on any open interval (including the whole real line).

EXAMPLE 5 Show first that the three solutions

$$
y_1(x) = x, \quad y_2(x) = x \ln x, \quad \text{and} \quad y_3(x) = x^2
$$

of the third-order equation

$$
x^3 y^{(3)} - x^2 y'' + 2xy' - 2y = 0 \tag{10}
$$

are linearly independent on the open interval $x > 0$. Then find a particular solution of Eq. (10) that satisfies the initial conditions

$$
y(1) = 3, \quad y'(1) = 2, \quad y''(1) = 1. \tag{11}
$$

Solution: Note that for $x > 0$, we could divide each term in (10) by x^3 to obtain a homogeneous linear equation of the standard form in (3). When we compute the Wronskian of the three given solutions, we find that

$$
W = \begin{vmatrix} x & x\ln x & x^2 \\ 1 & 1+\ln x & 2x \\ 0 & \dfrac{1}{x} & 2 \end{vmatrix} = x.
$$

Thus $W \neq 0$ for $x > 0$, so y_1, y_2, and y_3 are linearly independent on the interval $x > 0$. To find the desired particular solution, we impose the initial conditions in (11) on

$$y(x) = c_1 x + c_2 x \ln x \quad + c_3 x^2,$$

$$y'(x) = c_1 \quad + c_2(1 + \ln x) + 2c_3 x,$$

$$y''(x) = 0 \quad + \frac{c_2}{x} \quad + 2c_3.$$

This yields the simultaneous equations

$$y(1) = c_1 \qquad + c_3 = 3,$$

$$y'(1) = c_1 + c_2 + 2c_3 = 2,$$

$$y''(1) = \qquad c_2 + 2c_3 = 1;$$

we solve to find $c_1 = 1$, $c_2 = -3$, and $c_3 = 2$. Thus the particular solution in question is

$$y(x) = x - 3x \ln x + 2x^2. \qquad \blacksquare$$

Provided that $W(y_1, y_2, \ldots, y_n) \neq 0$, it turns out (Theorem 4) that we can always find values of the coefficients in the linear combination

$$y = c_1 y_1 + c_2 y_2 + \cdots + c_n y_n$$

in order to satisfy any given initial conditions of the form in (5). Theorem 3 provides the necessary nonvanishing of W in the case of linearly independent solutions.

THEOREM 3: Wronskians of Solutions

Suppose that $y_1, y_2, \ldots, y_n$ are n solutions of the homogeneous nth-order linear equation

$$y^{(n)} + p_1(x)y^{(n-1)} + \cdots + p_{n-1}(x)y' + p_n(x)y = 0 \tag{3}$$

on an open interval I where each p_i is continuous. Let

$$W = W(y_1, y_2, \ldots, y_n).$$

(a) If $y_1, y_2, \ldots, y_n$ are linearly dependent, then $W \equiv 0$ on I.

(b) If $y_1, y_2, \ldots, y_n$ are linearly independent, then $W \neq 0$ at each point of I.

Thus there are just two possibilities: Either $W = 0$ everywhere on I, or $W \neq 0$ everywhere on I.

Proof: We have already proven part (a). To prove part (b), it is sufficient to assume that $W(a) = 0$ at some point of I, and show that this implies the solutions y_1, $y_2, \ldots, y_n$ are linearly dependent. But $W(a)$ is simply the determinant of coefficients of the system of n homogeneous linear equations

$$c_1 y_1(a) + c_2 y_2(a) \quad + \cdots + \quad c_n y_n(a) = 0,$$

$$c_1 y_1'(a) + c_2 y_2'(a) \quad + \cdots + \quad c_n y_n'(a) = 0,$$

$$\vdots$$

$$c_1 y_1^{(n-1)}(a) + c_2 y_2^{(n-1)}(a) + \cdots + c_n y_n^{(n-1)}(a) = 0 \tag{12}$$

in the n unknowns $c_1, c_2, \ldots, c_n$. Because $W(a) = 0$, the basic fact from linear algebra quoted just after (9) implies that the equations in (12) have a nontrivial solution. That is, the numbers $c_1, c_2, \ldots, c_n$ are not all zero.

We now use these values to define the particular solution

$$Y(x) = c_1 y_1(x) + c_2 y_2(x) + \cdots + c_n y_n(x) \tag{13}$$

of Eq. (3). The equations in (12) then imply that Y satisfies the trivial initial conditions

$$Y(a) = Y'(a) = \cdots = Y^{(n-1)}(a) = 0.$$

Theorem 2 (uniqueness) therefore implies that $Y(x) \equiv 0$ on I. In view of (13) and the fact that $c_1, c_2, \ldots, c_n$ are not all zero, this is the desired conclusion that the solutions $y_1, y_2, \ldots, y_n$ are linearly dependent. This completes the proof of Theorem 3. ∎

General Solutions

We can now show that every solution of a *homogeneous* nth-order solution is a linear combination of n given linearly independent solutions. Using the fact from Theorem 3 that the Wronskian of n linearly independent solutions is nonzero, the proof of the following theorem is essentially the same as the proof of Theorem 4 of Section 3.1 (the case $n = 2$).

THEOREM 4: General Solutions of Homogeneous Equations

Let $y_1, y_2, \ldots, y_n$ be n linearly independent solutions of the homogeneous equation

$$y^{(n)} + p_1(x)y^{(n-1)} + \cdots + p_{n-1}(x)y' + p_n(x)y = 0 \tag{3}$$

on an open interval I where the p_i are continuous. If Y is any solution whatsoever of Eq. (3), then there exist numbers $c_1, c_2, \ldots, c_n$ such that

$$Y(x) = c_1 y_1(x) + c_2 y_2(x) + \cdots + c_n y_n(x)$$

for all x in I. ∎

Thus *every* solution of a homogeneous nth-order linear differential equation is a linear combination

$$y = c_1 y_1 + c_2 y_2 + \cdots + c_n y_n$$

of any n given linearly independent solutions. On this basis we call such a linear combination the **general solution** of the differential equation.

Nonhomogeneous Equations

We now consider the *nonhomogeneous* nth-order linear differential equation

$$Ly = y^{(n)} + p_1(x)y^{(n-1)} + \cdots + p_{n-1}(x)y' + p_n(x)y = f(x) \tag{2}$$

with associated homogeneous equation

$$Ly = y^{(n)} + p_1(x)y^{(n-1)} + \cdots + p_{n-1}(x)y' + p_n(x)y = 0. \tag{3}$$

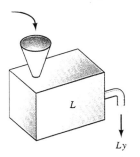

FIGURE 3.2.1. The idea of L "operating" on the function y

Here we introduce the symbol L to represent an **operator;** given an n times differentiable function y, L *operates* on y (as suggested in Fig. 3.2.1) to produce the linear combination

$$Ly = y^{(n)} + p_1 y^{(n-1)} + \cdots + p_{n-1} y' + p_n y \qquad (14)$$

of y and its first n derivatives. The principle of superposition (Theorem 1) means simply that the operator L is *linear;* that is,

$$L(c_1 y_1 + c_2 y_2) = c_1 L y_1 + c_2 L y_2 \qquad (15)$$

if c_1 and c_2 are constants.

Suppose that a single particular solution y_p of the nonhomogeneous equation in (2) is known and that Y is any other solution of Eq. (2). Then Eq. (15) implies that

$$L(Y - y_p) = LY - Ly_p = f - f = 0.$$

Thus $y_c = Y - y_p$ is a solution of the associated homogeneous equation in (3). Then

$$Y = y_c + y_p, \qquad (16)$$

and it follows from Theorem 4 that

$$y_c = c_1 y_1 + c_2 y_2 + \cdots + c_n y_n, \qquad (17)$$

where $y_1, y_2, \ldots, y_n$ are linearly independent solutions of the associated *homogeneous* equation. We call y_c a **complementary function** of the nonhomogeneous equation and have thus proved that a *general solution* of the nonhomogeneous equation in (2) is the sum of its complementary function y_c and a single particular solution y_p of Eq. (2).

THEOREM 5: Solutions of Nonhomogeneous Equations

Let y_p be a particular solution of the nonhomogeneous equation in (2) on an open interval I where the functions p_i and f are continuous. Let $y_1, y_2, \ldots, y_n$ be linearly independent solutions of the associated homogeneous equation in (3). If Y is any solution whatsoever of Eq. (2) on I, then there exist numbers $c_1, c_2, \ldots, c_n$ such that

$$Y(x) = c_1 y_1(x) + c_2 y_2(x) + \cdots + c_n y_n(x) + y_p(x) \qquad (18)$$

for all x in I. ∎

EXAMPLE 6 It is evident that $y_p(x) = 3x$ is a particular solution of the equation

$$y'' + 4y = 12x, \qquad (19)$$

and that $y_c(x) = c_1 \cos 2x + c_2 \sin 2x$ is its complementary solution. Find a solution of Eq. (19) that satisfies the initial conditions $y(0) = 5$, $y'(0) = 7$.

Solution: The general solution of Eq. (19) is

$$y(x) = c_1 \cos 2x + c_2 \sin 2x + 3x.$$

Now

$$y'(x) = -2c_1 \sin 2x + 2c_2 \cos 2x + 3.$$

Hence the initial conditions give

$$y(0) = c_1 = 5,$$

$$y'(0) = 2c_2 + 3 = 7.$$

We find that $c_1 = 5$ and $c_2 = 2$. Thus the desired solution is

$$y(x) = 5 \cos 2x + 2 \sin 2x + 3x.$$

3.2 Problems

In Problems 1 through 6, show directly that the given functions are linearly dependent on the real line. That is, find a nontrivial linear combination of the given functions that vanishes identically.

1. $f(x) = 2x$, $g(x) = 3x^2$, $h(x) = 5x - 8x^2$

2. $f(x) = 5$, $g(x) = 2 - 3x^2$, $h(x) = 10 + 15x^2$

3. $f(x) = 0$, $g(x) = \sin x$, $h(x) = e^x$

4. $f(x) = 17$, $g(x) = 2 \sin^2 x$, $h(x) = 3 \cos^2 x$

5. $f(x) = 17$, $g(x) = \cos^2 x$, $h(x) = \cos 2x$

6. $f(x) = e^x$, $g(x) = \cosh x$, $h(x) = \sinh x$

In Problems 7 through 12, use the Wronskian to prove that the given functions are linearly independent on the indicated interval.

7. $f(x) = 1$, $g(x) = x$, $h(x) = x^2$; the real line

8. $f(x) = e^x$, $g(x) = e^{2x}$, $h(x) = e^{3x}$; the real line

9. $f(x) = e^x$, $g(x) = \cos x$, $h(x) = \sin x$; the real line

10. $f(x) = e^x$, $g(x) = x^{-2}$, $h(x) = x^{-2} \ln x$; $x > 0$

11. $f(x) = x$, $g(x) = xe^x$, $h(x) = x^2 e^x$; the real line

12. $f(x) = x$, $g(x) = \cos(\ln x)$, $h(x) = \sin(\ln x)$; $x > 0$

In Problems 13 through 20, a third-order homogeneous linear equation and three linearly independent solutions are given. Find a particular solution satisfying the given initial conditions.

13. $y^{(3)} + 2y'' - y' - 2y = 0$; $y(0) = 1$, $y'(0) = 2$, $y''(0) = 0$; $y_1 = e^x$, $y_2 = e^{-x}$, $y_3 = e^{-2x}$

14. $y^{(3)} - 6y'' + 11y' - 6y = 0$; $y(0) = 0$, $y'(0) = 0$, $y''(0) = 3$; $y_1 = e^x$, $y_2 = e^{2x}$, $y_3 = e^{3x}$

15. $y^{(3)} - 3y'' + 3y' - y = 0$; $y(0) = 2$, $y'(0) = 0$, $y''(0) = 0$; $y_1 = e^x$, $y_2 = xe^x$, $y_3 = x^2 e^x$

16. $y^{(3)} - 5y'' + 8y' - 4y = 0$; $y(0) = 1$, $y'(0) = 4$, $y''(0) = 0$; $y_1 = e^x$, $y_2 = e^{2x}$, $y_3 = xe^{2x}$

17. $y^{(3)} + 9y'' = 0$; $y(0) = 3$, $y'(0) = -1$, $y''(0) = 2$; $y_1 = 1$, $y_2 = \cos 3x$, $y_3 = \sin 3x$

18. $y^{(3)} - 3y'' + 4y' - 2y = 0$; $y(0) = 1$, $y'(0) = 0$, $y''(0) = 0$; $y_1 = e^x$, $y_2 = e^x \cos x$, $y_3 = e^x \sin x$

19. $x^3 y^{(3)} - 3x^2 y'' + 6xy' - 6y = 0$; $y(1) = 6$, $y'(1) = 14$, $y''(1) = 22$; $y_1 = x$, $y_2 = x^2$, $y_3 = x^3$

20. $x^3 y^{(3)} + 6x^2 y'' + 4xy' - 4y = 0$; $y(1) = 1$, $y'(1) = 5$, $y''(1) = -11$; $y_1 = x$, $y_2 = x^{-2}$, $y_3 = x^{-2} \ln x$

In Problems 21 through 24, a nonhomogeneous differential equation, a complementary solution y_c, and a particular solution y_p are given. Find a solution satisfying the given initial conditions.

21. $y'' + y = 3x$; $y(0) = 2$, $y'(0) = -2$;
$y_c = c_1 \cos x + c_2 \sin x$; $y_p = 3x$

22. $y'' - 4y = 12$; $y(0) = 0$, $y'(0) = 10$;
$y_c = c_1 e^{2x} + c_2 e^{-2x}$; $y_p = -3$

23. $y'' - 2y' - 3y = 6$; $y(0) = 3$, $y'(0) = 11$;
$y_c = c_1 e^{-x} + c_2 e^{3x}$; $y_p = -2$

24. $y'' - 2y' + 2y = 2x$; $y(0) = 4$, $y'(0) = 8$;
$y_c = c_1 e^x \cos x + c_2 e^x \sin x$; $y_p = x + 1$

25. Let $Ly = y'' + py' + qy$. Suppose that y_1 and y_2 are two functions such that

$$Ly_1 = f(x) \qquad \text{and} \qquad Ly_2 = g(x).$$

Show that their sum $y = y_1 + y_2$ satisfies the nonhomogeneous equation $Ly = f(x) + g(x)$.

26. (a) Find by inspection particular solutions of the two nonhomogeneous equations

$$y'' + 2y = 4 \qquad \text{and} \qquad y'' + 2y = 6x.$$

(b) Use the method of Problem 25 to find a particular solution of the differential equation $y'' + 2y = 6x + 4$.

27. Prove directly that the functions

$$f_1(x) \equiv 1, \quad f_2(x) = x, \quad \text{and} \quad f_3(x) = x^2$$

are linearly independent on the whole real line. *(Suggestion:* Assume that $c_1 + c_2 x + c_3 x^2 = 0$. Differentiate this equation twice. You now have three equations that must be satisfied by every real number x, including $x = 0$. Conclude that $c_1 = c_2 = c_3 = 0$.)

28. Generalize the method of Problem 27 to prove directly that the functions

$$f_0(x) \equiv 1, \quad f_1(x) = x, \quad f_2(x) = x^2, \quad \ldots, \quad f_n(x) = x^n$$

are linearly independent on the real line.

29. Use the result of Problem 28 and the definition of linear independence to prove directly that, for any constant r, the functions

$$f_0(x) = e^{rx}, \quad f_1(x) = xe^{rx}, \quad \ldots, \quad f_n(x) = x^n e^{rx}$$

are linearly independent on the whole real line.

30. Verify that $y_1 = x$ and $y_2 = x^2$ are linearly independent solution on the entire real line of the equation

$$x^2 y'' - 2xy' + 2y = 0,$$

but that $W(x, x^2)$ vanishes at $x = 0$. Why do these observations not contradict part (b) of Theorem 3?

31. This problem indicates why we can impose *only n* initial conditions on a solution of an nth-order linear differential equation. (a) Given the equation

$$y'' + py + qy = 0,$$

explain why the value of $y''(a)$ is determined by the values of $y(a)$ and $y'(a)$. (b) Prove that the equation

$$y'' - 2y' - 5y = 0$$

has a solution satisfying the conditions

$$y(0) = 1, \quad y'(0) = 0, \quad y''(0) = C \quad \text{if and only if} \quad C = 5.$$

32. Prove that an nth-order homogeneous linear differential equation satisfying the hypotheses of Theorem 2 has n *linearly independent solutions* $y_1, y_2, \ldots, y_n$. *(Suggestion:* Let y_i be the unique solution such that

$$y_i^{(i-1)}(a) = 1 \quad \text{and} \quad y_i^{(k)}(a) = 0 \quad \text{if } k \neq i - 1.)$$

33. Suppose that the three numbers r_1, r_2, and r_3 are distinct. Show that the three functions $\exp(r_1 x)$, $\exp(r_2 x)$, and $\exp(r_3 x)$ are linearly independent by showing that their Wronskian

$$W = \exp([r_1 + r_2 + r_3]x) \cdot \begin{vmatrix} 1 & 1 & 1 \\ r_1 & r_2 & r_3 \\ r_1^2 & r_2^2 & r_3^2 \end{vmatrix}$$

is nonzero for all x.

34. Assume as known that the **Vandermonde determinant**

$$V = \begin{vmatrix} 1 & 1 & \cdots & 1 \\ r_1 & r_2 & \cdots & r_n \\ r_1^2 & r_2^2 & \cdots & r_n^2 \\ \cdot & \cdot & & \cdot \\ \cdot & \cdot & & \cdot \\ \cdot & \cdot & & \cdot \\ r_1^{n-1} & r_2^{n-1} & \cdots & r_n^{n-1} \end{vmatrix}$$

is nonzero if the numbers $r_1, r_2, \ldots, r_n$ are distinct. Prove by the method of Problem 33 that the functions

$$f_i(x) = \exp(r_i x), \quad 1 \leq i \leq n$$

are linearly independent.

35. According to Problem 32 of Section 3.1, the Wronskian $W(y_1, y_2)$ of two solutions of the second-order equation

$$y'' + p_1(x)y' + p_2(x)y = 0$$

is given by Abel's formula

$$W(x) = K \exp\left(-\int p_1(x)\, dx\right)$$

for some constant K. It can be shown that the Wronskian of n solutions $y_1, y_2, \ldots, y_n$ of the n-th order equation

$$y^{(n)} + p_1(x)y^{(n-1)} + \cdots + p_{n-1}(x)y' + p_n(x)y = 0$$

satisfies the same identity. Prove this for the case $n = 3$ as follows: (a) The derivative of a determinant of functions is the sum of the determinants obtained by separately differentiating the rows of the original determinant. Conclude that

$$W' = \begin{vmatrix} y_1 & y_2 & y_3 \\ y_1' & y_2' & y_3' \\ y_1^{(3)} & y_2^{(3)} & y_3^{(3)} \end{vmatrix}.$$

(b) Substitute for $y_1^{(3)}$, $y_2^{(3)}$, and $y_3^{(3)}$ from the equation $y^{(3)} + p_1 y'' + p_2 y' + p_3 y = 0$, and then show that $W' = -p_1 W$. Integration now gives Abel's formula.

3.3 Homogeneous Equations with Constant Coefficients

In Section 3.2 we saw that a general solution of an nth-order homogeneous linear equation is a linear combination of n linearly independent particular solutions, but we said little about how to actually find even a single solution. The solution of a linear differential equation with *variable* coefficients ordinarily requires numerical methods (Chapter 2) or infinite series methods (Chapter 8). But we can now show how to find, explicitly and in a rather straightforward way, n linearly independent solutions of a given nth-order homogeneous linear equation if it has *constant* coefficients. The general such equation may be written in the form

▶ $$a_n y^{(n)} + a_{n-1} y^{(n-1)} + \cdots + a_2 y'' + a_1 y' + a_0 y = 0, \qquad (1)$$

where the coefficients $a_0, a_1, a_2, \ldots, a_n$ are real constants with $a_n \neq 0$.

The Characteristic Equation

We first look for a *single* solution of Eq. (1), and begin with the observation that

$$\frac{d^k}{dx^k}(e^{rx}) = r^k e^{rx}, \qquad (2)$$

so any derivative of e^{rx} is a constant multiple of e^{rx}. Hence, if we substituted $y = e^{rx}$ in Eq. (1), each term would be a constant multiple of e^{rx}, with the constant coefficients depending upon r and the coefficients a_i. This suggests that we try to find r so that all these multiples of e^{rx} will have sum zero, in which case $y = e^{rx}$ will be a solution of Eq. (1).

For example, in Section 3.1 we substituted $y = e^{rx}$ in the second-order equation

$$ay'' + by' + cy = 0$$

to derive the characteristic equation

$$ar^2 + br + c = 0$$

that r must satisfy.

To carry out this technique in the general case, we substitute $y = e^{rx}$ in Eq. (1), and with the aid of Eq. (2) we find the result to be

$$a_n r^n e^{rx} + a_{n-1} r^{n-1} e^{rx} + \cdots + a_2 r^2 e^{rx} + a_1 r e^{rx} + a_0 e^{rx} = 0;$$

that is,

$$e^{rx}(a_n r^n + a_{n-1} r^{n-1} + \cdots + a_2 r^2 + a_1 r + a_0) = 0.$$

Because e^{rx} is never zero, we see that $y = e^{rx}$ will be a solution of Eq. (1) precisely when r is a root of the equation

▶ $$a_n r^n + a_{n-1} r^{n-1} + \cdots + a_2 r^2 + a_1 r + a_0 = 0. \qquad (3)$$

This equation is called the **characteristic equation** or **auxiliary equation** of the differential equation in (1). Our problem, then, is reduced to the solution of this purely algebraic equation.

According to the fundamental theorem of algebra, every nth-degree polynomial—such as the one in (3)—has n zeros, though not necessarily distinct and not necessarily real. Finding the exact values of these zeros may be difficult or even impossible; the quadratic formula is sufficient for second-degree equations, but for equations of high degree we may need to spot a fortuitous factorization, or restore to numerical techniques (such as Newton's method or Müller's method—see any numerical analysis text).

Distinct Real Roots

Whatever the method we use, let us suppose that we have solved the characteristic equation. Then we can always write a general solution of the differential equation. The situation is slightly more complicated in the case of repeated roots or complex roots of Eq. (3), so let us first examine the simplest case—in which the characteristic equation has n distinct (no two equal) *real* roots $r_1, r_2, \ldots, r_n$. Then the functions

$$e^{r_1 x}, \quad e^{r_2 x}, \quad \ldots, \quad e^{r_n x}$$

are all solutions of Eq. (1), and (by Problem 34 of Section 3.2) these n solutions are linearly independent on the entire real line. In summary, we have proved Theorem 1.

◤ *THEOREM 1:* Distinct Real Roots

If the roots $r_1, r_2, \ldots, r_n$ of the characteristic equation in (3) are real and distinct, then

$$\blacktriangleright \qquad y(x) = c_1 e^{r_1 x} + c_2 e^{r_2 x} + \cdots + c_n e^{r_n x} \qquad (4)$$

is the general solution of Eq. (1). $\blacksquare$

EXAMPLE 1 Solve the initial value problem

$$y'' + 2y' - 8y = 0; \quad y(0) = 5, \quad y'(0) = -2.$$

Solution: According to Theorem 1 we need only solve the characteristic equation

$$r^2 + 2r - 8 = (r - 2)(r + 4) = 0$$

for $r = 2, -4$. Hence the general solution is

$$y(x) = c_1 e^{2x} + c_2 e^{-4x}.$$

Then

$$y'(x) = 2c_1 e^{2x} - 4c_2 e^{-4x},$$

so the given initial conditions yield the equations

$$y(0) = c_1 + c_2 = 5,$$
$$y'(0) = 2c_1 - 4c_2 = -2$$

that we readily solve for $c_1 = 3, c_2 = 2$. Thus the desired particular solution is

$$y(x) = 3e^{2x} + 2e^{-4x}.$$

EXAMPLE 2 Find a general solution of

$$y^{(3)} - y'' - 6y' = 0.$$

Solution: The characteristic equation of this differential equation is

$$r^3 - r^2 - 6r = 0,$$

which we solve by factoring:

$$r(r^2 - r - 6) = r(r - 3)(r + 2) = 0,$$

so the three roots are $r = 0$, $r = 3$, and $r = -2$. They are real and distinct, and therefore—because $e^0 = 1$—a general solution of the given differential equation is

$$y(x) = c_1 + c_2 e^{3x} + c_3 e^{-2x}. \qquad \blacksquare$$

Polynomial Operators

If the roots of the characteristic equation in (3) are *not* distinct—there are repeated roots—then we cannot produce n linearly independent solutions of Eq. (1) by the method of Theorem 1. For example, if the roots are 1, 2, 2, and 2, we obtain only the *two* functions e^x and e^{2x}. The problem, then, is to produce the missing linearly independent solutions. For this purpose it is convenient to adopt the operator notation introduced near the conclusion of Section 3.2. Equation (1) corresponds to the operator equation $Ly = 0$ where L is the operator

$$L = a_n \frac{d^n}{dx^n} + a_{n-1} \frac{d^{n-1}}{dx^{n-1}} + \cdots + a_2 \frac{d^2}{dx^2} + a_1 \frac{d}{dx} + a_0. \qquad (5)$$

We also denote by $D = d/dx$ the operation of differentiation with respect to x, so that

$$Dy = y', \qquad D^2 y = y'', \qquad D^3 y = y^{(3)},$$

and so on. In terms of D, the operator L in (5) may be written

$$L = a_n D^n + a_{n-1} D^{n-1} + \cdots + a_2 D^2 + a_1 D + a_0, \qquad (6)$$

and we will find it useful to think of the right-hand side in (6) as a (formal) nth-degree polynomial in the "variable" D; it is a **polynomial operator.**

A first-degree polynomial operator has the form $D - a$ where a is a real number. It operates on the function $y = y(x)$ to produce

$$(D - a)y = Dy - ay = y' - ay.$$

The important fact about such operators is that any two of them *commute:*

$$(D - a)(D - b)y = (D - b)(D - a)y \qquad (7)$$

for any twice differentiable function $y = y(x)$. The proof of the formula in (7) is the following computation:

$$\begin{aligned}
(D - a)(D - b)y &= (D - a)(y' - by) \\
&= D(y' - by) - a(y' - by) \\
&= y'' - (b + a)y' + aby = y'' - (a + b)y' + bay \\
&= D(y' - ay) - b(y' - ay) \\
&= (D - b)(y' - ay) = (D - b)(D - a)y.
\end{aligned}$$

Repeated Roots

Let us now consider the possibility that the characteristic equation

$$a_n r^n + a_{n-1} r^{n-1} + \cdots + a_2 r^2 + a_1 r + a_0 = 0 \tag{3}$$

has *repeated* roots. For example, suppose that Eq. (3) has only two distinct roots, r_0 of multiplicity 1 and r_1 of multiplicity $k > 0$. Then Eq. (3) can be rewritten in the form

$$(r - r_1)^k (r - r_0) = (r - r_0)(r - r_1)^k = 0. \tag{8}$$

Similarly, the operator L in (6) can be written as

$$L = (D - r_1)^k (D - r_0) = (D - r_0)(D - r_1)^k, \tag{9}$$

the order of the factors making no difference because of the formula in (7).

Two solutions of the differential equation $Ly = 0$ are certainly $y_0 = e^{r_0 x}$ and $y_1 = e^{r_1 x}$. This is, however, not sufficient; we need $k + 1$ linearly independent solutions in order to construct a general solution, because the equation is of order $k + 1$. To find the missing $k - 1$ solutions, we note that

$$Ly = (D - r_0)[(D - r_1)^k y] = 0.$$

Consequently, *every* solution of the kth-order equation

$$(D - r_1)^k y = 0 \tag{10}$$

will also be a solution of the original equation $Ly = 0$. Hence our problem is reduced to that of finding the general solution of the differential equation in (10).

The fact that $e^{r_1 x}$ is one solution of (10) suggests that we try the substitution

$$y(x) = u(x) e^{r_1 x}, \tag{11}$$

where $u(x)$ is a function yet to be determined. Observe that

$$(D - r_1)[ue^{r_1 x}] = (Du)e^{r_1 x} + r_1 u e^{r_1 x} - r_1 u e^{r_1 x},$$

so

$$(D - r_1)[ue^{r_1 x}] = (Du)e^{r_1 x}. \tag{12}$$

It therefore follows by induction on k that

$$(D - r_1)^k [ue^{r_1 x}] = (D^k u)e^{r_1 x} \tag{13}$$

for any function $u(x)$. Hence $y = u e^{r_1 x}$ will be a solution of (10) if and only if $D^k u = u^{(k)} = 0$. But this is so if and only if

$$u(x) = c_1 + c_2 x + c_3 x^2 + \cdots + c_k x^{k-1},$$

a polynomial of degree at most $k - 1$. Hence our desired solution of (10) is

$$y(x) = u e^{r_1 x} = (c_1 + c_2 x + \cdots + c_k x^{k-1}) e^{r_1 x}.$$

In particular, we see here the additional solutions $x e^{r_1 x}, x^2 e^{r_1 x}, \ldots, x^{k-1} e^{r_1 x}$ of the original differential equation $Ly = 0$.

The preceding analysis can be carried out with the operator $D - r_0$ replaced with an arbitrary polynomial operator. When this is done, the result is a proof of the following theorem.

◼THEOREM 2: Repeated Roots

If the characteristic equation in (3) has a repeated root r of multiplicity k, then the part of the general solution of the differential equation in (1) corresponding to r is of the form

▶
$$(c_1 + c_2 x + c_3 x^2 + \cdots + c_k x^{k-1})e^{rx}. \tag{14}$$
◼

We may observe that according to Problem 29 of Section 3.2, the k functions e^{rx}, xe^{rx}, $x^2 e^{rx}$, . . . , and $x^{k-1}e^{rx}$ involved in (14) are linearly independent on the real line. Thus a root of multiplicity k corresponds to k linearly independent solutions of the differential equation.

EXAMPLE 3   The differential equation

$$y'' + 4y' + 4y = 0$$

has the characteristic equation

$$r^2 + 4r + 4 = (r + 2)^2 = 0$$

with double root $r = -2, -2$. Hence with $k = 2$ Theorem 2 yields the general solution

$$y(x) = (c_1 + c_2 x)e^{-2x}.$$

EXAMPLE 4   Find a general solution of

$$y^{(4)} + 3y^{(3)} + 3y'' + y' = 0.$$

Solution: The characteristic equation of this differential equation is

$$r^4 + 3r^3 + 3r^2 + r = r(r + 1)^3 = 0.$$

It has the simple root $r_1 = 0$, which contributes $y_1 \equiv c_1$ to the general solution. It has also the triple ($k = 3$) root $r_2 = -1$, which contributes $y_2 = (c_2 + c_3 x + c_4 x^2)e^{-x}$ to the solution. Hence the general solution of the differential equation is

$$y(x) = c_1 + (c_2 + c_3 x + c_4 x^2)e^{-x}. \qquad ◼$$

Complex-Valued Functions and Euler's Formula

Because we have assumed that the coefficients of the differential equation and its characteristic equation are real, any complex (nonreal) roots will occur in complex conjugate pairs $a \pm bi$ where a and b are real and $i = \sqrt{-1}$. This raises the question as to what might be meant by an exponential such as $\exp([a + bi]x)$.

To answer this question, we recall from elementary calculus the Taylor series for the exponential function:

$$e^t = \sum_{n=0}^{\infty} \frac{t^n}{n!} = 1 + t + \frac{t^2}{2!} + \frac{t^3}{3!} + \frac{t^4}{4!} + \cdots.$$

If we substitute $t = ix$ in this series, we get

$$e^{ix} = \sum_{n=0}^{\infty} \frac{(ix)^n}{n!}$$

$$= 1 + ix - \frac{x^2}{2!} - \frac{ix^3}{3!} + \frac{x^4}{4!} + \frac{ix^5}{5!} - \cdots$$

$$= \left(1 - \frac{x^2}{2!} + \frac{x^4}{4!} - \cdots\right) + i\left(x - \frac{x^3}{3!} + \frac{x^5}{5!} - \cdots\right).$$

Because the two real series in the last line are the Taylor series for $\cos x$ and $\sin x$, respectively, this implies that

$$e^{ix} = \cos x + i \sin x. \tag{15}$$

This result is known as **Euler's formula.** Because of it we *define* the exponential function e^z, for $z = x + iy$ an arbitrary complex number, to be

$$e^z = e^{x+iy} = e^x e^{iy} = e^x(\cos y + i \sin y). \tag{16}$$

Thus it appears that complex roots of the characteristic equation will lead to complex-valued solutions of the differential equations. A **complex-valued function** F of the real variable x associates with each real number x (in its domain of definition) the complex number

$$z = F(x) = f(x) + ig(x). \tag{17}$$

The real-valued functions f and g are called the **real** and **imaginary** parts, respectively, of F. If they are differentiable, we define the **derivative** F' of F to be

$$F'(x) = f'(x) + ig'(x). \tag{18}$$

Thus we simply differentiate the real and imaginary parts of F separately. Similarly, we say that the complex-valued function $y = F(x)$ **satisfies** the differential equation in (1) provided that its real and imaginary parts separately satisfy that differential equation.

The particular complex-valued functions of interest here are of the form $F(x) = e^{rx}$ where $r = a \pm bi$. We note from Euler's formula that

$$e^{(a+bi)x} = e^{ax}(\cos bx + i \sin bx). \tag{19a}$$

and

$$e^{(a-bi)x} = e^{ax}(\cos bx - i \sin bx). \tag{19b}$$

The most important property of e^{rx} is

$$D_x(e^{rx}) = re^{rx} \tag{20}$$

even if r should be a complex number. The proof of this assertion is a straightforward computation based on the definitions and formulas given earlier:

$$D_x(e^{rx}) = D_x(e^{ax} \cos bx) + iD_x(e^{ax} \sin bx)$$

$$= [ae^{ax} \cos bx - be^{ax} \sin bx] + i[ae^{ax} \sin bx + be^{ax} \cos bx]$$

$$= (a + bi)(e^{ax} \cos bx + ie^{ax} \sin bx) = re^{rx}.$$

Complex Roots

It follows from Eq. (20) that when r is complex (just as when r is real), e^{rx} will be a solution of the differential equation in (1) if and only if r is a root of its characteristic equation. If the complex conjugate pairs of roots $r_1 = a + bi$ and $r_2 = a - bi$ are simple (nonrepeated), then the corresponding part of a general solution of (1) is

$$C_1 e^{(a+bi)x} + C_2 e^{(a-bi)x} = C_1 e^{ax}(\cos bx + i \sin bx) + C_2 e^{ax}(\cos bx - i \sin bx)$$

$$= e^{ax}(c_1 \cos bx + c_2 \sin bx),$$

where $c_1 = C_1 + C_2$ and $c_2 = (C_1 - C_2)i$. Thus the conjugate pair of roots $a \pm bi$ leads to the linearly independent *real-valued* solutions $e^{ax} \cos bx$ and $e^{ax} \sin bx$. This yields the following result.

THEOREM 3: Complex Roots

If the characteristic equation in (3) has an unrepeated pair of complex conjugate roots $a \pm bi$ (with $b \neq 0$), then the corresponding part of a general solution of (1) is of the form

$$e^{ax}(c_1 \cos bx + c_2 \sin bx). \qquad \blacksquare \quad (21)$$

EXAMPLE 5   The characteristic equation of

$$y'' + b^2 y = 0 \qquad (b > 0)$$

is $r^2 + b^2 = 0$, with roots $r = \pm bi$. So Theorem 3 (with $a = 0$) gives the general solution

$$y(x) = c_1 \cos bx + c_2 \sin bx.$$

EXAMPLE 6   Find the particular solution of

$$y'' - 4y' + 5y = 0$$

for which $y(0) = 1$ and $y'(0) = 5$.

Solution: The characteristic equation is

$$r^2 - 4r + 5 = (r - 2)^2 + 1 = 0,$$

with roots $2 + i$ and $2 - i$. Hence a general solution is

$$y(x) = e^{2x}(c_1 \cos x + c_2 \sin x).$$

Then

$$y'(x) = 2e^{2x}(c_1 \cos x + c_2 \sin x) + e^{2x}(-c_1 \sin x + c_2 \cos x),$$

so the initial conditions give

$$y(0) = c_1 = 1 \qquad \text{and} \qquad y'(0) = 2c_1 + c_2 = 5.$$

It follows that $c_2 = 3$, and so the desired particular solution is

$$y(x) = e^{2x}(\cos x + 3 \sin x).$$

EXAMPLE 7   Find a general solution of $y^{(4)} + 4y = 0$.

Solution: The characteristic equation is

$$r^4 + 4 = (r^2 + 2i)(r^2 - 2i) = 0,$$

and its four roots are $\pm\sqrt{\pm 2i}$. Now $i = e^{i\pi/2}$ and $-i = e^{3i\pi/2}$, so

$$\sqrt{i} = (e^{i\pi/2})^{1/2} = e^{i\pi/4} = \frac{1+i}{\sqrt{2}}$$

and

$$\sqrt{-i} = (e^{3i\pi/2})^{1/2} = e^{3i\pi/4} = \frac{-1+i}{\sqrt{2}}.$$

Thus the four (distinct) roots of the characteristic equation are $r = \pm(1 \pm i)$. These two pairs of complex conjugate roots, $1 \pm i$ and $-1 \pm i$, give a general solution

$$y(x) = e^x(c_1 \cos x + c_2 \sin x) + e^{-x}(c_3 \cos x + c_4 \sin x)$$

of the differential equation $y^{(4)} + 4y = 0$. ∎

In Example 7 we employed the polar form

$$x + iy = re^{i\theta} \tag{22}$$

of a complex number. The relation between the real and imaginary parts x, y and the **modulus** r and **argument** θ is indicated in Fig. 3.3.1. One consequence of (22) is that the nonzero complex number $x + iy$ has the two square roots

$$\pm(x + iy)^{1/2} = \pm(re^{i\theta})^{1/2} = \pm r^{1/2}e^{i\theta/2}. \tag{23}$$

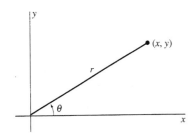

FIGURE 3.3.1. Modulus and argument of the complex number $x + iy$

Repeated Complex Roots

Theorem 2 holds for repeated complex roots. If the conjugate pair $a \pm bi$ has multiplicity k, then the corresponding part of the general solution has the form

$$(A_1 + A_2x + \cdots + A_kx^{k-1})e^{(a+bi)x} + (B_1 + B_2x + \cdots + B_kx^{k-1})e^{(a-bi)x}$$

$$= \sum_{p=0}^{k-1} x^p e^{ax}(c_i \cos bx + d_i \sin bx). \tag{24}$$

It can be shown that the $2k$ functions

$$x^p e^{ax} \cos bx, \qquad x^p e^{ax} \sin bx, \qquad 0 \leqq p \leqq k-1$$

that appear in (24) are linearly independent.

EXAMPLE 8 Find a general solution of $(D^2 + 6D + 13)^2 y = 0$.

Solution By completing the square, we see that the characteristic equation

$$(r^2 + 6r + 13)^2 = [(r+3)^2 + 4]^2 = 0$$

has as its roots the conjugate pair $-3 \pm 2i$ of multiplicity 2. Hence Eq. (24) gives the general solution

$$y(x) = e^{-3x}(c_1 \cos 2x + d_1 \sin 2x) + xe^{-3x}(c_2 \cos 2x + d_2 \sin 2x). \qquad ∎$$

In applications we are seldom presented in advance with a factorization as convenient as the one in Example 8. Often the most difficult part of solving a homogeneous linear equation is finding the roots of its characteristic equation. Example 9 illustrates an approach that may succeed when a root of the characteristic equation can be found by inspection. The project material for this section illustrates other possibilities.

EXAMPLE 9 The characteristic equation of the differential equation

$$y^{(3)} + y' - 10y = 0$$

is the cubic equation

$$r^3 + r - 10 = 0.$$

By a standard theorem of elementary algebra, the only possible rational roots are the factors ± 1, ± 2, ± 5, and ± 10 of the constant term 10. By trial-and-error (if not by immediate inspection) we discover the root $r = 2$. The factor theorem of elementary algebra implies that $r - 2$ is a factor of $r^3 + r - 10$, and division of the former into the latter produces as quotient the quadratic polynomial

$$r^2 + 2r + 5 = (r + 1)^2 + 4.$$

The roots of this quotient are the complex conjugates $-1 \pm 2i$. The three roots we have found now yield the general solution

$$y(x) = c_1 e^{2x} + e^{-x}(c_2 \cos 2x + c_3 \sin 2x).$$

EXAMPLE 10 The roots of the characteristic equation of a certain differential equation are 3, -5, 0, 0, 0, 0, -5, $2 \pm 3i$, and $2 \pm 3i$. Write the general solution of this homogeneous differential equation.

Solution The solution can be read directly from the list of roots. It is

$$y(x) = c_1 + c_2 x + c_3 x^2 + c_4 x^3 + c_5 e^{3x} + c_6 e^{-5x} + c_7 x e^{-5x}$$
$$+ e^{2x}(c_8 \cos 3x + c_9 \sin 3x) + x e^{2x}(c_{10} \cos 3x + c_{11} \sin 3x).$$

3.3 Problems

Find the general solutions of the differential equations in Problems 1 through 20.

1. $y'' - 4y = 0$

2. $2y'' - 3y' = 0$

3. $y'' + 3y' - 10y = 0$

4. $2y'' - 7y' + 3y = 0$

5. $y'' + 6y' + 9y = 0$

6. $y'' + 5y' + 5y = 0$

7. $4y'' - 12y' + 9y = 0$

8. $y'' - 6y' + 13y = 0$

9. $y'' + 8y' + 25y = 0$

10. $5y^{(4)} + 3y^{(3)} = 0$

11. $y^{(4)} - 8y^{(3)} + 16y'' = 0$

12. $y^{(4)} - 3y^{(3)} + 3y'' - y' = 0$

13. $9y^{(3)} + 12y'' + 4y' = 0$

14. $y^{(4)} + 3y'' - 4y = 0$

15. $y^{(4)} - 8y'' + 16y = 0$

16. $y^{(4)} + 18y'' + 81y = 0$

17. $6y^{(4)} + 11y'' + 4y = 0$

18. $y^{(4)} = 16y$

19. $y^{(3)} + y'' - y' - y = 0$

20. $y^{(4)} + 2y^{(3)} + 3y'' + 2y' + y = 0$ (*Suggestion:* Compute $(r^2 + r + 1)^2$.)

Solve the initial value problems given in Problems 21 through 26.

21. $y'' - 4y' + 3y = 0$; $y(0) = 7$, $y'(0) = 11$

22. $9y'' + 6y' + 4y = 0$; $y(0) = 3$, $y'(0) = 4$

23. $y'' - 6y' + 25y = 0$; $y(0) = 3$, $y'(0) = 1$

24. $2y^{(3)} - 3y'' - 2y' = 0$; $y(0) = 1$, $y'(0) = 1$, $y''(0) = 3$

25. $3y^{(3)} + 2y'' = 0$; $\quad y(0) = -1, \quad y'(0) = 0,$
$\quad y''(0) = 1$

26. $y^{(3)} + 10y'' + 25y' = 0$; $\quad y(0) = 3, \quad y'(0) = 4,$
$\quad y''(0) = 5$

Find the general solutions of the equations in Problems 27 through 32. First find a small integral root of the characteristic equation by inspection; then factor by division.

27. $y^{(3)} + 3y'' - 4y = 0$

28. $2y^{(3)} - y'' - 5y' - 2y = 0$

29. $y^{(3)} + 27y = 0$

30. $y^{(4)} - y^{(3)} + y'' - 3y' - 6y = 0$

31. $y^{(3)} + 3y'' + 4y' - 8y = 0$

32. $y^{(4)} + y^{(3)} - 3y'' - 5y' - 2y = 0$

In Problems 33 through 36, one solution of the differential equation is given. Find the general solution.

33. $y^{(3)} + 3y'' - 54y = 0$; $\quad y = e^{3x}$

34. $3y^{(3)} - 2y'' + 12y' - 8y = 0$; $\quad y = e^{2x/3}$

35. $6y^{(4)} + 5y^{(3)} + 25y'' + 20y' + 4y = 0$; $\quad y = \cos 2x$

36. $9y^{(3)} + 11y'' + 4y' - 14y = 0$; $\quad y = e^{-x}\sin x$

Problems 37 through 41 pertain to the solution of differential equations with complex coefficients.

37. (a) Use Euler's formula to show that every complex number can be written in the form $re^{i\theta}$, where $r \geqq 0$ and $-\pi < \theta \leqq \pi$. (b) Express the numbers $4, -2, 3i, 1 + i$, and $-1 + i\sqrt{3}$ in the form $re^{i\theta}$. (c) The two square roots of $re^{i\theta}$ are $\pm e^{i\theta/2}\sqrt{r}$. Find the square roots of the numbers $2 - 2i\sqrt{3}$ and $-2 + 2i\sqrt{3}$.

38. Use the quadratic formula to solve the following equations. Note in each case that the roots are not complex conjugates.
(a) $x^2 + ix + 2 = 0$. (b) $x^2 - 2ix + 3 = 0$.

39. Find a general solution of $y'' - 2iy' + 3y = 0$.

40. Find a general solution of $y'' - iy' + 6y = 0$.

41. Find a general solution of $y'' = (-2 + 2i\sqrt{3})y$.

42. Solve the initial value problem

$$y^{(3)} = y; \qquad y(0) = 1, \qquad y'(0) = y''(0) = 0.$$

(*Suggestion:* Impose the given initial conditions on the general solution

$$y(x) = Ae^x + Be^{\alpha x} + Ce^{\beta x},$$

where α and β are the complex conjugate roots of $r^3 - 1 = 0$, to discover that

$$y(x) = \frac{1}{3}\left(e^x + 2e^{-x/2}\cos\frac{x\sqrt{3}}{2}\right)$$

is a solution.)

43. Solve the initial value problem

$$y^{(4)} = y^{(3)} + y'' + y' + 2y;$$

$$y(0) = y'(0) = y''(0) = 0, \qquad y^{(3)}(0) = 30.$$

44. The differential equation

$$y'' + (\text{sgn } x)y = 0 \tag{25}$$

has the discontinuous coefficient function

$$\text{sgn } x = \begin{cases} +1 & \text{if } x > 0, \\ -1 & \text{if } x < 0. \end{cases}$$

Show that Eq. (25) nevertheless has two linearly independent solutions $y_1(x)$ and $y_2(x)$ defined for all x such that:

- Each satisfies Eq. (25) at each point $x \neq 0$.
- Each has a continuous derivative at $x = 0$.
- $y_1(0) = y_2'(0) = 1$ and $y_2(0) = y_1'(0) = 0$.

(*Suggestion:* Each $y_i(x)$ will be defined by one formula for $x \leqq 0$ and by another for $x \geqq 0$.)

$\mathit{3.3}$ Computing Project

To meet the needs of applications such as those of this section, polynomial-solving utilities are now a common feature of calculator and computer systems, and can be used to solve a characteristic equation numerically even when no simple factorization is evident or even possible. For instance, suppose that we want to solve the homogeneous linear differential equation

$$y^{(3)} - 3y'' + y = 0 \tag{1}$$

with characteristic polynomial

$$r^3 - 3r^2 + 1 = 0. \tag{2}$$

With a calculator (like the TI-85) having a built-in polynomial solver, we can simply enter the coefficients $1, -3, 0, 1$ of this cubic polynomial and get the three (approximate) roots $r = -0.5321, 0.6527, 2.8794$ at the press of a key.

With a system like *Maple* or *Mathematica* we can enter a one-line command like

```
NSolve[ r^3 - 3 r^2 + 1 == 0, r ]
```

to solve Eq. (2) numerically for the approximate roots of the characteristic equation. However we find them, it follows that a general solution of the differential equation in (1) is given (approximately) by

$$y(x) = c_1 e^{-0.5321x} + c_2 e^{0.6527x} + c_3 e^{2.8794x}. \tag{3}$$

Systems like *Maple* and *Mathematica* also offer simple commands for the direct solution of differential equations. Using *Maple,* for instance, we can first define the differential equation in (1) by entering the command

```
> diffeq := diff(y(x),x$3) - 3*diff(y(x),x$2) + y(x) = 0;
```

$$diffeq := \left(\frac{\partial^3}{\partial x^3}y(x)\right) - 3\left(\frac{\partial^2}{\partial x^2}y(x)\right) + y(x) = 0$$

and then ask for the solution by means of the command

```
> dsolve( diffeq, y(x) );
```

$$y(x) = \_C1 \; e^{(2\cos(1/9\;\pi)\;+\;1)x}$$
$$+ \_C2 \; e^{-(\cos(1/9\;\pi)\;-\;1\;+\;\sqrt{3}\,\sin(1/9\;\pi))x}$$
$$+ \_C3 \; e^{-x(\cos(1/9\;\pi)\;-\;1\;-\;\sqrt{3}\,\sin(1/9\;\pi))}$$

Evidently *Maple* has solved the cubic characteristic equation exactly in terms of trigonometric functions! To compare this result with the solution given in (3), we can apply the function **evalf** to convert exact expressions to floating point approximations:

```
> evalf(");
```

$$y(x) = \_C1 \; e^{2.8794x} + \_C2 \; e^{-.53209x} + \_C3 \; e^{.65271x}$$

Use calculator or computer methods like those indicated above to find general solutions (in approximate numerical form) of the following differential equations.

1. $y^{(3)} - 3y' + y = 0$
2. $y^{(3)} + 3y'' - 3y = 0$
3. $y^{(3)} + y' + y = 0$
4. $y^{(3)} + 3y' + 5y = 0$
5. $y^{(4)} + 2y^{(3)} - 3y = 0$
6. $y^{(4)} + 3y' - 4y = 0$

3.4 Mechanical Vibrations

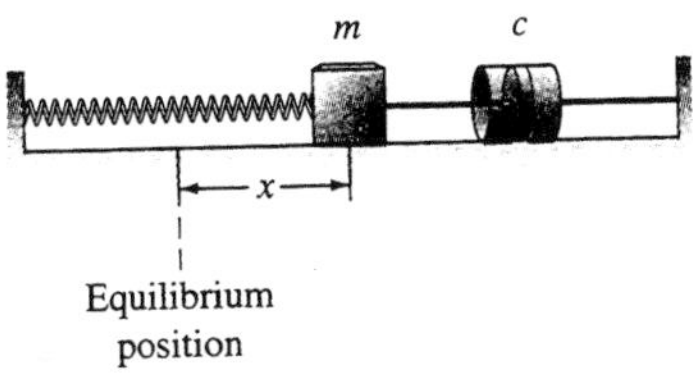

FIGURE 3.4.1. A mass-spring-dashpot system

The motion of a mass attached to a spring serves as a relatively simple example of the vibrations that occur in more complex mechanical systems. For many such systems, the analysis of these vibrations is a problem in the solution of linear differential equations with constant coefficients.

We consider a body of mass m attached to one end of an ordinary spring that resists compression as well as stretching; the other end of the spring is attached to a fixed wall, as shown in Fig. 3.4.1. Assume that the body rests on a frictionless horizontal plane, so that it can move only back and forth as the spring stretches and compresses. Denote by x the distance of the body from its **equilibrium position**—its position when the spring is unstretched. We take $x > 0$ when the spring is stretched, and thus $x < 0$ when it is compressed.

According to Hooke's law, the restorative force F_S that the spring exerts on the mass is proportional to the distance x that the spring has been stretched or compressed. Because this is the same as the displacement x of the mass m from its equilibrium position, it follows that

$$F_S = -kx. \tag{1}$$

The positive constant of proportionality k is called the **spring constant.** Note that F_S and x have opposite signs: $F_S < 0$ when $x > 0$, $F_S > 0$ when $x < 0$.

Figure 3.4.1 shows the mass attached to a dashpot—a device, like a shock absorber, that provides a force directed opposite to the instantaneous direction of motion of the mass m. We assume the dashpot is so designed that this force F_R is proportional to the velocity $v = dx/dt$ of the mass; that is,

$$F_R = -cv = -c\frac{dx}{dt}. \tag{2}$$

The positive constant c is the **damping constant** of the dashpot. More generally, we may regard (2) as specifying frictional forces in our system (including air resistance to the motion of m).

If, in addition to the forces F_S and F_R, the mass is subjected to a given **external force** $F_E = F(t)$, then the total force acting on the mass is $F = F_S + F_R + F_E$. Using Newton's law

$$F = ma = m\frac{d^2x}{dt^2} = mx'',$$

we obtain the second-order linear differential equation

$$\blacktriangleright \qquad mx'' + cx' + kx = F(t) \tag{3}$$

that governs the motion of the mass.

If there is no dashpot (and we ignore all frictional forces), then we set $c = 0$ in (3) and call the motion **undamped;** it is **damped** motion if $c > 0$. If there is no external force we replace $F(t)$ by 0 in (3). We refer to the motion as **free** in this case and **forced** in the case $F(t) \neq 0$. Thus the homogeneous equation

$$\blacktriangleright \qquad mx'' + cx' + kx = 0 \tag{4}$$

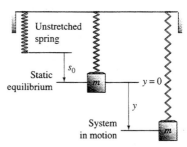

FIGURE 3.4.2. A mass suspended vertically from a spring

describes free motion of a mass on a spring with dashpot but with no external forces applied. We will defer discussion of forced motion until Section 3.6.

For an alternative example, we might attach the mass to the lower end of a spring that is suspended vertically from a fixed support, as in Fig. 3.4.2. In this case the weight $W = mg$ of the mass would stretch the spring a distance s_0 determined by Eq. (1) with $F_S = -W$ and $x = s_0$. That is, $mg = ks_0$, so that $s_0 = mg/k$. This gives the **static** equilibrium position of the mass. If y denotes the displacement of the mass in motion, measured downward from its static equilibrium position, then we ask you to show in Problem 9 that y satisfies Eq. (3); specifically, that

$$my'' + cy' + ky = F(t) \tag{5}$$

if we include damping and external forces.

The Simple Pendulum

The importance of the differential equation that appears in Eqs. (3) and (5) stems from the fact that it describes the motion of many other simple mechanical systems. For example, a **simple pendulum** consists of a mass m swinging back and forth on the end of a string (or better, a *massless rod*) of length L, as shown in Fig. 3.4.3. We may specify the position of the mass at time t by giving the counterclockwise angle $\theta = \theta(t)$ that the string or rod makes with the vertical at time t. To analyze the motion of the mass m, we will apply the law of the conservation of mechanical energy, according to which the sum of the kinetic energy and the potential energy of m remains constant.

The distance along the circular arc from 0 to m is $s = L\theta$, so the velocity of the mass is $v = ds/dt = L(d\theta/dt)$, and therefore its kinetic energy is

$$T = \frac{1}{2} mv^2 = \frac{1}{2} m \left(\frac{ds}{dt} \right)^2 = \frac{1}{2} mL^2 \left(\frac{d\theta}{dt} \right)^2.$$

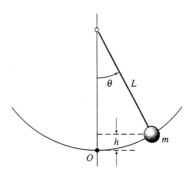

FIGURE 3.4.3. The simple pendulum

We next choose as reference point the lowest point O reached by the mass (see Fig. 3.4.3). Then its potential energy V is the product of its weight mg and its vertical height $h = L(1 - \cos \theta)$ above O, so

$$V = mgL(1 - \cos \theta).$$

The fact that the sum of T and V is a constant C therefore gives

$$\frac{1}{2} mL^2 \left(\frac{d\theta}{dt} \right)^2 + mgL (1 - \cos \theta) = C.$$

We differentiate both sides of this identity with respect to t to obtain

$$mL^2 \left(\frac{d\theta}{dt} \right) \left(\frac{d^2\theta}{dt^2} \right) + mgL (\sin \theta) \frac{d\theta}{dt} = 0,$$

so

$$\frac{d^2\theta}{dt^2} + \frac{g}{L} \sin \theta = 0 \tag{6}$$

after removal of the common factor $mL^2(d\theta/dt)$.

Now recall that $\sin \theta \approx \theta$ when θ is small; in fact, $\sin \theta$ and θ agree to two decimal places when $|\theta|$ is at most $\pi/12$ (15°). In a typical pendulum clock, for example, θ would never exceed 15°. It therefore seems reasonable to simplify our mathematical model of the simple pendulum by replacing $\sin \theta$ with θ in Eq. (6). If we also insert a term $c\theta'$ to account for the frictional resistance of the surrounding medium, the result is an equation of the form of Eq. (4):

$$\theta'' + c\theta' + k\theta = 0, \tag{7}$$

where $k = g/L$. Note that this equation is independent of the mass m on the end of the rod. We might, however, expect for the effects of the discrepancy between θ and $\sin \theta$ to accumulate over a period of time, so that Eq. (7) will probably not describe accurately the actual motion of the pendulum over a long period of time.

In the remainder of this section, we first analyze free undamped motion and then free damped motion.

Free Undamped Motion

If we have only a mass on a spring, with neither damping nor external force, then Eq. (3) takes the simpler form

$$mx'' + kx = 0. \tag{8}$$

It is convenient to define

$$\omega_0 = \sqrt{\frac{k}{m}}, \tag{9}$$

and rewrite Eq.(8) as

$$x'' + \omega_0^2 x = 0. \tag{8'}$$

The general solution of Eq. (8') is

$$x(t) = A \cos \omega_0 t + B \sin \omega_0 t. \tag{10}$$

To analyze the motion described by this solution, we choose constants C and α so that

$$C = \sqrt{A^2 + B^2}, \qquad \cos \alpha = \frac{A}{C}, \qquad \text{and} \qquad \sin \alpha = \frac{B}{C}, \tag{11}$$

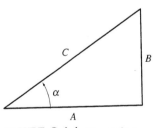

FIGURE 3.4.4. The angle α

as indicated in Fig. 3.4.4. Note that, though $\tan \alpha = B/A$, the angle α is *not* given by the principal branch of the inverse tangent function (which gives values only in the interval $(-\pi/2, \pi/2)$). Instead, α is the angle between 0 and 2π whose cosine and sine have the signs given in (11), where either A or B or both may be negative.

In any event, from (10) and (11) we get

$$x(t) = C\left(\frac{A}{C} \cos \omega_0 t + \frac{B}{C} \sin \omega_0 t\right) = C(\cos \alpha \cos \omega_0 t + \sin \alpha \sin \omega_0 t).$$

With the aid of the cosine addition formula, we find that

$$x(t) = C\cos(\omega_0 t - \alpha). \tag{12}$$

Thus the mass oscillates to-and-fro about its equilibrium position with

Amplitude	$C,$
Circular frequency	$\omega_0,$ and
Phase angle	$\alpha.$

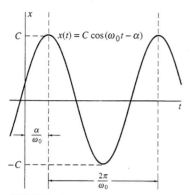

FIGURE 3.4.5. Simple harmonic motion

Such motion is called **simple harmonic motion.** A typical graph of $x(t)$ is shown in Fig. 3.4.5. If time t is measured in seconds, the circular frequency ω_0 has dimensions of radians per second (rad/s). The **period** of the motion is the time required for the system to complete one full oscillation, so is given by

$$T = \frac{2\pi}{\omega_0} \tag{13}$$

seconds; its **frequency** is

$$\frac{1}{T} = \frac{\omega_0}{2\pi} \tag{14}$$

in hertz (Hz), which measures the number of complete cycles per second. Note that frequency is measured in cycles per second, whereas circular frequency has the dimensions of radians per second.

If the initial position $x(0) = x_0$ and initial velocity $x'(0) = v_0$ of the mass are given, we first determine the values of the coefficients A and B in (10), and then find the amplitude C and phase angle α by carrying out the transformation of $x(t)$ to the form in (12), as indicated above.

EXAMPLE 1 A body with mass $m = \frac{1}{2}$ kilogram (kg) is attached to the end of a spring that is stretched 2 meters (m) by a force of 100 Newtons (N). It is set in motion with initial position $x_0 = 0.5$ (m) and initial velocity $v_0 = -10$ (m/s). (Note that these data indicate that the body is displaced to the right and moving to the left at time $t = 0$.) Find the position function of the body as well as the amplitude, frequency, period of oscillation, and phase angle of its motion.

Solution The spring constant is $k = (100 \text{ N})/(2 \text{ m}) = 50$ (N/m), so Eq. (8) yields $\frac{1}{2}x'' + 50x = 0$; that is,

$$x'' + 100x = 0.$$

Consequently, the circular frequency will be $\omega_0 = 10$ (rad/s). So the body will oscillate with

$$\text{frequency:} \quad \frac{10}{2\pi} \approx 1.59 \text{ Hz}$$

and

$$\text{period:} \quad \frac{2\pi}{10} \approx 0.63 \text{ s}.$$

We now impose the initial conditions $x(0) = 0.5$ and $x'(0) = 10$ on the general solution $x(t) = A \cos 10t + B \sin 10t$, and it follows that $A = 0.5$ and $B = -1$. So the position function of the body is

$$x(t) = \frac{1}{2} \cos 10t - \sin 10t.$$

Hence its amplitude of motion is

$$C = \sqrt{\left(\frac{1}{2}\right)^2 + 1^2} = \frac{1}{2}\sqrt{5} \approx 1.12 \quad \text{(m)}.$$

To find the phase angle, we write

$$x(t) = \frac{\sqrt{5}}{2}\left(\frac{1}{\sqrt{5}}\cos 10t - \frac{2}{\sqrt{5}}\sin 10t\right) = \frac{\sqrt{5}}{2}\cos(10t - \alpha).$$

Thus we require $\cos\alpha = 1/\sqrt{5} > 0$ and $\sin\alpha = -2/\sqrt{5} < 0$. Hence α is the fourth-quadrant angle

$$\alpha = 2\pi - \tan^{-1}\left(\frac{2/\sqrt{5}}{1/\sqrt{5}}\right) \approx 5.1760 \quad (\text{rad}).$$

In the form in which the amplitude and phase angle are made explicit, the position function is

$$x(t) \approx \frac{\sqrt{5}}{2}\cos(10t - 5.1760).$$

Free Damped Motion

With damping but no external force, the differential equation we have been studying takes the form $mx'' + cx' + kx = 0$; alternatively,

$$x'' + 2px' + \omega_0^2 x = 0, \tag{15}$$

where $\omega_0 = \sqrt{k/m}$ is the corresponding *undamped* circular frequency and

$$p = \frac{c}{2m} > 0. \tag{16}$$

The characteristic equation $r^2 + 2pr + \omega_0^2 = 0$ of (15) has roots

$$r_1, r_2 = -p \pm (p^2 - \omega_0^2)^{1/2} \tag{17}$$

that depend upon the sign of

$$p^2 - \omega_0^2 = \frac{c^2}{4m^2} - \frac{k}{m} = \frac{c^2 - 4km}{4m^2}.$$

The **critical damping** c_{CR} is given by $c_{CR} = \sqrt{4km}$, and we distinguish three cases, according as $c > c_{CR}$, $c = c_{CR}$, or $c < c_{CR}$.

Overdamped Case: $c > c_{CR}$ $(c^2 > 4km)$. Because c is relatively large in this case, we are dealing with a strong resistance in comparison with a relatively weak spring or small mass. Then (17) gives distinct real roots r_1 and r_2, both of which are negative. The position function has the form

$$x(t) = c_1 e^{r_1 t} + c_2 e^{r_2 t}. \tag{18}$$

It is easy to see that $x(t) \to 0$ as $t \to +\infty$ and that the body settles to its equilibrium position without any oscillations (Problem 27). Fig. 3.4.6 shows some typical graphs of the position function for the overdamped case; we chose x_0 a fixed positive number and illustrated the effects of changing the initial velocity v_0. In every case the would-be oscillations are damped out.

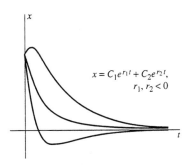

$$x = C_1 e^{r_1 t} + C_2 e^{r_2 t},$$
$$r_1, r_2 < 0$$

FIGURE 3.4.6. Overdamped motion

Critically Damped Case: $c = c_{CR}$ *($c^2 = 4km$).* In this case (17) gives equal roots $r_1 = r_2 = -p$ of the characteristic equation, so the general solution is

$$x(t) = e^{-pt}(c_1 + c_2 t). \tag{19}$$

Because $e^{-pt} > 0$ and $c_1 + c_2 t$ has at most one positive zero, the body passes through its equilibrium position at most once, and it is clear that $x(t) \to 0$ as $t \to +\infty$. Some graphs of the motion in the critically damped case appear in Fig. 3.4.7, and they resemble those of the overdamped case (Fig. 3.4.6). In the critically damped case, the resistance of the dashpot is just large enough to damp out any oscillations, but even a slight decrease in resistance will bring us to the remaining case, the one that shows the most dramatic behavior.

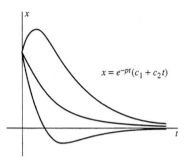

$$x = e^{-pt}(c_1 + c_2 t)$$

FIGURE 3.4.7. Critically damped motion

Underdamped Case: $c < c_{CR}$ *($c^2 < 4km$).* The characteristic equation now has the two complex conjugate roots $-p \pm i\sqrt{\omega_0^2 - p^2}$, and the general solution is

$$x(t) = e^{-pt}(c_1 \cos \omega_1 t + c_2 \sin \omega_1 t), \tag{20}$$

where

$$\omega_1 = \sqrt{\omega_0^2 - p^2} = \frac{\sqrt{4km - c^2}}{2m}. \tag{21}$$

Using the cosine addition formula as in the derivation of Eq. (12), we may rewrite (20) as

$$x(t) = Ce^{-pt}\cos(\omega_1 t - \alpha), \tag{22}$$

where $C = \sqrt{c_1^2 + c_2^2}$ and $\tan \alpha = c_2/c_1$.

The solution in (22) represents exponentially damped oscillations of the body about its equilibrium position. The graph of $x(t)$ lies between the curves $x = Ce^{-pt}$ and $x = Ce^{-pt}$ and touches them when $\omega_1 t - \alpha$ is an integral multiple of π. The motion is not actually periodic, but it nevertheless is useful to call ω_1 its **circular frequency**, $T_1 = 2\pi/\omega_1$ its **pseudoperiod** of oscillation, and Ce^{-pt} its **time-varying amplitude.** Most of these quantities are shown in the typical graph of underdamped motion shown in Fig. 3.4.8. Note from Eq. (21) that in this case ω_1 is less than the undamped circular frequency ω_0, so T_1 is larger than the period T of oscillation of the same mass without damping on the same spring. Thus the action of the dashpot has at least three effects:

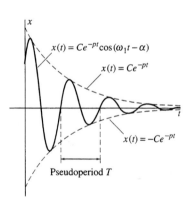

$$x(t) = Ce^{-pt}\cos(\omega_1 t - \alpha)$$
$$x(t) = Ce^{-pt}$$
$$x(t) = -Ce^{-pt}$$

Pseudoperiod T

FIGURE 3.4.8. Underdamped oscillations

1. It exponentially damps the oscillations, in accord with the time-varying amplitude.

2. It slows the motion; that is, the dashpot decreases the frequency of the motion.

3. It delays the motion—this is the effect of the phase angle in Eq. (22).

EXAMPLE 2   The mass and spring of Example 1 are now attached also to a dashpot that provides 6 N of resistance for each meter per second of velocity. The mass is set in motion with the same initial position $x(0) = 0.5$ (m) and the same initial velocity $x'(0) = -10$ (m/s). Find the position function of the mass, its new frequency and pseudoperiod, its phase angle, and the amplitudes of its first four (local) maxima and minima.

Solution Rather than memorizing the various formulas given in the preceding discussion, it is better practice in a particular case to set up the differential equation and then solve it directly. Recall that $m = \frac{1}{2}$ and $k = 50$; we are now given $c = 6$ in mks units. Hence Eq. (3) is $\frac{1}{2} x'' + 6x' + 50x = 0$; that is,

$$x'' + 12x' + 100x = 0.$$

The roots of the characteristic equation $r^2 + 12r + 100 = 0$ are

$$\frac{-12 \pm \sqrt{144 - 400}}{2} = -6 \pm 8i,$$

so the general solution is

$$x(t) = e^{-6t}(A \cos 8t + B \sin 8t). \tag{23}$$

The new circular frequency is $\omega_1 = 8$ (rad/s) and the pseudoperiod and new frequency are

$$T_1 = \frac{2\pi}{8} \approx 0.79 \quad (s)$$

and

$$\frac{1}{T_1} = \frac{8}{2\pi} \approx 1.27 \quad (Hz)$$

(in contrast with 0.63 s and 1.59 Hz, respectively, in the undamped case).

From (23) we compute

$$x'(t) = e^{-6t}(-8A \sin 8t + 8B \cos 8t) - 6e^{-6t}(A \cos 8t + B \sin 8t).$$

The initial conditions therefore produce the equations

$$x(0) = A = \frac{1}{2} \quad \text{and} \quad x'(0) = -6A + 8B = -10,$$

so $A = \frac{1}{2}$ and $B = -\frac{7}{8}$. Thus

$$x(t) = e^{-6t}\left(\frac{1}{2}\cos 8t - \frac{7}{8}\sin 8t\right),$$

and so with

$$C = \sqrt{\left(\frac{1}{2}\right)^2 + \left(\frac{7}{8}\right)^2} = \frac{1}{8}\sqrt{65}$$

we have

$$x(t) = \frac{\sqrt{65}}{8} e^{-6t}\left(\frac{4}{\sqrt{65}}\cos 8t - \frac{7}{\sqrt{65}}\sin 8t\right).$$

We require $\cos \alpha = 4/\sqrt{65} > 0$ and $\sin \alpha = -7/\sqrt{65} < 0$, so α is the fourth-quadrant angle

$$\alpha = 2\pi - \tan^{-1}\left(\frac{7}{4}\right) \approx 5.2315 \quad (rad).$$

Finally,

$$x(t) \approx \frac{\sqrt{65}}{8} e^{-6t} \cos(8t - 5.2315). \tag{24}$$

The local maxima and minima of $x(t)$ occur when

$$0 = x'(t)$$

$$\approx \frac{\sqrt{65}}{8} [-6e^{-6t} \cos(8t - 5.2315) - 8e^{-6t} \sin(8t - 5.2315)],$$

and thus when

$$\tan(8t - 5.2315) \approx -0.75.$$

Because $\tan^{-1}(-0.75) \approx -0.6435$, we want to find the first four positive values of t such that $8t - 5.2315$ is the sum of -0.6435 and an integral multiple of π. These values of t and the corresponding values of x computed with the aid of (24) are as follows:

t (s)	0.1808	0.5735	0.9662	1.3589
x (m)	-0.2725	0.0258	-0.0024	0.0002

We see that the oscillations are damped out very rapidly, with their amplitude decreasing by a factor of about 10 every half-cycle. See Problems 30 and 31 for a more general discussion of this phenomenon. ∎

3.4 Problems

1. Determine the period and frequency of the simple harmonic motion of a 4-kg mass on the end of a spring with spring constant 16 N/m.

2. Determine the period and frequency of the simple harmonic motion of a body of mass 0.75 kg on the end of a spring with spring constant 48 N/m.

3. A mass of 3 kg is attached to the end of a spring that is stretched 20 cm by a force of 15 N. It is set in motion with initial position $x_0 = 0$ and initial velocity $v_0 = -10$ m/s. Find the amplitude, period, and frequency of the resulting motion.

4. A body with mass 250 g is attached to the end of a spring that is stretched 25 cm by a force of 9 N. At time $t = 0$ the body is pulled 1 m to the right, stretching the spring, and set in motion with an initial velocity of 5 m/s to the left. (a) Find $x(t)$ in the form $C \cos(\omega_0 t + \alpha)$. (b) Find the amplitude and period of the motion of the body.

In Problems 5 through 8, assume that the differential equation of a simple pendulum of length L is $L\theta'' + g\theta = 0$, where $g = GM/R^2$ is the gravitational acceleration at the location of

the pendulum (at distance R from the center of the earth; M denotes the mass of the earth).

5. Two pendulums are of lengths L_1 and L_2, and—when located at the respective distances R_1 and R_2 from the center of the earth—have periods p_1 and p_2. Show that

$$\frac{p_1}{p_2} = \frac{R_1\sqrt{L_1}}{r_2\sqrt{L_2}}.$$

6. A certain pendulum clock keeps perfect time in Paris, where the radius of the earth is $R = 3956$ (mi). But this clock loses 2 min 40 s per day at a location on the equator. Use the result of Problem 5 to find the amount of the equatorial bulge of the earth.

7. A pendulum of length 100.10 in., located at a point at sea level where the radius of the earth is $R = 3960$ (mi), has the same period as does a pendulum of length 100.00 in. atop a nearby mountain. Use the result of Problem 5 to find the height of the mountain.

8. Most grandfather clocks have pendulums with adjustable lengths. One such clock loses 10 min per day when the length of its pendulum is 30 in. With what length pendulum will this clock keep perfect time?

9. Derive Eq. (5) describing the motion of a mass attached to the bottom of a vertically suspended spring. (*Suggestion:* First denote by $x(t)$ the displacement of the mass below the unstretched position of the spring; set up the differential equation for x. Then substitute $y = x - x_0$ in this differential equation.)

10. Consider a floating cylindrical buoy with radius r, height h, and density $\rho \leqq 0.5$ (recall that the density of water is 1 g/cm^3). The buoy is initially suspended at rest with its bottom at the top surface of the water and is released at time $t = 0$. Thereafter it is acted on by two forces: a downward gravitational force equal to its weight $mg = \rho\pi r^2 hg$ and an upward force of buoyancy equal to the weight $\pi r^2 xg$ of water displaced, where $x = x(t)$ is the depth of the bottom of the buoy beneath the surface at time t (Fig. 3.4.9). Conclude that the buoy undergoes simple harmonic motion about the equilibrium position $x_e = \rho h$ with period $p = 2\pi\sqrt{\rho h/g}$. Compute p and the amplitude of the motion if $\rho = 0.5$ g/cm^3, $h = 200$ cm, and $g = 980$ cm/s^2.

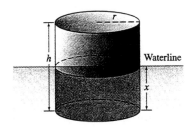

FIGURE 3.4.9. The buoy of Problem 10

11. A cylindrical buoy weighing 100 lb (thus of mass $m = 3.125$ slugs in ft-lb-s (fps) units) floats in water with its axis vertical (as in Problem 10). When depressed slightly and released, it oscillates up and down four times every 10 s. Assume that friction is negligible. Find the radius of the buoy.

12. Assume that the earth is a solid sphere of uniform density, with mass M and radius $R = 3960$ (mi). For a particle of mass m *within* the earth at distance r from the center of the earth, the gravitational force attracting m toward the center is $F_r = -GM_r m/r^2$, where M_r is the mass of the part of the earth within a sphere of radius r. (a) Show that $F_r = -GMmr/R^3$. (b) Now suppose that a hole is drilled straight through the center of the earth, thus connecting two antipodal points on its surface. Let a particle of mass m be dropped at time $t = 0$ into this hole with initial speed zero, and let $r(t)$ be its distance from the center of the earth at time t (Fig. 3.4.10). Conclude from Newton's second law and part (a) that $r''(t) = -k^2 r(t)$, where

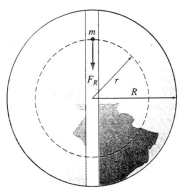

FIGURE 3.4.10. A mass m falling down a hole through the center of the earth (Problem 12)

$k^2 = GM/R^3 = g/R$. (c) Take $g = 32.2$ ft/s^2, and conclude from part (b) that the particle undergoes simple harmonic motion back and forth between the ends of the hole, with a period of about 84 min. (d) Look up (or derive) the period of a satellite that just skims the surface of the earth; compare with the results in part (c). How do you explain the coincidence? Or *is it* a coincidence? (e) With what speed (in miles per hour) does the particle pass through the center of the earth? (f) Look up or derive the orbital velocity of a satellite that just skims the surface of the earth; compare the value with the result in part (e). How do you explain the coincidence? Or *is it* a coincidence?

The remaining problems in this section deal with free damped motion. In Problems 13 through 19, a mass m is attached to both a spring (with given spring constant k) and a dashpot (with given damping constant c). The mass is set in motion with initial position x_0 and initial velocity v_0. Find the position function $x(t)$ and determine whether the motion is overdamped, critically, damped, or underdamped. If it is underdamped, write $x(t)$ in the form $Ce^{-pt}\cos(\omega_1 t - \alpha)$.

13. $m = \frac{1}{2}$, $\quad c = 3$, $\quad k = 4$; $\quad x_0 = 2$, $\quad v_0 = 0$
14. $m = 3$, $\quad c = 30$, $\quad k = 63$; $\quad x_0 = 2$, $\quad v_0 = 2$
15. $m = 1$, $\quad c = 8$, $\quad k = 16$; $\quad x_0 = 5$, $\quad v_0 = -10$
16. $m = 2$, $\quad c = 12$, $\quad k = 50$; $\quad x_0 = 0$, $\quad v_0 = -8$
17. $m = 4$, $\quad c = 20$, $\quad k = 169$; $\quad x_0 = 4$, $\quad v_0 = 16$
18. $m = 2$, $\quad c = 16$, $\quad k = 40$; $\quad x_0 = 5$, $\quad v_0 = 4$
19. $m = 1$, $\quad c = 10$, $\quad k = 125$; $\quad x_0 = 6$, $\quad v_0 = 50$

20. A 12-lb weight (mass $m = 0.375$ slugs in fps units) is attached both to a vertically suspended spring that it stretches 6 in. and to a dashpot that provides 3 lb of resistance for every foot per second of velocity. (a) If the weight is pulled down 1 ft below its static equilibrium position and then released from rest at time $t = 0$, find its position function $x(t)$. (b) Find the frequency, time-varying amplitude, and phase angle of the motion.

21. This problem deals with a highly simplified model of a car of weight 3200 lb (mass $m = 100$ slugs in fps units). Assume that the suspension system of the car acts like a single spring and its shock absorbers like a single dashpot, so that its vertical vibrations satisfy Eq. (4) with appropriate values of the coefficients. (a) Find the stiffness coefficient k of the spring if the car undergoes free vibrations at 80 cycles per minute (cycles/min) when its shock absorbers are disconnected. (b) With the shock absorbers connected the car is set into vibration by driving it over a bump, and the resulting damped vibrations have a frequency of 78 cycles/min. After how long will the time-varying amplitude be 1% of its initial value?

Problems 22 through 32 deal with a mass-spring-dashpot system having position function $x(t)$ satisfying Eq. (4). We write $x_0 = x(0)$ and $v_0 = x'(0)$ and recall that $p = c/(2m)$, $\omega_0^2 = k/m$, and $\omega_1^2 = \omega_0^2 - p^2$. The system is critically damped, overdamped, or underdamped, as specified in each problem.

22. (Critically damped) Show in this case that

$$x(t) = (x_0 + v_0 t + p x_0 t) e^{-pt}.$$

23. (Critically damped) Deduce from Problem 22 that the mass passes through $x = 0$ at some instant $t > 0$ if and only if x_0 and $v_0 + p x_0$ have opposite signs.

24. (Critically damped) Deduce from Problem 22 that $x(t)$ has a local maximum or minimum at some instant $t > 0$ if and only if v_0 and $v_0 + p x_0$ have the same sign.

25. (Overdamped) Show in this case that

$$x(t) = \frac{1}{2\gamma} [(v_0 - r_2 x_0) e^{r_1 t} - (v_0 - r_1 x_0) e^{r_2 t}],$$

where $r_1, r_2 = -p \pm \sqrt{p^2 - \omega_0^2}$ and $\gamma = (r_1 - r_2)/2 > 0$.

26. (Overdamped) If $x_0 = 0$, deduce from Problem 25 that

$$x(t) = \frac{v_0}{\gamma} e^{-pt} \sinh \gamma t.$$

27. (Overdamped) Prove that in this case the mass can pass through its equilibrium position $x = 0$ at most once.

28. (Underdamped) Show that in this case

$$x(t) = e^{-pt} \left(x_0 \cos \omega_1 t + \frac{v_0 + p x_0}{\omega_1} \sin \omega_1 t \right).$$

29. (Underdamped) If the damping constant c is small in comparison with $\sqrt{8mk}$, apply the binomial series to show that

$$\omega_1 \approx \omega_0 \left(1 - \frac{c^2}{8mk} \right).$$

30. (Underdamped) Show that the local maxima and minima of $x(t) = Ce^{-pt} \cos(\omega_1 t - \alpha)$ occur where

$$\tan(\omega_1 t - \alpha) = -\frac{p}{\omega_1}.$$

Conclude that $t_2 - t_1 = 2\pi/\omega_1$ if two consecutive maxima occur at times t_1 and t_2.

31. (Underdamped) Let x_1 and x_2 be two consecutive local maximum values of $x(t)$. Deduce from the result of Problem 30 that

$$\ln \frac{x_1}{x_2} = \frac{2\pi p}{\omega_1}.$$

The constant $\Delta = 2\pi p/\omega_1$ is called the **logarithmic decrement** of the oscillation. Note also that $c = m\omega_1 \Delta/\pi$ because $p = c/(2m)$.

Note: The result of Problem 31 provides an accurate method for measuring the *viscosity* of a fluid, which is an important parameter in fluid dynamics, but which is not easy to measure directly. According to Stokes' drag law, a spherical body of radius a moving at a (relatively slow) speed v through a fluid of viscosity m experiences a resistive force $F_R = 6\pi\mu av$. Thus if a spherical mass on a spring is immersed in the fluid and set in motion, this drag resistance damps its oscillations with damping constant $c = 6\pi a\mu$. The frequency ω_1 and logarithmic decrement Δ of the oscillations can be measured by direct observation. The final formula in Problem 31 then gives c and hence the viscosity of the fluid.

32. (Underdamped) A body weighing 100 lb (mass $m = 3.125$ slugs in fps units) is oscillating attached to a spring and a dashpot. Its first two maximum displacements of 6.73 in. and 1.46 in. are observed to occur at times 0.34 s and 1.17 s, respectively. Compute the damping constant (in pound-seconds per foot) and spring constant (in pounds per foot).

Differential Equations and Determinism

Given a mass m, a dashpot constant c, and a spring constant k, Theorem 2 of Section 3.1 implies that the equation

$$mx'' + cx' + kx = 0 \tag{25}$$

has a *unique* solution for $t \geq 0$ satisfying given initial conditions $x(0) = x_0$, $x'(0) = v_0$. Thus the future motion of an ideal mass-spring-dashpot system is completely determined by the differential equation and the initial conditions. Of course in a real physical system it is impossible to measure the parameters m, c, and k *precisely*. Problems 33 through 36 explore the resulting uncertainty in predicting the future behavior of a physical system.

33. Suppose that $m = 1$, $c = 2$, and $k = 1$ in Eq. (25). Show that the solution with $x(0) = 0$ and $x'(0) = 1$ is

$$x_1(t) = te^{-t}.$$

34. Suppose that $m = 1$ and $c = 2$ but $k = 1 - 10^{-2n}$. Show that the solution of Eq. (25) with $x(0) = 0$ and $x'(0) = 1$ is

$$x_2(t) = 10^n e^{-t} \sinh 10^{-n} t.$$

35. Suppose that $m = 1$ and $c = 2$ but $k = 1 + 10^{-2n}$. Show that the solution of Eq. (25) with $x(0) = 0$ and $x'(0) = 1$ is

$$x_3(t) = 10^n e^{-t} \sin 10^{-n} t.$$

36. Whereas the graphs of $x_1(t)$ and $x_2(t)$ resemble those shown in Figs. 3.4.6 and 3.4.7, the graph of $x_3(t)$ exhibits damped oscillations like those illustrated in Fig. 3.4.8, but with a very long pseudoperiod. Nevertheless, show that for each fixed $t > 0$ it is true that

$$\lim_{n \to \infty} x_2(t) = \lim_{n \to \infty} x_3(t) = x_1(t).$$

Conclude that *on a given finite time interval* the three solutions are in "practical" agreement if n is sufficiently large.

3.5 Nonhomogeneous Equations and the Method of Undetermined Coefficients

We learned in Section 3.3 how to solve homogeneous linear equations wth constant coefficients, but we saw in Section 3.4 that an external force in a simple mechanical system contributes a nonhomogeneous term to its differential equation. The general nonhomogeneous nth-order linear equation with constant coefficients has the form

$$a_n y^{(n)} + a_{n-1} y^{(n-1)} + \cdots + a_1 y' + a_0 y = f(x). \tag{1}$$

By Theorem 5 of Section 3.2, a general solution of (1) has the form

$$\blacktriangleright \qquad\qquad y = y_c + y_{p'} \tag{2}$$

where the complementary function $y_c(x)$ is a general solution of the associated homogeneous equation

$$a_n y^{(n)} + a_{n-1} y^{(n-1)} + \cdots + a_1 y' + a_0 y = 0, \tag{3}$$

and $y_p(x)$ is a particular solution of (1). Thus our remaining task is to find y_p.

   The **method of undetermined coefficients** is a straightforward way of doing this when the given function $f(x)$ in (1) is sufficiently simple that we can make an intelligent guess as to the general form of y_p. For example, suppose that $f(x)$ is a polynomial of degree m. Then, because the derivatives of a polynomial are themselves polynomials of lower degree, it is reasonable to suspect a particular solution

$$y_p(x) = A_m x^m + A_{m-1} x^{m-1} + \cdots + A_1 x + A_0$$

that is also a polynomial of degree m, but with as yet undetermined coefficients. We may, therefore, substitute this expression for y_p into (1), and then—by equating coefficients of like powers of x on the two sides of the resulting equation—attempt to determine the coefficients $A_0, A_1, \ldots, A_m$ so that y_p will, indeed, be a particular solution of Eq. (1).

   Similarly, suppose that

$$f(x) = a \cos kx + b \sin kx.$$

Then it is reasonable to expect a particular solution of the same form:

$$y_p(x) = A \cos kx + B \sin kx,$$

a linear combination with undetermined coefficients A and B. The reason is that any derivative of such a linear combination of $\cos kx$ and $\sin kx$ has the same form. We may therefore substitute this form of y_p in (1), and then—by equating coefficients of cos kx and of sin kx on both sides of the resulting equation—attempt to determine the coefficients A and B so that y_p will, indeed, be a particular solution.

It turns out that this approach does succeed whenever all the derivatives of $f(x)$ have the same form as $f(x)$ itself. Before describing the method in full generality, we illustrate it with several preliminary examples.

EXAMPLE 1   Find a particular solution of $y'' + 3y' + 4y = 3x + 2$.

Solution Here $f(x) = 3x + 2$ is a polynomial of degree 1, so our guess is that

$$y_p(x) = Ax + B.$$

Then $y_p' = A$ and $y_p'' = 0$, so y_p will satisfy the differential equation provided that

$$(0) + 3(A) + 4(Ax + B) = 3x + 2.$$

This is so if and only if $4A = 3$ and $3A + 4B = 2$. These two equations yield $A = \frac{3}{4}$ and $B = -\frac{1}{16}$, so we have found the particular solution

$$y_p(x) = \frac{3}{4}x - \frac{1}{16}.$$

EXAMPLE 2   Find a particular solution of $y'' - 4y = 2e^{3x}$.

Solution Any derivative of e^{3x} is a constant multiple of e^{3x}, so it is reasonable to try

$$y_p(x) = Ae^{3x}.$$

Then $y_p'' = 9Ae^{3x}$, so the given differential equation will be satisfied provided that

$$9Ae^{3x} - 4(Ae^{3x}) = 2e^{3x};$$

that is, $5A = 2$, so that $A = \frac{2}{5}$. Thus our particular solution is $y_p(x) = \frac{2}{5}e^{3x}$.

EXAMPLE 3   Find a particular solution of $3y'' + y' - 2y = 2\cos x$.

Solution A first guess might be $y_p(x) = A\cos x$, but the presence of y' on the left-hand side signals that we probably need a term involving sin x as well. So we try

$$y_p(x) = A\cos x + B\sin x;$$
$$y_p'(x) = -A\sin x + B\cos x,$$
$$y_p''(x) = -A\cos x - B\sin x.$$

Then substitution of y_p and its derivatives into the given differential equation yields

$$3(-A\cos x - B\sin x) + (-A\sin x + B\cos x) - 2(A\cos x + B\sin x) = 2\cos x.$$

We equate the coefficient of cos x on the left-hand side with that of cos x on the right and do the same with sin x to get the equations

$$-5A + B = 2,$$
$$-A - 5B = 0,$$

with solution $A = -\frac{5}{13}$, $B = \frac{1}{13}$. Hence a particular solution is

$$y_p(x) = -\frac{5}{13}\cos x + \frac{1}{13}\sin x.$$ ∎

The following example, which superficially resembles Example 2, indicates that the method of undetermined coefficients is not always quite so simple as we have made it appear.

EXAMPLE 4 Find a particular solution of $y'' - 4y = 2e^{2x}$.

Solution If we try $y_p(x) = Ae^{2x}$, we find that

$$y_p'' - 4y_p = 4Ae^{2x} - 4Ae^{2x} = 0 \neq 2e^{2x};$$

so, no matter what A is, Ae^{2x} cannot satisfy the given nonhomogeneous equation. In fact, the above computation shows that Ae^{2x} satisfies instead the associated *homogeneous* equation. Therefore, we should begin with a trial function $y_p(x)$ whose derivative involves both e^{2x} *and something else* that can cancel upon substitution into the differential equation to leave the e^{2x} term that we need. A reasonable guess is

$$y_p(x) = Axe^{2x},$$

with

$$y_p'(x) = Ae^{2x} + 2Axe^{2x} \qquad \text{and} \qquad y_p''(x) = 4Ae^{2x} + 4Axe^{2x}.$$

Substitution into the original differential equation yields

$$(4Ae^{2x} + 4Axe^{2x}) - 4(Axe^{2x}) = 2e^{2x}.$$

The terms involving xe^{2x} obligingly cancel, leaving only $4Ae^{2x} = 2e^{2x}$, so that $A = \frac{1}{2}$. Thus a particular solution is

$$y_p(x) = \frac{1}{2}xe^{2x}.$$ ∎

The General Approach

Our initial difficulty in Example 4 resulted from the fact that $f(x) = 2e^{2x}$ satisfied the associated homogeneous equation. Rule 1, given shortly, tells what to do when we do not have this difficulty, and Rule 2 tells what to do when we do have it.

The method of undetermined coefficients applies whenever the function $f(x)$ in Eq. (1) is a linear combination of (finite) products of functions of the following three types:

1. A polynomial in x;
2. An exponential function e^{rx};   (4)
3. $\cos kx$ or $\sin kx$.

Any such function, for example

$$f(x) = (3 - 4x^2)e^{5x} - 4x^3\cos 10x,$$

has the crucial property that only *finitely* many linearly independent functions appear as terms (summands) in $f(x)$ and its derivatives of all orders. In Rules 1 and 2 below we assume that $Ly = f(x)$ is a nonhomogeneous linear equation with constant coefficients and that $f(x)$ is a function of this kind.

▪ RULE 1: Method of Undetermined Coefficients

Suppose that no term appearing either in $f(x)$ or in any of its derivatives satisfies the associated homogeneous equation $Ly = 0$. Then take as a trial solution for y_p a linear combination of all linearly independent such terms and their derivatives. Determine the coefficients by substitution of this trial solution into the nonhomogeneous equation $Ly = f(x)$. ▪

Note that this rule is not a theorem requiring proof; it is merely a procedure to be following in searching for a particular solution y_p. If we succeed in finding y_p, then nothing more need be said. It can be proved, however, that this procedure will always succeed under the conditions specified here.

In practice we check the supposition made in Rule 1 by first using the characteristic equation to find the complementary function y_c, and then write a list of all the terms appearing in $f(x)$ and its successive derivatives. If none of the terms in this list duplicates a term in y_c, then we're in business!

EXAMPLE 5 Find a particular solution of

$$y'' + 4y = 3x^3. \tag{5}$$

Solution The (familiar) complementary function of this equation is

$$y_c(x) = c_1 \cos 2x + c_2 \sin 2x.$$

The function $f(x) = 3x^3$ and its derivatives are constant multiples of the linearly independent functions x^3, x^2, x, and 1. Because none of these appears in y_c, we try

$$y_p = Ax^3 + Bx^2 + Cx + D,$$
$$y_p' = 3Ax^2 + 2Bx + C,$$
$$y_p'' = 6Ax + 2B.$$

Substitution in Eq. (5) gives

$$y_p'' + 4y_p = (6Ax + 2B) + 4(Ax^3 + Bx^2 + Cx + D)$$
$$= 4Ax^3 + 4Bx^2 + (6A + 4C)x + (2B + D)$$
$$= 3x^3.$$

We equate coefficients of like powers of x to get the equations

$$4A = 3, \qquad 4B = 0,$$
$$6A + 4C = 0, \qquad 2B + D = 0$$

with solution $A = \frac{3}{4}$, $B = 0$, $C = -\frac{9}{8}$, and $D = 0$. Hence a particular solution of Eq.

(5) is

$$y_p(x) = \frac{3}{4}x^3 - \frac{9}{8}x.$$

EXAMPLE 6   Solve the initial value problem

$$y'' - 3y' + 2y = 3e^{-x} - 10\cos 3x;$$

$$y(0) = 1, \qquad y'(0) = 2. \tag{6}$$

Solution   The characteristic equation $r^2 - 3r + 2 = 0$ has roots $r = 1$ and $r = 2$, so the complementary function is

$$y_c(x) = c_1 e^x + c_2 e^{2x}.$$

The terms involved in $f(x) = 3e^{-x} - 10\cos 3x$ and its derivatives are e^{-x}, $\cos 3x$, and $\sin 3x$. Because none of these appears in y_c, we try

$$
\begin{aligned}
y_p &= Ae^{-x} &+ B\cos 3x &+ C\sin 3x, \\
y_p' &= -Ae^{-x} - 3B\sin 3x &+ 3C\cos 3x, \\
y_p'' &= Ae^{-x} &- 9B\cos 3x &- 9C\sin 3x.
\end{aligned}
$$

After we substitute these expressions into the differential equation in (6) and collect coefficients, we get

$$
\begin{aligned}
y_p'' - 3y_p' + 2y_p &= 6Ae^{-x} + (-7B - 9C)\cos 3x + (9B - 7C)\sin 3x \\
&= 3e^{-x} - 10\cos 3x.
\end{aligned}
$$

We equate the coefficients of the terms involving e^{-x}, those involving $\cos 3x$, and those involving $\sin 3x$. The result is the system

$$6A = 3,$$

$$-7B - 9C = -10,$$

$$9B - 7C = 0$$

with solution $A = \frac{1}{2}$, $B = \frac{7}{13}$, and $C = \frac{9}{13}$. This gives the particular solution

$$y_p(x) = \frac{1}{2}e^{-x} + \frac{7}{13}\cos 3x + \frac{9}{13}\sin 3x$$

which, however, does not have the required initial values in (6).

To satisfy those initial conditions, we begin with the *general* solution

$$
\begin{aligned}
y(x) &= y_c(x) + y_p(x) \\
&= c_1 e^x + c_2 e^{2x} + \frac{1}{2}e^{-x} + \frac{7}{13}\cos 3x + \frac{9}{13}\sin 3x,
\end{aligned}
$$

with derivative

$$y'(x) = c_1 e^x + 2c_2 e^{2x} - \frac{1}{2}e^{-x} - \frac{21}{13}\sin 3x + \frac{27}{13}\cos 3x.$$

The initial conditions in (6) lead to the equations

$$y(0) = c_1 + c_2 + \frac{1}{2} + \frac{7}{13} = 1,$$

$$y'(0) = c_1 + 2c_2 - \frac{1}{2} + \frac{27}{13} = 2$$

with solution $c_1 = -\frac{1}{2}$, $c_2 = \frac{6}{13}$. The desired particular solution is therefore

$$y(x) = -\frac{1}{2} e^x + \frac{6}{13} e^{2x} + \frac{1}{2} e^{-x} + \frac{7}{13} \cos 3x + \frac{9}{13} \sin 3x.$$

EXAMPLE 7   Find the general form of a particular solution of

$$y^{(3)} + 9y' = x \sin x + x^2 e^{2x}. \tag{7}$$

Solution   The characteristic equation $r^3 + 9r = 0$ has roots $r = 0$, $r = -3i$, and $r = 3i$. So the complementary function is

$$y_c(x) = c_1 + c_2 \cos 3x + c_3 \sin 3x.$$

The derivatives of the right-hand side in Eq. (7) involve the terms

$$\cos x, \qquad \sin x, \qquad x \cos x, \qquad x \sin x,$$

$$e^{2x}, \qquad xe^{2x}, \quad \text{and} \quad x^2 e^{2x}.$$

Because there is no duplication with the terms of the complementary function, the trial function takes the form

$$y_p(x) = A \cos x + B \sin x + Cx \cos x + Dx \sin x + Ee^{2x} + Fxe^{2x} + Gx^2 e^{2x}.$$

Upon substituting y_p in (7) and equating coefficients of like terms, we get seven equations determining the seven coefficients A, B, C, D, E, F, and G.   ∎

The Case of Duplication

Now we turn our attention to the situation in which Rule 1 does not apply: Some of the terms involved in $f(x)$ and its derivatives satisfy the associated homogeneous equation. For instance, suppose that we want to find a particular solution of the differential equation

$$(D - r)^3 y = (2x - 3)e^{rx}. \tag{8}$$

Proceeding as in Rule 1, our first guess would be

$$y_p(x) = Ae^{rx} + Bxe^{rx}. \tag{9}$$

This form of $y_p(x)$ will not be adequate because the complementary function of (8) is

$$y_c(x) = c_1 e^{rx} + c_2 xe^{rx} + c_3 x^2 e^{rx}, \tag{10}$$

so substitution of (9) in the left-hand side of (8) would yield zero rather than $(2x - 3)e^{rx}$.

To see how to amend our first guess, we observe that

$$(D - r)^2[(2x - 3)e^{rx}] = [D^2(2x - 3)]e^{rx} = 0$$

by Eq. (13) of Section 3.3. If $y(x)$ is *any* solution of Eq. (8) and we apply the operator $(D - r)^2$ to both sides, we therefore see that $y(x)$ is also a solution of the equation $(D - r)^5 y = 0$. The general solution of this *homogeneous* equation can be written as

$$y(x) = \underbrace{c_1 e^{rx} + c_2 x e^{rx} + c_3 x^2 e^{rx}}_{y_c} + \underbrace{Ax^3 e^{rx} + Bx^4 e^{rx}}_{y_p}.$$

Thus *every* solution of our original equation in (8) is the sum of a complementary function and a *particular solution* of the form

$$y_p(x) = Ax^3 e^{rx} + Bx^4 e^{rx}. \tag{11}$$

Note that (11) may be obtained by multiplying each term of our first guess in (9) by the least power of x (in this case, x^3) that suffices to eliminate duplication between the terms of the resulting trial solution $y_p(x)$ and the complementary function $y_c(x)$ given in (10). This procedure succeeds in the general case.

To simplify the general statement of Rule 2, we observe that in order to find a particular solution of the nonhomogeneous linear differential equation

$$Ly = f_1(x) + f_2(x), \tag{12}$$

it suffices to find *separately* particular solutions Y_1 and Y_2 of the two equations

$$Ly = f_1(x) \qquad \text{and} \qquad Ly = f_2(x), \tag{13}$$

respectively. For linearity then gives

$$L[Y_1 + Y_2] = LY_1 + LY_2 = f_1(x) + f_2(x),$$

and therefore $y_p = Y_1 + Y_2$ is a particular solution of (12). This is the **principle of superposition** for nonhomogeneous linear equations.

Now our problem is to find a particular solution of the equation $Ly = f(x)$, where $f(x)$ is a linear combination of products of the elementary functions listed in (4). Thus $f(x)$ can be written as a sum of terms each of the form

$$P_m(x)e^{rx} \cos kx \qquad \text{or} \qquad P_m(x)e^{rx} \sin kx, \tag{14}$$

where $P_m(x)$ is a polynomial in x of degree m. Note that any derivative of such a term is of the same form but with *both* sines and cosines appearing. The procedure by which we arrived earlier at the particular solution in (11) of Eq. (8) can be generalized to show that the following procedure is always successful.

▮ *RULE 2:* Method of Undetermined Cofficients

If the function $f(x)$ is of either form in (14), take as the trial solution

$$y_p(x) = x^s[(A_0 + A_1 x + \cdots + A_m x^m)e^{rx} \cos kx$$
$$+ (B_0 + B_1 x + \cdots + B_m x^m)e^{rx} \sin kx], \tag{15}$$

where s is the smallest nonnegative integer such that no term in y_p duplicates a term in the complementary function y_c. Then determine the coefficients in (15) by substituting y_p into the nonhomogeneous equation. ▮

$f(x)$	y_p
$P_m(x) = b_0 + b_1 x + b_2 x^2 + \cdots + b_m x^m$	$x^s(A_0 + A_1 x + A_2 x^2 + \cdots + A_m x^m)$
$a \cos kx + b \sin kx$	$x^s(A \cos kx + B \sin kx)$
$e^{rx}(a \cos kx + b \sin kx)$	$x^s e^{rx}(A \cos kx + B \sin kx)$
$P_m(x) e^{rx}$	$x^s(A_0 + A_1 x + A_2 x^2 + \cdots + A_m x^m) e^{rx}$
$P_m(x)\,(a \cos kx + b \sin kx)$	$x^s[(A_0 + A_1 x + \cdots + A_m x^m) \cos kx$
	$\qquad + (B_0 + B_1 x + \cdots + B_m x^m) \sin kx]$

FIGURE 3.5.1. Substitutions in the method of undetermined coefficients

In practice we seldom need to deal with a function $f(x)$ exhibiting the full generality in (14). The table in Fig. 3.5.1 lists the form of y_p in various common cases, corresponding to the possibilities $m = 0$, $r = 0$, and $k = 0$.

On the other hand, it is not uncommon to have

$$f(x) = f_1(x) + f_2(x),$$

where $f_1(x)$ and $f_2(x)$ are different functions of the sort listed in the table of Fig. 3.5.1. In this event we take as y_p the sum of the indicated particular functions, choosing s *separately* for each part to eliminate duplication with the complementary function. This procedure is illustrated in Examples 8 through 10.

EXAMPLE 8   Find a particular solution of

$$y^{(3)} + y'' = 3e^x + 4x^2. \tag{16}$$

Solution   The characteristic equation $r^3 + r^2 = 0$ has roots $r_1 = r_2 = 0$ and $r_3 = -1$, so the complementary function is

$$y_c(x) = c_1 + c_2 x + c_3 e^{-x}.$$

As a first step toward our particular solution, we form the sum

$$(Ae^x) + (B + Cx + Dx^2).$$

The part Ae^x corresponding to $3e^x$ does not duplicate any part of the complementary function, but the part $B + Cx + Dx^2$ must be multiplied by x^2 to eliminate duplication. Hence we take

$$y_p = Ae^x + Bx^2 + Cx^3 + Dx^4,$$
$$y_p' = Ae^x + 2Bx + 3Cx^2 + 4Dx^3,$$
$$y_p'' = Ae^x + 2B + 6Cx + 12Dx^2, \quad \text{and}$$
$$y_p^{(3)} = Ae^x + 6C + 24Dx,$$

Substitution of these derivatives in (16) yields

$$2Ae^x + (2B + 6C) + (6C + 24D)x + 12Dx^2 = 3e^x + 4x^2.$$

The system of equations

$$2A = 3, \qquad 2B + 6C = 0,$$
$$6C + 24D = 0, \qquad 12D = 4$$

has the solution $A = \frac{3}{2}, B = 4, C = -\frac{4}{3}$, and $D = \frac{1}{3}$. Hence the desired particular solution is

$$y_p(x) = \frac{3}{2}e^x + 4x^2 - \frac{4}{3}x^3 + \frac{1}{3}x^4.$$

EXAMPLE 9   Determine the appropriate form for a particular solution of

$$y'' + 6y' + 13y = e^{-3x}\cos 2x.$$

Solution   The characteristic equation $r^2 + 6r + 13 = 0$ has roots $-3 \pm 2i$, so the complementary function is

$$y_c(x) = e^{-3x}(c_1\cos 2x + c_2\sin 2x).$$

This is the same form as a first attempt $e^{-3x}(A\cos 2x + B\sin 2x)$ at a particular solution, so we must multiply by x to eliminate duplication. Hence we would take

$$y_p(x) = e^{-3x}(Ax\cos 2x + Bx\sin 2x).$$

EXAMPLE 10   Determine the appropriate form for a particular solution of the fifth-order equation

$$(D - 2)^3(D^2 + 9)y = x^2e^{2x} + x\sin 3x.$$

Solution   The characteristic equation $(r - 2)^3(r^2 + 9) = 0$ has roots $r = 2, 2, 2, 3i$, and $-3i$, so the complementary function is

$$y_c(x) = c_1e^{2x} + c_2xe^{2x} + c_3x^2e^{2x} + c_4\cos 3x + c_5\sin 3x.$$

As a first step toward the form of a particular solution, we examine the sum

$$[(A + Bx + Cx^2)e^{2x}] + [(D + Ex)\cos 3x + (F + Gx)\sin 3x].$$

To eliminate duplication with terms of $y_c(x)$, the first part—corresponding to x^2e^{2x}—must be multiplied by x^3, and the second part—corresponding to $x\sin 3x$—must be multiplied by x. Hence we would take

$$y_p(x) = (Ax^3 + Bx^4 + Cx^5)e^{2x} + (Dx + Ex^2)\cos 3x + (Fx + Gx^2)\sin 3x. \quad \blacksquare$$

Variation of Parameters

Finally, let us point out the kind of situation in which the method of undetermined coefficients cannot be used. Consider, for instance, the equation

$$y'' + y = \tan x, \tag{17}$$

which at first glance may appear similar to those considered in the preceding examples. Not so; the function $f(x) = \tan x$ has *infinitely many* linearly independent derivatives

$$\sec^2 x, \quad 2\sec^2 x\tan x, \quad 4\sec^2 x\tan^2 x + 2\sec^4 x, \quad \ldots.$$

Therefore we do not have available a *finite* linear combination to use as a trial solution.

We discuss here the method of **variation of parameters** which—in principle (that is, if the integrals that appear can be evaluated)—can always be used to find a particular solution of the nonhomogeneous linear differential equation

$$y^{(n)} + p_{n-1}(x)y^{(n-1)} + \cdots + p_1(x)y' + p_0(x)y = f(x), \tag{18}$$

provided that we already know the general solution

$$y_c = c_1 y_1 + c_2 y_2 + \cdots + c_n y_n \tag{19}$$

of the associated homogeneous equation

$$y^{(n)} + p_{n-1}(x)y^{(n-1)} + \cdots + p_1(x)y' + p_0(x)y = 0. \tag{20}$$

Here, in brief, is the basic idea of the method of variation of parameters. Suppose that we replace the constants, or *parameters,* $c_1, c_2, \ldots, c_n$ in the complementary function in (19) by variables: functions $u_1, u_2, \ldots, u_n$ of x. We ask whether it is possible to choose these functions in such a way that the combination

$$y_p(x) = u_1(x)y_1(x) + u_2(x)y_2(x) + \cdots + u_n(x)y_n(x) \tag{21}$$

is a particular solution of the nonhomogeneous Eq. (18). It turns out that this *is* always possible.

The method is essentially the same for all orders $n \geqq 2$, but we will describe it in detail only for the case $n = 2$. So we begin with the second-order nonhomogeneous equation

$$\blacktriangleright \qquad L[y] = y'' + P(x)y' + Q(x)y = f(x) \tag{22}$$

with complementary function

$$y_c = c_1 y_1 + c_2 y_2 \tag{23}$$

on some open interval I where the functions P and Q are continuous. We want to find functions u_1 and u_2 such that

$$\blacktriangleright \qquad y_p = u_1 y_1 + u_2 y_2 \tag{24}$$

is a particular solution of Eq. (22).

One condition on the two functions u_1 and u_2 is that $L[y_p] = f(x)$. Because two conditions are required to determine two functions, we are free to impose an additional condition of our choice. We will do this in a way that simplifies the computations as much as possible. But first, to impose the condition $L[y_p] = f(x)$, we must compute the derivatives y_p' and y_p''. The product rule gives

$$y_p' = (u_1 y_1' + u_2 y_2') + (u_1' y_1 + u_2' y_2).$$

To avoid the appearance of the second derivatives u_1'' and u_2'', our additional condition will be that the second sum here must vanish:

$$u_1' y_1 + u_2' y_2 = 0. \tag{25}$$

Then

$$y_p' = u_1 y_1' + u_2 y_2', \tag{26}$$

and the product rule gives

$$y_p'' = (u_1 y_1'' + u_2 y_2'') + (u_1' y_1' + u_2' y_2'). \tag{27}$$

But both y_1 and y_2 satisfy the homogeneous equation

$$y'' + Py' + Qy = 0$$

associated with the nonhomogeneous equation in (22), so

$$y_i'' = -Py_i' - Qy_i \tag{28}$$

for $i = 1, 2$. It therefore follows from Eq. (27) that

$$y_p'' = (u_1'y_1' + u_2'y_2') - P \cdot (u_1y_1' + u_2y_2') - Q \cdot (u_1y_1 + u_2y_2).$$

In view of Eqs. (24) and (26), this means that

$$y_p'' = (u_1'y_1' + u_2'y_2') - Py_p' - Qy_p;$$

that is, that

$$L[y_p] = u_1'y_1' + u_2'y_2'. \tag{29}$$

The requirement that y_p satisfy the nonhomogeneous equation in (22)—that is, that $L[y_p] = f(x)$—therefore implies that

$$u_1'y_1' + u_2'y_2' = f(x). \tag{30}$$

Finally, Eqs. (25) and (30) determine the functions u_1 and u_2 that we need. Collecting these equations, we obtain a system

$$\blacktriangleright \qquad \begin{aligned} u_1'y_1 + u_2'y_2 &= 0, \\ u_1'y_1' + u_2'y_2' &= f(x) \end{aligned} \tag{31}$$

of two linear equations in the two *derivatives* u_1' and u_2'. Note that the determinant of coefficients in (31) is simply the Wronskian $W(y_1, y_2)$. Once we have solved the equations in (31) for the derivatives u_1' and u_2', we integrate each to obtain the functions u_1 and u_2 such that

$$\blacktriangleright \qquad y_p = u_1y_1 + u_2y_2$$

is the desired particular solution of Eq. (22).

EXAMPLE 11 Find a particular solution of $y'' + y = \tan x$.

Solution The complementary function is $y_c(x) = c_1 \cos x + c_2 \sin x$, so

$$\begin{aligned} y_1 &= \cos x, & y_2 &= \sin x, \\ y_1' &= -\sin x, & y_2' &= \cos x. \end{aligned}$$

Hence the equations in (31) are

$$u_1'(\cos x) + u_2'(\sin x) = 0,$$

$$u_1'(-\sin x) + u_2'(\cos x) = \tan x.$$

We easily solve these equations for

$$u_1' = -\sin x \tan x = -\frac{\sin^2 x}{\cos x} = \cos x - \sec x,$$

$$u_2' = \cos x \tan x = \sin x.$$

Hence we take

$$u_1 = \int (\cos x - \sec x)\, dx = \sin x - \ln|\sec x + \tan x|$$

and

$$u_2 = \int \sin x\, dx = -\cos x.$$

Thus our particular solution is

$$y_p(x) = u_1(x)y_1(x) + u_2(x)y_2(x)$$
$$= (\sin x - \ln|\sec x + \tan x|)\cos x + (-\cos x)\sin x;$$

that is,

$$y_p(x) = -(\cos x)\ln|\sec x + \tan x|.$$

3.5 Problems

In Problems 1 through 20, find a particular solution y_p of the given equation.

1. $y'' + 16y = e^{3x}$

2. $y'' - y' - 2y = 3x + 4$

3. $y'' - y' - 6y = 2\sin 3x$

4. $4y'' + 4y' + y = 3xe^x$

5. $y'' + y' + y = \sin^2 x$

6. $2y'' + 4y' + 7y = x^2$

7. $y'' - 4y = \sinh x$

8. $y'' - 4y = \cosh 2x$

9. $y'' + 2y' - 3y = 1 + xe^x$

10. $y'' + 9y = 2\cos 3x + 3\sin 3x$

11. $y^{(3)} + 4y' = 3x - 1$

12. $y^{(3)} + y' = 2 - \sin x$

13. $y'' + 2y' + 5y = e^x \sin x$

14. $y^{(4)} - 2y'' + y = xe^x$

15. $y^{(5)} + 5y^{(4)} - y = 17$

16. $y'' + 9y = 2x^2 e^{3x} + 5$

17. $y'' + y = \sin x + x\cos x$

18. $y^{(4)} - 5y'' + 4y = e^x - xe^{2x}$

19. $y^{(5)} + 2y^{(3)} + 2y'' = 3x^2 - 1$

20. $y^{(3)} - y = e^x + 7$

In Problems 21 through 30, set up the appropriate form of a particular solution y_p, but do not determine the values of the coefficients.

21. $y'' - 2y' + 2y = e^x \sin x$

22. $y^{(5)} - y^{(3)} = e^x + 2x^2 - 5$

23. $y'' + 4y = 3x\cos 2x$

24. $y^{(3)} - y'' - 12y' = x - 2xe^{-3x}$

25. $y'' + 3y' + 2y = x(e^{-x} - e^{-2x})$

26. $y'' - 6y' + 13y = xe^{3x}\sin 2x$

27. $y^{(4)} + 5y'' + 4y = \sin x + \cos 2x$

28. $y^{(4)} + 9y'' = (x^2 + 1)\sin 3x$

29. $(D - 1)^3(D^2 - 4)y = xe^x + e^{2x} + e^{-2x}$

30. $y^{(4)} - 2y'' + y = x^2 \cos x$

Solve the initial value problems in Problems 31 through 40.

31. $y'' + 4y = 2x$; $y(0) = 1$, $y'(0) = 2$

32. $y'' + 3y' + 2y = e^x$; $y(0) = 0$, $y'(0) = 3$

33. $y'' + 9y = \sin 2x$; $y(0) = 1$, $y'(0) = 0$

34. $y'' + y = \cos x$; $y(0) = 1$, $y'(0) = -1$

35. $y'' - 2y' + 2y = x + 1$; $y(0) = 3$, $y'(0) = 0$

36. $y^{(4)} - 4y'' = x^2$; $y(0) = y'(0) = 1$,
$y''(0) = y^{(3)}(0) = -1$

37. $y^{(3)} - 2y'' + y' = 1 + xe^x$; $y(0) = y'(0) = 0$,
$y''(0) = 1$

38. $y'' + 2y' + 2y = \sin 3x$; $y(0) = 2$, $y'(0) = 0$

39. $y^{(3)} + y'' = x + e^{-x}$; $y(0) = 1$, $y'(0) = 0$,
$y''(0) = 1$

40. $y^{(4)} - y = 5$; $y(0) = y'(0) = y''(0) = y^{(3)}(0) = 0$

41. Find a particular solution of the equation

$$y^{(4)} - y^{(3)} - y'' - y' - 2y = 8x^5.$$

42. Find the solution of the initial value problem consisting of the differential equation of Problem 41 and the initial conditions

$$y(0) = y'(0) = y''(0) = y^{(3)}(0) = 0.$$

43. (a) Write

$$\cos 3x + i\sin 3x = e^{3ix} = (\cos x + i\sin x)^3$$

by Euler's formula, expand, and equate real and imaginary parts to derive the identities

$$\cos^3 x = \frac{3}{4} \cos x + \frac{1}{4} \cos 3x,$$

$$\sin^3 x = \frac{3}{4} \sin x - \frac{1}{4} \sin 3x.$$

(b) Use the result of part (a) to find a general solution of

$$y'' + 4y = \cos^3 x.$$

Use trigonometric identities to find general solutions of the equations in Problems 44 through 46.

44. $y'' + y' + y = \sin x \sin 3x$

45. $y'' + 9y = \sin^4 x$

46. $y'' + y = x \cos^3 x$

In Problems 47 through 56, use the method of variation of parameters to find a particular solution of the given differential equation.

47. $y'' + 3y' + 2y = 4e^x$ **48.** $y'' - 2y' - 8y = 3e^{-2x}$

49. $y'' - 4y' + 4y = 2e^{2x}$ **50.** $y'' - 4y = \sinh 2x$

51. $y'' + 4y = \cos 3x$ **52.** $y'' + 9y = \sin 3x$

53. $y'' + 9y = 2 \sec 3x$ **54.** $y'' + y = \csc^2 x$

55. $y'' + 4y = \sin^2 x$ **56.** $y'' - 4y = xe^x$

57. You can verify by substitution that $y_c = c_1 x + c_2 x^{-1}$ is a complementary function for the nonhomogeneous second-order equation $x^2 y'' + xy' - y = 72x^5$. But before applying the method of variation of parameters, you first must divide this equation by the leading coefficient x^2 to rewrite it in the standard form

$$y'' + \frac{1}{x} y' - \frac{1}{x^2} y = 72x^3.$$

Thus $f(x) = 72x^3$ in Eq. (22). Now proceed to solve the equations in (31) and thence derive the particular solution $y_p = 3x^5$.

In Problems 58 through 63 a nonhomogeneous second-order linear equation and a complementary function y_c are given. Apply the method of Problem 57 to find a particular solution of the equation.

58. $x^2 y'' - 4xy' + 6y = x^3$; $y_c = c_1 x^2 + c_2 x^3$

59. $x^2 y'' - 3xy' + 4y = x^4$; $y_c = x^2(c_1 + c_2 \ln x)$

60. $4x^2 y'' - 4xy' + 3y = 8x^{4/3}$; $y_c = c_1 x + c_2 x^{3/4}$

61. $x^2 y'' + xy' + y = \ln x$; $y_c = c_1 \cos (\ln x)$
    $+ c_2 \sin(\ln x)$

62. $(x^2 - 1) y'' - 2xy' + 2y = x^2 - 1$; $y_c = c_1 x$
    $+ c_2 (1 + x^2)$

3.5 Computing Projects

The use of a computer algebra system can lighten the burden of algebraic computation associated with the method of undetermined coefficients. For example, consider the differential equation

$$L[y] = y^{(5)} + 2y^{(4)} + 2y^{(3)} - 300x^2 - 30e^x = 0 \tag{1}$$

with complementary function

$$y_c(x) = A + Bx + Cx^2 + e^{-x}(D \cos x + E \sin x).$$

Using *Mathematica*, for instance, we first specify the form

y = a x^3 + b x^4 + c x^5 + d E^x;

of the desired particular solution. We then calculate the result of substituting **y** in the left-hand side of Eq. (1) with the command

Ly = D[y,{x,5}] + 2 D[y,{x,4}] +

2 D[y,{x,3}] - 300 x^2 - 30 E^x

120 c - 30 E^x + d E^x - 300 x^2 + 2 (24 b + d E^x + 120 c x) +

2 (6 a + d E^x + 24 b x + 60 c x^2)

where **D[y, {x,n}]** yields the *n*th derivative of the expression **y** with respect to the variable **x**. Upon collecting coefficients of the types of terms that appear,

> **Collect[Ly, {1, x, x^2, E^x}]**

> 12 a + 48 b + 120 c + (−30 + 5 d) E^X + (48 b + 240 c) x +
>
> (−300 + 120 c) x²

we can readily read off the four linear equations to be solved for the four coefficients a, b, c, d.

> **Solve [{ 12 a + 48 b + 120 c == 0,**
>
> **−30 + 5 d == 0,**
>
> **(48 b + 240 c) == 0,**
>
> **−300 + 120 c == 0}, {a, b, c, d}]**

> {{a -> 25, d -> 6, b -> − ($\frac{25}{2}$), c -> $\frac{5}{2}$ }}

Thus the desired particular solution of Eq. (1) is

$$y_p(x) = \frac{1}{2}(50x^3 - 25x^4 + 5x^5) + 6e^x.$$

If a computer algebra system is available, use it to find particular solutions of the differential equations given in Problems 21 through 30 of this section.

The method of variation of parameters also is readily automated using a computer algebra system. To solve Example 11 using *Maple,* for instance, we first enter the given homogeneous solutions y_1 and y_2 and the nonhomogeneous term $f(x)$ in the equation $y'' + y = \tan x$.

> **>y1 := cos(x):**
>
> **y2 := sin(x):**
>
> **f := tan(x):**

We next set up and solve the equations in (31).

> **>y1p := diff(y1, x):**
>
> **y2p := diff(y2, x):   # Derivatives of y1 and y2**
>
> **eqs := { u1p*y1 + u2p*y2 = 0,**
>
> **u1p*y1p + u2p*y2p = f }:**

> **soln := solve(eqs, {u1p, u2p});**

> soln:=$\left\{ u2p = \dfrac{\cos(x)\,\tan(x)}{\sin(x)^2 + \cos(x)^2}, \quad u1p = -\dfrac{\tan(x)\,\sin(x)}{\sin(x)^2 + \cos(x)^2} \right\}$

> **>u1p := rhs(soln[2]):   # Select the derivatives**
>
> **u2p := rhs(soln[1]):   # of u1 and u2**

Finally we integrate **u1p** = u_1' and **u2p** = u_2' and assemble the desired particular solution $y_p = u_1 y_1 + u_2 y_2$.

```
>u1 := int(u1p, x):
 u2 := int(u2p, x);
 y := simplify( u1*y1 + u2*y2);
 y := ln(1 - cos(x) - sin(x)) cos(x)
      - ln(1 - cos(x) + sin(x)) cos(x) - sin(x)
```

By combining the two logarithms on the right and then converting sines and cosines into secants and tangents, you should be able to verify that this solution is equivalent to the one we found manually in the text.

To solve a different second-order variation of parameters problem (as in Problems 47 through 62 in this section), one need only substitute the appropriate functions y_1, y_2, and $f(x)$ in the initial lines above, then re-execute the remaining lines.

3.6 Forced Oscillations and Resonance

In Section 3.4 we derived the differential equation

$$mx'' + cx' + kx = F(t) \tag{1}$$

that governs the one-dimensional motion of a mass m that is attached to a spring (with constant k) and a dashpot (with constant c) and is also acted on by an external force $F(t)$. Machines with rotating components commonly involve mass-spring systems (or their equivalents) in which the external force is simple harmonic:

$$F(t) = F_0 \cos \omega t \quad \text{or} \quad F(t) = F_0 \sin \omega t, \tag{2}$$

where the constant F_0 is the amplitude of the periodic force and ω is its circular frequency.

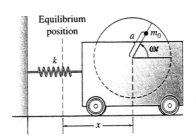

FIGURE 3.6.1. The cart-with-flywheel system

For an example of how a rotating machine component can provide a simple harmonic force, consider the cart with a rotating vertical flywheel shown in Fig. 3.6.1. The cart has mass $m - m_0$, not including the flywheel of mass m_0. The centroid of the flywheel is off-center at distance a from its center, and its angular speed is ω radians per second. The cart is attached to a spring (with constant k) as shown. Assume that the centroid of the cart itself is directly beneath the center of the flywheel, and denote by $x(t)$ its displacement from its equilibrium position (where the spring is unstretched). Figure 3.6.1 helps us to see that the displacement $\bar{x}$ of the centroid of the combined cart plus flywheel is given by

$$\bar{x} = \frac{(m - m_0) x + m_0 (x + a \cos \omega t)}{m} = x + \frac{m_0 a}{m} \cos \omega t.$$

Let us ignore friction and apply apply Newton's second law $m\bar{x}'' = -kx$, because the force exerted by the spring is $-kx$. We substitute for $\bar{x}$ in the last equation to obtain

$$mx'' - m_0 a \omega^2 \cos \omega t = -kx;$$

that is,

$$mx'' + kx = m_0 a\omega^2 \cos \omega t. \tag{3}$$

Thus the cart with its rotating flywheel acts like a mass on a spring under the influence of a simple harmonic external force with amplitude $F_0 = m_0 a\omega^2$. Such a system is a reasonable model of a front-loading washing machine with the clothes being washed loaded off-center. This illustrates the practical importance of analyzing solutions of Eq. (1) with external forces as in (2).

Undamped Forced Oscillations

To study undamped oscillations under the influence of the external force $F(t) = F_0 \cos \omega t$, we set $c = 0$ in Eq. (1), and thereby begin with the equation

▶
$$mx'' + kx = F_0 \cos \omega t \tag{4}$$

whose complementary function is $x_c = c_1 \cos \omega_0 t + c_2 \sin \omega_0 t$. Here,

$$\omega_0 = \sqrt{\frac{k}{m}}$$

is the (circular) **natural frequency** of the mass-spring system. Let us assume initially that the external and natural frequencies are *unequal:* $\omega \neq \omega_0$. We substitute $x_p = A \cos \omega t$ in (4) to find a particular solution. (No sine term is needed in x_p because there is no term involving x' on the left-hand side in Eq. (4).) This gives

$$-m\omega^2 A \cos \omega t + kA \cos \omega t = F_0 \cos \omega t,$$

so

$$A = \frac{F_0}{k - m\omega^2} = \frac{F_0/m}{\omega_0^2 - \omega^2}, \tag{5}$$

and thus

$$x_p(t) = \frac{F_0/m}{\omega_0^2 - \omega^2} \cos \omega t. \tag{6}$$

Therefore the general solution $x = x_c + x_p$ is given by

$$x(t) = c_1 \cos \omega_0 t + c_2 \sin \omega_0 t + \frac{F_0/m}{\omega_0^2 - \omega^2} \cos \omega t, \tag{7}$$

where the constants c_1 and c_2 are determined by the initial values $x(0)$ and $x'(0)$. Equivalently, as in Eq. (12) of Section 3.4, we can rewrite Eq. (7) as

$$x(t) = C \cos(\omega_0 t - \alpha) + \frac{F_0/m}{\omega_0^2 - \omega^2} \cos \omega t, \tag{8}$$

so we see that the resulting motion is a superposition of two oscillations, one with natural circular frequency ω_0, the other with the frequency ω of the external force.

EXAMPLE 1   Suppose that $m = 1$, $k = 9$, $F_0 = 80$, and $\omega = 5$, so the differential equation in (4) is

$$x'' + 9x = 80 \cos 5t.$$

Find $x(t)$ if $x(0) = x'(0) = 0$.

Solution Here the natural frequency $\omega_0 = 3$ and the frequency $\omega = 5$ of the external force are unequal, as in the preceding discussion. First we substitute $x_p = A \cos 5t$ in the differential equation and find that $-25A + 9A = 80$, so that $A = -5$. Thus a particular solution is

$$x_p(t) = -5 \cos 5t.$$

The complementary function is $x_c = c_1 \cos 3t + c_2 \sin 3t$, so the general solution of the given nonhomogeneous equation is

$$x(t) = c_1 \cos 3t + c_2 \sin 3t - 5 \cos 5t,$$

with derivative

$$x'(t) = -3c_1 \sin 3t + 3c_2 \cos 3t + 25 \sin 5t.$$

The initial conditions $x(0) = 0$ and $x'(0) = 0$ now yield $c_1 = 5$ and $c_2 = 0$, so the desired particular solution is

$$x(t) = 5 \cos 3t - 5 \cos 5t. \qquad \blacksquare$$

Beats

If we impose the initial conditions $x(0) = x'(0) = 0$ on the solution in (7), we find that

$$c_1 = -\frac{F_0}{m(\omega_0^2 - \omega^2)} \quad \text{and} \quad c_2 = 0,$$

so the particular solution is

$$x(t) = \frac{F_0}{m(\omega_0^2 - \omega^2)} (\cos \omega t - \cos \omega_0 t). \tag{9}$$

The trigonometric identity $2 \sin A \sin B = \cos (A - B) - \cos(A + B)$, applied with $A = \frac{1}{2}(\omega_0 + \omega)t$ and $B = \frac{1}{2}(\omega_0 - \omega)t$, enables us to rewrite Eq. (9) in the form

$$x(t) = \frac{2F_0}{m(\omega_0^2 - \omega^2)} \sin \frac{1}{2} (\omega_0 - \omega)t \sin \frac{1}{2} (\omega_0 + \omega)t. \tag{10}$$

Suppose now that $\omega \approx \omega_0$, so that $\omega_0 + \omega$ is very large in comparison with $|\omega_0 - \omega|$. Then $\sin \frac{1}{2}(\omega_0 + \omega)t$ is a *rapidly* varying function, whereas $\sin \frac{1}{2}(\omega_0 - \omega)t$ is a *slowly* varying function. We may therefore interpret (10) as a rapid oscillation with circular frequency $\frac{1}{2}(\omega_0 + \omega)$,

$$x(t) = A(t) \sin \frac{1}{2} (\omega_0 + \omega)t,$$

but with a slowly varying amplitude

$$A(t) = \frac{2F_0}{m(\omega_0^2 - \omega^2)} \sin \frac{1}{2} (\omega_0 - \omega)t.$$

EXAMPLE 2 With $m = 0.1$, $F_0 = 50$, $\omega_0 = 55$, and $\omega = 45$, Eq. (10) gives

$$x(t) = \sin 5t \sin 50t.$$

Figure 3.6.2 shows the corresponding oscillation of frequency $\frac{1}{2}(\omega_0 + \omega) = 50$ that is "modulated" by the amplitude function $A(t) = \sin 5t$ of frequency $\frac{1}{2}(\omega_0 - \omega) = 5$. ∎

A rapid oscillation with a (comparatively) slowly varying periodic amplitude exhibits the phenomenon of *beats*. For example, if two horns not exactly attuned to one another simultaneously play their middle C, one at $\omega_0/(2\pi) = 258$ Hz and the other at $\omega/(2\pi) = 254$ Hz, then one hears a beat—an audible variation in the *amplitude* of the combined sound—with a frequency of

Resonance

$$\frac{(\omega_0 - \omega)/2}{2\pi} = \frac{1}{2}(258 - 254) = 2 \text{ Hz}.$$

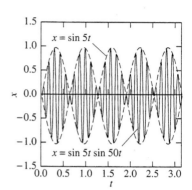

FIGURE 3.6.2. The phenomenon of beats

Looking at Eq. (6), we see that the amplitude A of x_p is large when the natural and external frequencies ω_0 and ω are approximately equal. It is sometimes useful to rewrite (5) in the form

$$A = \frac{F_0}{k - m\omega^2} = \frac{F_0/k}{1 - (\omega/\omega_0)^2} = \pm\frac{\rho F_0}{k}, \tag{11}$$

where F_0/k is the **static displacement** of a spring with constant k due to a *constant* force F_0, and the **amplification factor** ρ is defined to be

$$\rho = \frac{1}{\left|1 - (\omega/\omega_0)^2\right|}. \tag{12}$$

It is clear that $\rho \to +\infty$ as $\omega \to \omega_0$. This is the phenomenon of **resonance**—the increase without bound (as $\omega \to \omega_0$) in the amplitude of the oscillations of an undamped system with natural frequency ω_0 in response to an external force with frequency $\omega \approx \omega_0$.

We have been assuming that $\omega \neq \omega_0$. What sort of catastrophe should one expect if ω and ω_0 are precisely equal? Then Eq. (4), upon division of each term by m, becomes

$$x'' + \omega_0^2 x = \frac{F_0}{m}\cos\omega_0 t. \tag{13}$$

Because $\cos\omega_0 t$ is a term of the complementary function, the method of undetermined coefficients calls for us to try

$$x_p = t(A\cos\omega_0 t + B\sin\omega_0 t).$$

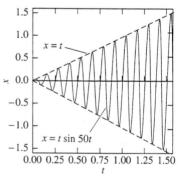

FIGURE 3.6.3. The phenomenon of resonance

We substitute this in (13), and thereby find that $A = 0$ and $B = F_0/(2m\omega_0)$. Hence the particular solution is

$$x_p(t) = \frac{F_0}{2m\omega_0}t\sin\omega_0 t. \tag{14}$$

The graph of $x_p(t)$ in Fig. 3.6.3 (in which $m = 1$, $F_0 = 100$, and $\omega_0 = 50$) shows vividly how the amplitude of the oscillation theoretically would increase without bound in this case of *pure resonance,* $\omega = \omega_0$. We may interpret the phenomenon as reinforcement of the natural vibrations of the system by externally impressed vibrations at the same frequency.

EXAMPLE 3   Suppose that $m = 5$ kg and that $k = 500$ N/m in the cart with the flywheel of Fig. 3.6.1. Then the natural frequency is $\omega_0 = \sqrt{k/m} = 10$ rad/s; that is, $10/(2\pi) \approx 1.59$ Hz. We would therefore expect oscillations of very large amplitude to occur if the flywheel revolves at about $(1.59)(60) \approx 95$ revolutions per minute (rpm).   ■

In practice, a mechanical system with very little damping can be destroyed by resonance vibrations. A spectacular example can occur when a column of soldiers marches in step over a bridge. Any complicated structure such as a bridge has many natural frequencies of vibration. If the frequency of the soldiers' cadence is approximately equal to one of the natural frequencies of the structure, then—just as in our simple example of a mass on a spring—resonance will occur. Indeed, the resulting resonance vibrations can be of such large amplitude that the bridge will collapse. This has actually happened—for example, the collapse of Broughton Bridge near Manchester, England, in 1831—and it is the reason for the now-standard practice of breaking cadence when crossing a bridge. Resonance may have been involved in the 1981 Kansas City disaster in which a hotel balcony (called a *skywalk*) collapsed with dancers on it. The collapse of a building in an earthquake is sometimes due to resonance vibrations caused by the ground oscillating at one of the natural frequencies of the structure; this happened to many buildings in the Mexico City earthquake of September 19, 1985. On occasion an airplane has crashed because of resonant wing oscillations caused by vibrations of the engines. It is reported that for some of the first commercial jet aircraft, the natural frequency of the vertical vibrations of the airplane during turbulence was almost exactly that of the mass-spring system consisting of the pilot's head (mass) and spine (spring). Resonance occurred, causing pilots to have difficulty in reading the instruments. Large modern commercial jets have different natural frequencies, so that this resonance problem no longer occurs.

Modeling Mechanical Systems

The avoidance of destructive resonance vibrations is a constant factor in the design of mechanical structures and systems of all types. Often the most important step in determining the natural frequency of vibration of a system is the formulation of its differential equation. In addition to Newton's law $F = ma$, the principle of conservation of energy is sometimes useful for this purpose (as in the derivation of the pendulum equation in Section 3.4). The following kinetic and potential energy formulas are often useful.

   1. *Kinetic energy:* $T = \frac{1}{2}mv^2$ for translation of a mass with velocity v;
   2. *Kinetic energy:* $T = \frac{1}{2}I\omega^2$ for rotation of a body of moment of inertia I with angular velocity ω;
   3. *Potential energy:* $V = \frac{1}{2}kx^2$ for a spring with constant k stretched or compressed a distance x;

4. *Potential energy:* $V = mgh$ for the gravitational potential energy of a mass m at height h above the reference level (the level at which $V = 0$), provided that g may be regarded as essentially constant.

EXAMPLE 4   Find the natural frequency of a mass m on a spring (with constant k) if, instead of sliding without friction, it is a uniform disk of radius a that rolls without slipping, as shown in Fig. 3.6.4.

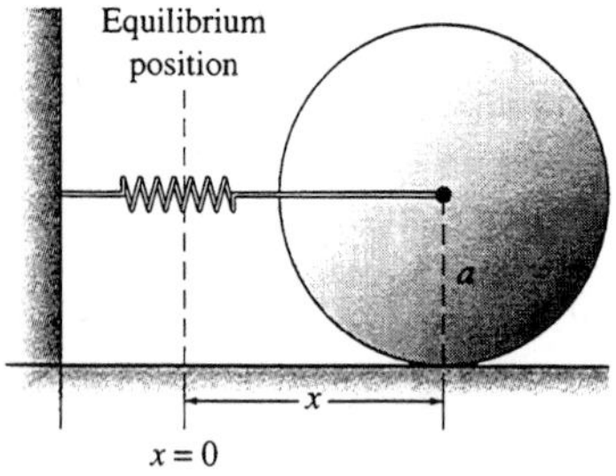

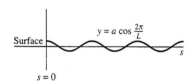

FIGURE 3.6.4. The rolling disk

Solution With the preceding notation, the principle of conservation of energy gives

$$\frac{1}{2}mv^2 + \frac{1}{2}I\omega^2 + \frac{1}{2}kx^2 = E$$

where E is a constant (the total mechanical energy of the system). We note that $v = a\omega$, and recall that $I = ma^2/2$ for a uniform circular disk. Thus we may simplify the last equation to

$$\frac{3}{4}mv^2 + \frac{1}{2}kx^2 = E.$$

Differentiation ($v = x'$, $v' = x''$) now gives

$$\frac{3}{2}mx'x'' + kxx' = 0.$$

We divide each term by $\frac{3}{2}mx'$ to obtain

$$x'' + \frac{2k}{3m}x = 0.$$

Thus the natural circular frequency is $\omega_0 = \sqrt{2k/3m}$, which is $\sqrt{2/3} \approx 0.8165$ times the frequency in the previous situation of sliding without friction.

EXAMPLE 5   Suppose that a car oscillates vertically as if it were a mass $m = 800$ kg on a single spring (with constant $k = 7 \times 10^4$ N/m), attached to a single dashpot (with constant $c = 2000$ N-s/m). Suppose that this car with the dashpot *disconnected* is driven along a washboard road surface with an amplitude of 5 cm and a wavelength of $L = 10$ m (Fig. 3.6.5). At what car speed will resonance vibrations occur?

FIGURE 3.6.5. The washboard road surface of Example 5

Solution We think of the car as a unicycle, as pictured in Fig. 3.6.6. Let $x(t)$ denote the upward displacement of the mass m from its equilibrium position; we ignore the force of gravity, because it merely displaces the equilibrium position as in Problem 9 of Section 3.4. We write the equation of the road surface as

$$y = a\cos\frac{2\pi s}{L} \qquad (a = 0.05\ \text{m}, L = 10\ \text{m}). \tag{15}$$

When the car is in motion, the spring is stretched by the amount $x - y$, so Newton's second law, $F = ma$, gives

$$mx'' = -k(x - y);$$

that is,

$$mx'' + kx = ky \tag{16}$$

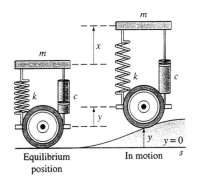

FIGURE 3.6.6. The "unicycle model" of a car

If the velocity of the car is v, then $s = vt$ in (15), so Eq. (16) takes the form

$$mx'' + kx = ka \cos \frac{2\pi vt}{L}. \tag{16'}$$

This is the differential equation that governs the vertical oscillations of the car. In comparing it with Eq. (4), we see that we have forced oscillations with circular frequency $\omega = 2\pi v/L$. Resonance will occur when $\omega = \omega_0 = \sqrt{k/m}$. We use our numerical data to find the speed of the car at resonance:

$$v = \frac{L}{2\pi} \sqrt{\frac{k}{m}} = \frac{10}{2\pi} \sqrt{\frac{7 \times 10^4}{800}} \approx 14.89 \quad (\text{m/s});$$

that is, about 33.3 mi/h (using the conversion factor of 2.237 mi/h per m/s).   ■

Damped Forced Oscillations

In real physical systems there is always some damping, from frictional effects if nothing else. The complementary function x_c of the equation

▶
$$mx'' + cx' + kx = F_0 \cos \omega t \tag{17}$$

is given by Eq. (18), (19), or (20) of Section 3.4, depending upon whether $c > c_{CR}$, $c = c_{CR}$, or $c < c_{CR}$. The specific form is not important here. What is important is that, in any case, these formulas show that $x_c(t) \to 0$ as $t \to +\infty$. Thus x_c is a **transient solution** of (17)—one that dies out with the passage of time, leaving only the particular solution x_p.

The method of undetermined coefficients indicates that we should substitute

$$x_p = A \cos \omega t + B \sin \omega t$$

in (17). When we do so, collect terms, and equate coefficients of $\cos \omega t$ and $\sin \omega t$, we obtain the two equations

$$(k - m\omega^2)A + c\omega B = F_0, \qquad -c\omega A + (k - m\omega^2)B = 0 \tag{18}$$

that we solve without difficulty for

$$A = \frac{(k - m\omega^2)F_0}{(k - m\omega^2)^2 + (c\omega)^2}, \qquad B = \frac{(c\omega)F_0}{(k - m\omega^2)^2 + (c\omega)^2}.$$

To simplify the notation, it is convenient to introduce the quantity

$$\rho = \frac{k}{\sqrt{(k - m\omega^2)^2 + (c\omega)^2}} \tag{19}$$

and the angle α of Fig. 3.6.7. Then we find that

$$A = \rho \frac{F_0}{k} \cos \alpha, \qquad B = \rho \frac{F_0}{k} \sin \alpha.$$

Hence our particular solution is

$$x_p = A \cos \omega t + B \sin \omega t = \rho \frac{F_0}{k} (\cos \omega t \cos \alpha + \sin \omega t \sin \alpha);$$

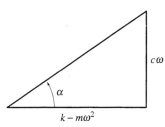

FIGURE 3.6.7. The angle α

more concisely,

$$x_p(t) = \rho \frac{F_0}{k} \cos(\omega t - \alpha). \tag{20}$$

Thus we get a **steady periodic solution** that remains after the transient solution has died away. This steady-state solution has amplitude $\rho F_0/k$, circular frequency ω, and phase angle α given by

$$\alpha = \tan^{-1} \frac{c\omega}{k - m\omega^2}, \qquad 0 \leqq \alpha \leqq \pi. \tag{21}$$

Note that α lies in the first or second quadrant, so the formula in (21) does not simply involve the principal value of the inverse tangent function. If a calculator gives a negative value for α, simply add π to obtain the correct value of α.

The **amplification factor** ρ, defined in (19), is the amount by which the static displacement F_0/k must be multiplied to get the amplitude of the steady periodic oscillation. Note that when $c > 0$, the amplitude always remains finite (unlike the undamped case). The amplitude may reach a maximum for some value of ω; this is *practical resonance*. To see when it occurs for various values of the constants m, c, and k, it is useful to express ρ in terms of the dimensionless ratios

$$\tilde{\omega} = \frac{\omega}{\omega_0} = \frac{\omega}{\sqrt{k/m}} \qquad \text{and} \qquad \tilde{c} = \frac{c}{c_{CR}} = \frac{c}{\sqrt{4km}}.$$

Then (19) is equivalent to

$$\rho = \frac{1}{\sqrt{(1 - \tilde{\omega}^2)^2 + 4\tilde{c}^2\tilde{\omega}^2}}. \tag{19'}$$

Figure 3.6.8 shows the graph of ρ versus $\tilde{\omega}$ for various values of $\tilde{c}$. It can be shown that if $c \geqq c_{CR}/\sqrt{2}$, then ρ steadily decreases as ω increases, but if $c < c_{CR}/\sqrt{2}$, then ρ reaches a maximum value—practical resonance—at some value of ω less than ω_0, and then approaches zero as $\omega \to +\infty$. It follows that an underdamped system typically will undergo forced oscillations whose amplitude is:

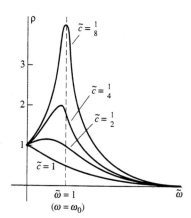

FIGURE 3.6.8. Practical resonance

1. Large if ω is close to the critical resonance frequency;
2. Close to F_0/k is ω is very small;
3. Very small if ω is very large.

EXAMPLE 6

Find the transient and steady periodic solutions of

$$x'' + 2x' + 2x = 20 \cos 2t, \qquad x(0) = x'(0) = 0.$$

Solution Instead of applying the general formulas derived above, it is better in a concrete problem to work the problem directly. The roots of the characteristic equation $r^2 + 2r + 2 = 0$ are $-1 \pm i$, so the complementary function is

$$x_c(t) = e^{-t}(c_1 \cos t + c_2 \sin t).$$

When we substitute

$$x_p(t) = A \cos 2t + B \sin 2t$$

in the given equation, collect coefficients, and equate coefficients of cos $2t$ and sin $2t$, we obtain the equations

$$-2A + 4B = 20,$$
$$-4A - 2B = 0,$$

with solution $A = -2, B = 4$. Hence the general solution is

$$x(t) = e^{-t}(c_1 \cos t + c_2 \sin t) - 2 \cos 2t + 4 \sin 2t.$$

At this point we impose the initial conditions $x(0) = x'(0) = 0$, and find easily that $c_1 = 2$ and $c_2 = -6$. Therefore, the transient solution x_{tr} and the steady periodic solution x_{sp} are given by

$$x_{tr}(t) = e^{-t}(2 \cos t - 6 \sin t)$$

and

$$x_{sp}(t) = -2 \cos 2t + 4 \sin 2t = 2\sqrt{5}\left(-\frac{1}{\sqrt{5}} \cos 2t + \frac{2}{\sqrt{5}} \sin 2t\right).$$

The latter can also be written in the form

$$x_{sp}(t) = 2\sqrt{5} \cos(2t - \alpha),$$

where $\alpha = \pi - \tan^{-1}(2) \approx 2.0344$. ∎

Figure 3.6.9 shows graphs of the solution

$$x(t) = x_{sp}(t) + x_{tr}(t)$$

of the initial value problem

$$x'' + 2x' + 2x = 20 \cos t, \tag{22}$$
$$x(0) = x_0, \qquad x'(0) = 0$$

for the different values $x_0 = -10, -8, -6, \ldots, 8$, and 10 of the initial position. Here we see clearly what it means for the transient solution $x_{tr}(t)$ to "die out with the passage of time," leaving only the steady periodic solution $x_{sp}(t)$. Indeed, because $x_{tr}(t) \to 0$ exponentially, within a few cycles the full solution $x(t)$ and the steady periodic solution $x_{sp}(t)$ are visually indistinguishable.

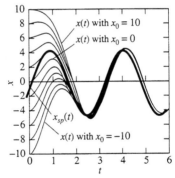

FIGURE 3.6.9. Solutions of the initial value problem (22) for $x_0 = -10, -8, -6, \ldots, 8, 10$

3.6 Problems

In Problems 1 through 6, express the solution of the given initial value problem as a sum of two oscillations (as in Eq. (8)).

1. $x'' + 9x = 10 \cos 2t;$ $x(0) = x'(0) = 0$

2. $x'' + 4x = 5 \sin 3t;$ $x(0) = x'(0) = 0$

3. $x'' + 100x = 15 \cos 5t + 20 \sin 5t;$ $x(0) = 25,$ $x'(0) = 0$

4. $x'' + 25x = 10 \cos 4t;$ $x(0) = 0,$ $x'(0) = 10$

5. $mx'' + kx = F_0 \cos \omega t$ with $\omega \neq \omega_0;$ $x(0) = x_0,$ $x'(0) = 0$

6. $mx'' + kx = F_0 \cos \omega t$ with $\omega = \omega_0;$ $x(0) = 0,$ $x'(0) = v_0$

In Problems 7 through 14, find the steady periodic solution in the form $x_{sp}(t) = C \cos(\omega t - \alpha)$ with $C > 0$. If initial conditions are given, also find the transient solution.

7. $x'' + 4x' + 4x = 10 \cos 3t$

8. $x'' + 3x' + 5x = -4 \cos 5t$

9. $2x'' + 2x' + x = 3 \sin 10t$

10. $x'' + 3x' + 3x = 8 \cos 10t + 6 \sin 10t$

11. $x'' + 4x' + 5x = 10 \cos 3t;\quad x(0) = x'(0) = 0$

12. $x'' + 6x' + 13x = 10 \sin 5t;\quad x(0) = x'(0) = 0$

13. $x'' + 2x' + 6x = 3 \cos 10t;\quad x(0) = 10,$
    $x'(0) = 0$

14. $x'' + 8x' + 25x = 5 \cos t + 13 \sin t;\quad x(0) = 5,$
    $x'(0) = 0$

15. A mass weighing 100 lb (mass $m = 3.125$ slugs in fps units) is attached to the end of a spring that is stretched 1 in. by a force of 100 lb. A force $F_0 \cos \omega t$ acts on the mass. At what frequency (in hertz) will resonance oscilllations occur? Neglect damping.

16. A front-loading washing machine is mounted on a thick rubber pad that acts like a spring; the weight $W = mg$ (with $g = 9.8$ m/s^2) of the machine depresses the pad exactly $\frac{1}{2}$ cm. When its rotor spins at ω radians per second, the rotor exerts a vertical force $F_0 \cos \omega t$ pounds on the machine. At what speed (in revolutions per minute) will resonance vibrations occur? Neglect damping.

17. See Fig. 3.6.10, which shows a mass m on the end of a pendulum (of length L) also attached to a horizontal spring (with constant k). Assume small oscillations of m so that the spring remains essentially horizontal, and neglect damping. Find the natural circular frequency ω_0 of motion of the mass in terms of L, k, m, and the gravitational constant g.

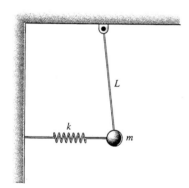

FIGURE 3.6.10. The pendulum-and-spring system of Problem 17

18. A mass m hangs on the end of a cord around a pulley of radius a and moment of inertia I, as shown in Fig. 3.6.11. The rim of the pulley is attached to a spring (with constant k). Assume small oscillations so that the spring remains essentially horizontal, and neglect friction. Find the natural circular frequency of the system in terms of m, a, k, I, and g.

19. A building consists of two floors. The first floor is attached rigidly to the ground, and the second floor is of mass $m = 1000$

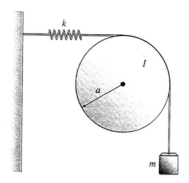

FIGURE 3.6.11. The mass-spring-pulley system of Problem 18

slugs (fps units) and weighs 16 tons (32,000 lb). The elastic frame of the building behaves as a spring that resists horizontal displacements of the second floor; it requires a horizontal force of 5 tons to displace the second floor a distance of 1 ft. Assume that in an earthquake the ground oscillates horizontally with amplitude A_0 and circular frequency ω, resulting in an external horizontal force $F(t) = mA_0\omega^2 \sin \omega t$ on the second floor. (a) What is the natural frequency (in hertz) of oscillations of the second floor? (b) If the ground undergoes one oscillation every 2.25 s with an amplitude of 3 in., what is the amplitude of the resulting forced oscillations of the second floor? .

20. A mass on a spring without damping is acted on by the external force $F(t) = F_0 \cos^3 \omega t$. Show that there are *two* values of ω for which resonance occurs, and find both.

21. Derive the steady periodic solution of

$$mx'' + cx' + kx = F_0 \sin \omega t.$$

In particular, show that it is what one would expect—the same as the formula in (20) with the same values of ρ and ω, except with $\sin(\omega t - \alpha)$ in place of $\cos(\omega t - \alpha)$.

22. Given the differential equation

$$mx'' + cx' + kx = E_0 \cos \omega t + F_0 \sin \omega t$$

—with both cosine and sine forcing terms—derive the steady periodic solution

$$x_{sp}(t) = \frac{\sqrt{E_0^2 + F_0^2}}{\sqrt{(k - m\omega^2)^2 + (c\omega)^2}} \cos(\omega t - \alpha - \beta),$$

where α is defined in Eq. (21) and $\beta = \tan^{-1}(F_0/E_0)$. *Suggestion:* Add the steady periodic solutions separately corresponding to $E_0 \cos \omega t$ and $F_0 \sin \omega t$ (see Problem 21).

23. Recall that the amplification factor ρ is given in terms of the impressed frequency ω by

$$\rho = \frac{k}{\sqrt{(k - m\omega^2)^2 + (c\omega)^2}}.$$

(a) If $c \geqq c_{CR} / \sqrt{2}$, where $c_{CR} = \sqrt{4km}$, show that ρ steadily decreases as ω increases. (b) If $c < c_{CR} / \sqrt{2}$, show that ρ attains a maximum value (practical resonance) when

$$\omega = \omega_m = \sqrt{\frac{k}{m} - \frac{c^2}{2m^2}} < \omega_0 = \sqrt{\frac{k}{m}}.$$

24. As indicated by the cart-with-flywheel example discussed in this section, an unbalanced rotating machine part typically results in a force having amplitude proportional to the *square* of the frequency ω. (a) Show that the amplitude of the steady periodic solution of the differential equation

$$mx'' + cx' + kx = mA\omega^2 \cos \omega t$$

(with a forcing term similar to that in Eq. (17)) is $\rho(mA/k)$, where the amplification factor is

$$\rho = \frac{k\omega^2}{\sqrt{(k - m\omega^2)^2 + (c\omega)^2}}.$$

(b) Suppose that $c^2 < 2mk$. Show that the maximum amplitude occurs at the frequency ω_m given by

$$\omega_m = \sqrt{\frac{k}{m} \left(\frac{2mk}{2mk - c^2} \right)}.$$

Thus the resonance frequency in this case is *larger* (in contrast to the result of Problem 23) than the natural frequency $\omega_0 = \sqrt{k/m}$. (*Suggestion:* Maximize the *square* of ρ.)

3.6 Computing Projects

Steady Periodic and Transient Solutions

For your personal project let $p = 2a$ and $q = a^2 + b^2$ where a and b are the two smallest nonzero digits of your student I.D. number (with $a < b$), and let r be the largest such digit. Then solve the initial value problem

$$x'' + px' + qx = r \cos t,$$

$$x(0) = x_0, \qquad x'(0) = v_0$$

in terms of x_0 and v_0. If a computer algebra system is available, you can use the *Mathematica* command

```
DSolve[ {x"[t] + p x'[t] + q x[t] == r Cos[t],
         x[0] == x0, x'[0] == v0}, x[t], t ]
```

the very similar *Maple* **dsolve** command, or the *Derive* command

```
DSOLVE_IV(p, q, r cos(t), t, 0, x0, v0)
```

(in the ODE2.MTH utility file). Then generate a figure like Fig. 3.6.9, except showing solution curves with $x_0 = 0$ and various different values of v_0.

Automobile Vibrations

The upward displacement function $x(t)$ of the car of Example 5 satisfies the equation

$$mx'' + cx' + kx = cy' + ky \tag{1}$$

when the car's shock absorber is connected (so $c > 0$). With $y = a \sin \omega t$ for the road surface, this equation becomes

$$mx'' + cx' + kx = E_0 \cos \omega t + F_0 \sin \omega t, \tag{2}$$

where $E_0 = c\omega a$ and $F_0 = ka$. Apply the result of Problem 22 in this section to show

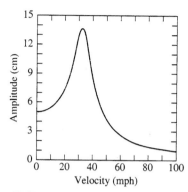

FIGURE 3.6.12. Amplitude of vibrations of the car on a washboard surface

that the amplitude C of the resulting steady periodic oscillation for the car is given by

$$C = \frac{a\sqrt{k^2 + (c\omega)^2}}{\sqrt{(k - m\omega^2)^2 + (c\omega)^2}}. \tag{3}$$

Because $\omega = 2\pi v/L$ when the car is moving with velocity v, this gives C as a function of v.

Using the numerical data given in Example 5 (including $c = 3000$ N-s/m), see whether you can use Eq. (3) to reproduce the plot in Fig. 3.6.12 showing the amplitude of the car's vibrations as a function of its velocity over the washboard surface. The graph indicates that, as the car accelerates gradually from rest, it initially oscillates with amplitude slightly over 5 cm. Maximum resonance oscillations with amplitude about 14 cm occur around 32 mi/h, but then subside to more tolerable levels at high speeds.

Can you verify the maximum point on the graph by maximizing C as a function of ω in Eq. (3)?

4 Introduction to Systems of Differential Equations

4.1 First-Order Systems and Applications

In the preceding chapters we have discussed methods for solving an ordinary differential equation that involves only one dependent variable. Many applications, however, require the use of two or more dependent variables, each a function of a single independent variable (typically time). Such a problem leads naturally to a *system* of simultaneous ordinary differential equations. We will usually denote the independent variable by t and the dependent variables (the unknown functions of t) by x_1, x_2, x_3, . . . , or by $x, y, z, ...$ Primes will denote differentiation with respect to t.

We will restrict our attention to systems in which the number of equations is the same as the number of dependent variables (unknown functions). For instance, a system of two first-order equations in the dependent variables x and y has the general form

$$f(t, x, y, x', y') = 0,$$
$$g(t, x, y, x', y') = 0,$$

(1)

where the functions f and g are given. A **solution** of this system is a pair $x(t)$, $y(t)$ of functions of t that satisfy both equations identically over some interval of values of t.

219

For an example of a second-order system, consider a particle of mass m that moves in space under the influence of a force field $\mathbf{F}$ that depends upon time t, the position $(x(t),\ y(t),\ z(t))$ of the particle, and its velocity $(x'(t),\ y'(t),\ z'(t))$. Applying Newton's law $m\mathbf{a} = \mathbf{F}$ componentwise, we get the system

$$
\begin{aligned}
mx'' &= F_1(t,\ x,\ y,\ z,\ x',\ y',\ z'), \\
my'' &= F_2(t,\ x,\ y,\ z,\ x',\ y',\ z'), \\
mz'' &= F_3(t,\ x,\ y,\ z,\ x',\ y',\ z'),
\end{aligned}
\tag{2}
$$

where F_1, F_2, and F_3, are the three components of the vector function $\mathbf{F}$.

Initial Applications

Examples 1 through 3 illustrate further how systems of differential equations arise naturally in scientific problems.

EXAMPLE 1   Consider the system of two masses and two springs shown in Fig. 4.1.1, with a given external force $f(t)$ acting on the right-hand mass m_2. We denote by $x(t)$ the displacement (to the right) of the mass m_1 from its static equilibrium position (when the system is motionless and in equilibrium and $f(t) = 0$), and by $y(t)$ the displacement of the mass m_2 from its static position. Thus the two springs are neither stretched nor compressed when x and y are zero.

In the configuration in Fig. 4.1.1, the first spring is stretched x units and the second by $y - x$ units. We apply Newton's law of motion to the two "free body dia-

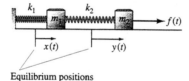

Equilibrium positions

FIGURE 4.1.1. The mass-and-spring system of Example 1

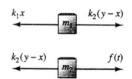

FIGURE 4.1.2. The "free body diagrams" for the system of Example 1

grams" shown in Fig. 4.1.2; we thereby obtain the system

$$
\begin{aligned}
m_1 x'' &= -k_1 x + k_2(y - x) \\
m_2 y'' &= -k_2(y - x) + f(t)
\end{aligned}
\tag{3}
$$

of differential equations that the position functions $x(t)$ and $y(t)$ must satisfy. For instance, if $m_1 = 2$, $m_2 = 1$, $k_1 = 4$, $k_2 = 2$, and $f(t) = 40\sin 3t$ in appropriate physical units, then the system in (3) reduces to

$$
\begin{aligned}
2x'' &= -6x + 2y \\
y'' &= 2x - 2y + 40\sin 3t.
\end{aligned}
\tag{4}
$$

EXAMPLE 2   Consider two brine tanks connected as shown in Fig. 4.1.3. Tank 1 contains $x(t)$ pounds of salt in 100 gal of brine and tank 2 contains $y(t)$ pounds of salt in 200 gal of brine. The brine in each tank is kept uniform by stirring, and brine is pumped from

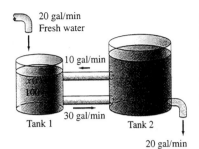

20 gal/min
Fresh water

10 gal/min

30 gal/min

Tank 1   Tank 2

20 gal/min

FIGURE 4.1.3. The two brine tanks of Example 2

each tank to the other at the rates indicated in Fig. 4.1.3. In addition, fresh water flows into tank 1 at 20 gal/min, and the brine in tank 2 flows out at 20 gal/min (so the total volume of brine in the two tanks remains constant). The salt concentrations in the two tanks are $x/100$ pounds per gallon and $y/200$ pounds per gallon, respectively. When we compute the rates of change of the amounts of salt in the two tanks, we therefore get the system of differential equations that $x(t)$ and $y(t)$ must satisfy:

$$x' = -30 \cdot \frac{x}{100} + 10 \cdot \frac{y}{200} = -\frac{3}{10}x + \frac{1}{20}y$$

$$y' = 30 \cdot \frac{x}{100} - 10 \cdot \frac{y}{200} - 20 \cdot \frac{y}{200} = \frac{3}{10}x - \frac{3}{20}y;$$

that is,

$$20x' = -6x + y$$
$$20y' = 6x - 3y. \tag{5}$$

EXAMPLE 3 Consider the electrical network shown in Fig. 4.1.4, where $I_1(t)$ denotes the current in the indicated direction through the inductor L and $I_2(t)$ denotes the current through the resistor R_2. The current through the resistor R_1 is $I = I_1 - I_2$ in the direction indicated.

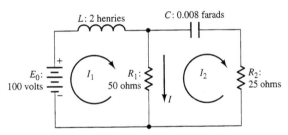

L: 2 henries C: 0.008 farads

E_0: 100 volts I_1 R_1: 50 ohms I_2 R_2: 25 ohms

I

FIGURE 4.1.4. The electrical network of Example 3

We recall Kirchhoff's voltage law to the effect that the (algebraic) sum of the voltage drops around any closed loop of such a network is zero. As in Section 3.7, the voltage drops across the three types of circuit elements are those shown in Fig. 4.1.5. We apply Kirchhoff's law to the left-hand loop of the network to obtain

$$2\frac{dI_1}{dt} + 50(I_1 - I_2) - 100 = 0, \tag{6}$$

because the voltage drop from the negative to the positive pole of the battery is -100. The right-hand loop yields the equation

$$125Q_2 + 25I_2 + 50(I_2 - I_1) = 0 \tag{7}$$

where $Q_2(t)$ is the charge on the capacitor. Because $dQ_2/dt = I_2$, differentiation of each side of Eq. (7) yields

$$-50\frac{dI_1}{dt} + 75\frac{dI_2}{dt} + 125I_2 = 0. \tag{8}$$

Circuit Element	Voltage Drop
Inductor	$L\dfrac{dI}{dt}$
Resistor	RI
Capacitor	$\dfrac{1}{C}Q$

FIGURE 4.1.5. Voltage drops across common circuit elements

Dividing Eqs. (6) and (8) by the factors 2 and -25, respectively, we get the system

$$\frac{dI_1}{dt} + 25I_1 - 25I_2 = 50$$

$$2\frac{dI_1}{dt} - 3\frac{dI_2}{dt} - 5I_2 = 0$$

(9)

of differential equations that the currents $I_1(t)$ and $I_2(t)$ must satisfy. ∎

First-Order Systems

Consider a system of differential equations that can be solved for the highest-order derivatives of the dependent variables that appear, as explicit functions of t and of lower-order derivatives of the dependent variables. For instance, in the case of a system of two second-order equations, our assumption is that it can be written in the form

$$x_1'' = f_1(t, x_1, x_2, x_1', x_2')$$

$$x_2'' = f_2(t, x_1, x_2, x_1', x_2').$$

(10)

It is of both practical and theoretical importance that any such higher-order system can be transformed into an equivalent system of *first-order* equations.

To describe how such a transformation is accomplished, we consider first the "system" consisting of the single nth-order equation

▶ $$x^{(n)} = f(t, x\, x', \ldots, x^{(n-1)}).$$ (11)

We introduce the dependent variables $x_1, x_2, \ldots, x_n$ defined as follows:

$$x_1 = x, \quad x_2 = x', \quad x_3 = x'', \quad \ldots, \quad x_n = x^{(n-1)}.$$

(12)

Note that $x_1' = x' = x_2$, $x_2' = x'' = x_3$, and so on. Hence the substitutions of (12) in Eq. (11) yield the system

$$x_1' = x_2$$

$$x_2' = x_3$$

▶ $$\vdots$$ (13)

$$x_{n-1}' = x_n$$

$$x_n' = f(t, x_1, x_2, \ldots, x_n)$$

of n *first-order* equations. Evidently, this system is equivalent to the original nth-order equation in (11), in the sense that $x(t)$ is a solution of Eq. (11) if and only if the functions $x_1(t), x_2(t), \ldots, x_n(t)$ defined in (12) satisfy the system of equations in (13).

EXAMPLE 4   The third-order equation

$$x''' + 3x'' + 2x' - 5x = \sin 2t$$

is of the form in (11) with

$$f(t, x, x', x'') = 5x - 2x' - 3x'' + \sin 2t.$$

Hence the substitutions

$$x_1 = x, \qquad x_2 = x' = x_1', \qquad x_3 = x'' = x_2'$$

yield the system

$$x_1' = x_2$$
$$x_2' = x_3$$
$$x_3' = 5x_1 - 2x_2 - 3x_3 + \sin 2t$$

of three first-order equations. ∎

It may appear that the first-order system obtained in Example 4 offers little advantage because we could use the methods of Chapter 3 to solve the original (linear) third-order equation. But suppose that we were confronted with the nonlinear equation

$$x'' = x^3 + (x')^3,$$

to which none of our earlier methods can be applied. The corresponding first-order system is

$$x_1' = x_2$$
$$x_2' = (x_1)^3 + (x_2)^3, \tag{14}$$

and we will see in Section 4.3 that there exist effective numerical techniques for approximating the solution of essentially any first-order system. So in this case the transformation to a first-order system *is* advantageous. From a practical viewpoint, large systems of higher-order differential equations typically are solved numerically with the aid of a computer, and the first step is to transform such a system into a first-order system for which a standard computer program is available.

EXAMPLE 5 The system

$$2x'' = -6x + 2y$$
$$y'' = 2x - 2y + 40 \sin 3t \tag{4}$$

of second-order equations was derived in Example 1. Transform this system into an equivalent first-order system.

Solution Motivated by the equations in (12), we define

$$x_1 = x, \qquad x_2 = x' = x_1', \qquad y_1 = y, \qquad y_2 = y' = y_1'.$$

Then the system in (4) yields the system

$$x_1' = x_2$$
$$2x_2' = -6x_1 + 2y_1$$
$$y_1' = y_2$$
$$y_2' = 2x_1 - 2y_1 + 40 \sin 3t \tag{15}$$

of four first-order equations in the dependent variables x_1, x_2, y_1, and y_2. ∎

Simple Two-Dimensional Systems

The linear second-order differential equation

$$x'' + px' + qx = 0 \tag{16}$$

(with constant coefficients and independent variable t) transforms via the substitutions $x' = y$, $x'' = y'$ into the two-dimensional linear system

$$\begin{aligned} x' &= y \\ y' &= -qx - py. \end{aligned} \tag{17}$$

Conversely, we can solve this system in (17) by solving the familiar single equation in (16).

EXAMPLE 6   To solve the two-dimensional system

$$\begin{aligned} x' &= -2y \\ y' &= \frac{1}{2}x, \end{aligned} \tag{18}$$

we begin with the observation that

$$x'' = -2y' = -2\left(\frac{1}{2}x\right) = -x.$$

This gives the single second-order equation $x'' + x = 0$ with general solution

$$x(t) = A \cos t + B \sin t = C \cos(t - \alpha)$$

where $A = C \cos \alpha$, $B = C \sin \alpha$. Then

$$y(t) = -\frac{1}{2}x'(t) = -\frac{1}{2}(-A \sin t + B \cos t)$$

$$= \frac{1}{2} C \sin(t - \alpha).$$

The identity $\cos^2 \theta + \sin^2 \theta = 1$ therefore implies that, for each value of t, the point $(x(t), y(t))$ lies on the ellipse

$$\frac{x^2}{C^2} + \frac{y^2}{(C/2)^2} = 1$$

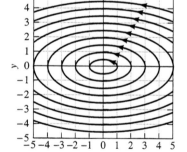

FIGURE 4.1.6. Trajectories of the system $x' = -2y$, $y' = x/2$

with semiaxes C and $C/2$. Figure 4.1.6 shows several such ellipses in the xy-plane.   ∎

A solution $(x(t), y(t))$ of a two-dimensional system

$$\begin{aligned} x' &= f(t, x, y) \\ y' &= g(t, x, y) \end{aligned}$$

may be regarded as a parametrization of a **solution curve** or **trajectory** of the system in the xy-plane. Thus the trajectories of the system in (18) are the ellipses of Fig. 4.1.6. The choice of an initial point $(x(0), y(0))$ determines which one of these trajectories a particular solution parametrizes.

Unfortunately, the picture showing a system's trajectories in the xy-plane—its so-called *phase plane portrait*—fails to reveal precisely how the point $(x(t), y(t))$ moves along its trajectory. This missing information can be shown in the separate graphs of $x(t)$ and $y(t)$ as functions of t.

EXAMPLE 6
Continued

With initial values $x(0) = 2, y(0) = 0$, the general solution in Example 6 yields

$$x(0) = A = 2, \qquad y(0) = -\frac{1}{2}B = 0.$$

The resulting particular solution is given by

$$x(t) = 2 \cos t, \qquad y(t) = \sin t.$$

The graphs of the two functions are shown in Fig. 4.1.7. We see that $x(t)$ initially decreases while $y(t)$ increases. It follows that, as t increases, the solution point $(x(t), y(t))$ traverses the trajectory $\frac{1}{4}x^2 + y^2 = 1$ in the counterclockwise direction, as indicated by the arrows labeling the elliptical trajectories in Fig. 4.1.6.

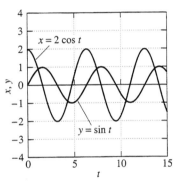

FIGURE 4.1.7. x- and y-solution curves for the initial value problem $x' = -2y, \quad y' = x/2, \quad x(0) = 2, \quad y(0) = 0$

EXAMPLE 7

To find a general solution of the system

$$x' = y$$
$$y' = 2x + y, \tag{19}$$

we begin with the observation that

$$x'' = y' = 2x + y = x' + 2x.$$

This gives the single linear second-order equation

$$x'' - x' - 2x = 0$$

with characteristic equation

$$r^2 - r - 2 = (r + 1)(r - 2) = 0$$

and general solution

$$x(t) = Ae^{-t} + Be^{2t}. \tag{20}$$

Then

$$y(t) = x'(t) = -Ae^{-t} + 2Be^{2t}. \tag{21}$$

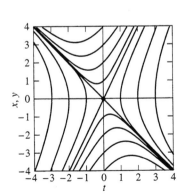

FIGURE 4.1.8. Trajectories of the system $x' = y, \quad y' = 2x + y$ of Example 7

Typical phase plane trajectories of the system in (19) parametrized by Eqs. (20) and (21) are shown in Fig. 4.1.8. See Problem 23 for further discussion of these trajectories.

EXAMPLE 8   To solve the initial value problem

$$x' = -y$$
$$y' = (1.01)x - (0.2)y, \tag{22}$$
$$x(0) = 0, \qquad y(0) = -1,$$

we begin with the observation that

$$x'' = -y' = -[(1.01)x - (0.2)y] = (-1.01)x - (0.2)x'.$$

This gives the single linear second-order equation

$$x'' + (0.2)x' + (1.01)x = 0$$

with characteristic equation

$$r^2 + (0.2)r + 1.01 = (r + 0.1)^2 + 1 = 0,$$

characteristic roots $-0.1 \pm i$, and general solution

$$x(t) = e^{-t/10}(A\cos t + B\sin t).$$

Then $x(0) = A = 0$, so

$$x(t) = Be^{-t/10}\sin t,$$
$$y(t) = -x'(t) = \frac{1}{10}Be^{-t/10}\sin t - Be^{-t/10}\cos t.$$

Finally, $y(0) = -B = -1$, so the desired solution of the system in (22) is

$$x(t) = e^{-t/10}\sin t,$$
$$y(t) = \frac{1}{10}e^{-t/10}(-10\cos t + \sin t). \tag{23}$$

These equations parametrize the spiral trajectory in Fig. 4.1.9; the trajectory approaches the origin as $t \to +\infty$. Figure 4.1.10 shows the x- and y-solution curves given in (23). ■

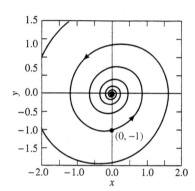

FIGURE 4.1.9. Trajectory parametrized by the equations in Eq. (23)

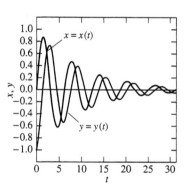

FIGURE 4.1.10. x- and y-solution curves for the initial value problem of Example 8

When we study linear systems in Chapter 5, we will learn why the superficially similar systems in Examples 6 through 8 have the markedly different trajectories shown in Figs. 4.1.6, 4.1.8, and 4.1.9.

Linear Systems

In addition to practical advantages for numerical computation, the general theory of systems and systematic solution techniques are more easily and more concisely described for first-order systems than for higher-order systems. For instance, consider a *linear* first-order system of the form

$$x_1' = p_{11}(t)x_1 + p_{12}(t)x_2 + \cdots + p_{1n}(t)x_n + f_1(t)$$

$$x_2' = p_{21}(t)x_1 + p_{22}(t)x_2 + \cdots + p_{2n}(t)x_n + f_2(t)$$

$$\vdots$$

$$x_n' = p_{n1}(t)x_1 + p_{n2}(t)x_2 + \cdots + p_{nn}(t)x_n + f_n(t)$$

(24)

We say that this system is **homogeneous** if the functions $f_1, f_2, \ldots, f_n$ are all identically zero; otherwise, it is **nonhomogeneous.** Thus the linear system in (5) is homogeneous, whereas the linear system in (15) is nonhomogeneous. The system in (14) is nonlinear because the right-hand side of the second equation is not a linear function of the dependent variables x_1 and x_2.

A **solution** of the system in (24) is an n-tuple of functions $x_1(t), x_2(t), \ldots, x_n(t)$ that (on some interval) identically satisfy each of the equations in (24). We will see that the general theory of a system of n linear first-order equations shares many similarities with the general theory of a single nth-order linear differential equation. Theorem 1 (proved in the Appendix) is analogous to Theorem 2 of Section 3.2. It tells us that if the coefficient functions p_{ij} and f_j in (24) are continuous, then the system has a unique solution satisfying given initial conditions.

■ THEOREM 1: Existence and Uniqueness for Linear Systems

Suppose that the functions $p_{11}, p_{12}, \ldots, p_{nn}$ and the functions $f_1, f_2, \ldots, f_n$ are continuous on the open interval I containing the point a. Then, given n numbers $b_1, b_2, \ldots, b_n$, the system in (24) has a unique solution on the entire interval I that satisfies the n initial conditions

$$x_1(a) = b_1, \qquad x_2(a) = b_2, \qquad \ldots, \qquad x_n(a) = b_n. \qquad (25)$$

■

Thus n initial conditions are needed to determine a solution of a system of n linear first-order equations, and we therefore expect a general solution of such a system to involve n arbitrary constants. For instance, we saw in Example 5 that the second-order system

$$2x'' = -6x + 2y$$

$$y'' = 2x - 2y + 40 \sin 3t,$$

which describes the position functions $x(t)$ and $y(t)$ of Example 1, is equivalent to the system of *four* first-order linear equations in (15). Hence four initial conditions would be needed to determine the subsequent motions of the two masses in Example 1; typical initial values would be the initial positions $x(0)$ and $y(0)$ and the initial velocities $x'(0)$ and $y'(0)$. On the other hand, we found that the amounts $x(t)$ and $y(t)$ of salt in the two tanks of Example 2 are described by the system

$$20x' = -6x + y$$

$$20y' = 6x + 3y$$

of *two* first-order linear equations. Hence the two initial values $x(0)$ and $y(0)$ should suffice to determine the solution. Given a higher-order system, we often must transform it into an equivalent first-order system to discover how many initial conditions are needed to determine a unique solution. Theorem 1 tells us that the number of such conditions is precisely the same as the number of equations in the equivalent first-order system.

4.1 Problems

In Problems 1 through 10, transform the given differential equation or system into an equivalent system of first-order differential equations.

1. $x'' + 3x' + 7x = t^2$

2. $x^{(4)} + 6x'' - 3x' + x = \cos 3t$

3. $t^2 x'' + tx' + (t^2 - 1)x = 0$

4. $t^3 x''' - 2t^2 x'' + 3tx' + 5x = \ln t$

5. $x''' = (x')^2 + \cos x$

6. $x'' - 5x + 4y = 0, \quad y'' + 4x - 5y = 0$

7. $x'' = -\dfrac{kx}{(x^2 + y^2)^{3/2}}, \quad y'' = -\dfrac{ky}{(x^2 + y^2)^{3/2}}$

8. $x'' + 3x' + 4x - 2y = 0, \quad y'' + 2y' - 3x + y = \cos t$

9. $x'' = 3x - y + 2z, \quad y'' = x + y - 4z, \quad z'' = 5x - y - z$

10. $x'' = (1 - y)x, \quad y'' = (1 - x)y$

Use the method of Examples 6, 7, and 8 to find general solutions of the systems in Problems 11 through 20. If initial conditions are given, find the corresponding particular solutions.

11. $\begin{aligned} x' &= y \\ y' &= -x \end{aligned}$

12. $\begin{aligned} x' &= y \\ y' &= x \end{aligned}$

13. $\begin{aligned} x' &= -2y \\ y' &= 2x, \\ x(0) &= 1, \quad y(0) = 0 \end{aligned}$

14. $\begin{aligned} x' &= 10y \\ y' &= -10x, \\ x(0) &= 3, \quad y(0) = 4 \end{aligned}$

15. $\begin{aligned} x' &= \tfrac{1}{2}y \\ y' &= -8x \end{aligned}$

16. $\begin{aligned} x' &= 8y \\ y' &= -2x \end{aligned}$

17. $\begin{aligned} x' &= y \\ y' &= 6x - y, \\ x(0) &= 1, \quad y(0) = 2 \end{aligned}$

18. $\begin{aligned} x' &= -y \\ y' &= 10x - 7y, \\ x(0) &= 2, \quad y(0) = -7 \end{aligned}$

19. $\begin{aligned} x' &= -y \\ y' &= 13x + 4y, \\ x(0) &= 0, \quad y(0) = 3 \end{aligned}$

20. $\begin{aligned} x' &= y \\ y' &= -9x + 6y \end{aligned}$

21. (a) Calculate $[x(t)]^2 + [y(t)]^2$ to show that the trajectories of the system $x' = y, y' = -x$ of Problem 11 are circles. (b) Calculate $[x(t)]^2 - [y(t)]^2$ to show that the trajectories of the system $x' = y, y' = x$ of Problem 12 are hyperbolas.

22. (a) Beginning with the general solution of the system $x' = -2y, y' = 2x$ of Problem 13, calculate $x^2 + y^2$ to show that the trajectories are circles. (b) Show similarly that the tra-

jectories of the system $x' = \frac{1}{2}y, y' = -8x$ of Problem 15 are ellipses with equations of the form $16x^2 + y^2 = C^2$.

23. First solve Eqs. (20) and (21) for e^{-t} and e^{2t} in terms of $x(t)$, $y(t)$, and the constants A and B. Then substitute the results in $(e^{2t})(e^{-t})^2 = 1$ to show that the trajectories of the system $x' = y$, $y' = 2x + y$ in Example 7 satisfy an equation of the form

$$4x^3 - 3xy^2 + y^3 = C \quad \text{(constant)}.$$

Then show that $C = 0$ yields the straight lines $y = -x$ and $y = 2x$ that are visible in Fig. 4.1.8.

24. Derive the equations

$$\begin{aligned} m_1 x_1'' &= -(k_1 + k_2)x_1 + k_2 x_2 \\ m_2 x_2'' &= k_2 x_1 - (k_2 + k_3)x_2 \end{aligned}$$

for the displacements (from equilibrium) of the two masses shown in Fig. 4.1.11.

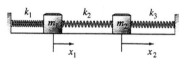

FIGURE 4.1.11. The system of Problem 24

25. Two particles each of mass m are attached to a string under (constant) tension T, as indicated in Fig. 4.1.12. Assume that the particles oscillate vertically (that is, parallel to the y-axis) with amplitudes so small that the sines of the angles shown are accurately approximated by their tangents. Show that the displacements y_1 and y_2 of the two masses satisfy the equations

$$ky_1'' = -2y_1 + y_2, \qquad ky_2'' = y_1 - 2y_2,$$

where $k = mL/T$.

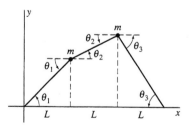

FIGURE 4.1.12. The mechanical system of Problem 25

26. Three 100-gal fermentation vats are connected as indicated in Fig. 4.1.13, and the mixtures in each tank are kept uniform by

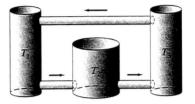

FIGURE 4.1.13. The fermentation tanks of Problem 26

stirring. Denote by $x_i(t)$ the amount (in pounds) of alcohol in tank T_i at time t ($i = 1, 2, 3$). Suppose that the mixture circulates between the tanks at the rate of 10 gal/min. Derive the equations

$$
\begin{aligned}
10x_1' &= -x_1 & &+ x_3 \\
10x_2' &= x_1 - x_2 & & \\
10x_3' &= & x_2 &- x_3.
\end{aligned}
$$

27. Set up a system of first-order differential equations for the currents in the electrical circuit shown in Fig. 4.1.14.

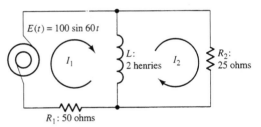

FIGURE 4.1.14. The electrical circuit of Problem 27

28. Repeat Problem 27, except with the generator replaced with a battery supplying an emf of 100 V and with the inductor replaced by a 1-millifarad (mF) capacitor.

29. A particle of mass m moves in the plane with coordinates $(x(t), y(t))$ under the influence of a force that is directed toward the origin and has magnitude $k/(x^2 + y^2)$—an inverse-square central force field. Show that

$$
mx'' = -\frac{kx}{r^3} \qquad \text{and} \qquad my'' = -\frac{ky}{r^3},
$$

where $r = \sqrt{x^2 + y^2}$.

30. Suppose that a projectile of mass m moves in a vertical plane in the atmosphere near the surface of the earth under the influence of two forces: a downward gravitational force of magnitude mg, and a resistive force $\mathbf{F}_R$ that is directed opposite to the velocity vector $\mathbf{v}$ and has magnitude kv^2 (where $v = |\mathbf{v}|$ is the speed of the projectile; see Fig. 4.1.15). Show that the equations of motion of the projectile are

$$
mx'' = -kvx', \qquad my'' = -kvy' - mg,
$$

where $v = \sqrt{(x')^2 + (y')^2}$.

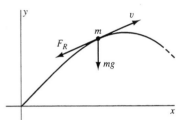

FIGURE 4.1.15. The trajectory of the projectile of Problem 30

31. Suppose that a particle with mass m and electrical charge q moves in the xy-plane under the influence of the magnetic field $\mathbf{B} = B\mathbf{k}$ (thus a uniform field parallel to the z-axis), so the force on the particle is $\mathbf{F} = q\mathbf{v} \times \mathbf{B}$ if its velocity is $\mathbf{v}$. Show that the equations of motion of the particle are

$$
mx'' = +qBy', \qquad my'' = -qBx'.
$$

5 Linear Systems of Differential Equations

5.1 Matrices and Linear Systems

Although the simple elimination techniques of Section 4.2 suffice for the solution of small linear systems containing only two or three equations with constant coefficients, the general properties of linear systems—as well as solution methods suitable for larger systems—are most easily and concisely described using the language and notation of vectors and matrices. For ready reference and review, this section begins with a complete and self-contained account of the matrix notation and terminology that is needed. Special techniques of linear algebra—specifically, those associated with eigenvalues and eigenvectors—are introduced as needed in subsequent sections of this chapter.

Review of Matrix Notation and Terminology

An $m \times n$ **matrix A** is a rectangular array of mn numbers (or **elements**) arranged in m (horizontal) **rows** and n (vertical) **columns**:

$$\mathbf{A} = \begin{bmatrix} a_{11} & a_{12} & a_{13} & \cdots & a_{1j} & \cdots & a_{1n} \\ a_{21} & a_{22} & a_{23} & \cdots & a_{2j} & \cdots & a_{2n} \\ a_{31} & a_{32} & a_{33} & \cdots & a_{3j} & \cdots & a_{3n} \\ \cdot & \cdot & \cdot & & \cdot & & \cdot \\ \cdot & \cdot & \cdot & & \cdot & & \cdot \\ a_{i1} & a_{i2} & a_{i3} & \cdots & a_{ij} & \cdots & a_{in} \\ \cdot & \cdot & \cdot & & \cdot & & \cdot \\ \cdot & \cdot & \cdot & & \cdot & & \cdot \\ a_{m1} & a_{m2} & a_{m3} & \cdots & a_{mj} & \cdots & a_{mn} \end{bmatrix} \tag{1}$$

We will ordinarily denote matrices by **boldface** capital letters. Sometimes we use the abbreviation $\mathbf{A} = [a_{ij}]$ for the matrix with the element a_{ij} in the ith row and jth column, as in Eq. (1). We denote the **zero matrix,** each entry of which is zero, by

$$\mathbf{0} = \begin{bmatrix} 0 & 0 & \cdots & 0 \\ 0 & 0 & \cdots & 0 \\ \cdot & \cdot & & \cdot \\ \cdot & \cdot & & \cdot \\ 0 & 0 & \cdots & 0 \end{bmatrix}. \tag{2}$$

Actually for each pair of positive integers m and n, there is an $m \times n$ zero matrix, but the single symbol $\mathbf{0}$ will suffice for all these zero matrices.

Two $m \times n$ matrices $\mathbf{A} = [a_{ij}]$ and $\mathbf{B} = [b_{ij}]$ are said to be **equal** if corresponding elements are equal; that is, if $a_{ij} = b_{ij}$ for $1 \leqq i \leqq m$ and $1 \leqq j \leqq n$. We **add** $\mathbf{A}$ and $\mathbf{B}$ by adding corresponding entries:

$$\mathbf{A} + \mathbf{B} = [a_{ij}] + [b_{ij}] = [a_{ij} + b_{ij}]. \tag{3}$$

Thus the element in row i and column j of $\mathbf{C} = \mathbf{A} + \mathbf{B}$ is $c_{ij} = a_{ij} + b_{ij}$. To multiply the matrix $\mathbf{A} = [a_{ij}]$ by the number c, we simply multiply each of its elements by c:

$$c\mathbf{A} = \mathbf{A}c = [ca_{ij}]. \tag{4}$$

EXAMPLE 1   If

$$\mathbf{A} = \begin{bmatrix} 2 & -3 \\ 4 & 7 \end{bmatrix}, \qquad \mathbf{B} = \begin{bmatrix} -13 & 10 \\ 7 & -5 \end{bmatrix}, \qquad \text{and} \qquad \mathbf{C} = \begin{bmatrix} 3 & 0 \\ 5 & -7 \end{bmatrix},$$

then

$$\mathbf{A} + \mathbf{B} = \begin{bmatrix} 2 & -3 \\ 4 & 7 \end{bmatrix} + \begin{bmatrix} -13 & 10 \\ 7 & -5 \end{bmatrix} = \begin{bmatrix} -11 & 7 \\ 11 & 2 \end{bmatrix}$$

and

$$6\mathbf{C} = 6 \cdot \begin{bmatrix} 3 & 0 \\ 5 & -7 \end{bmatrix} = \begin{bmatrix} 18 & 0 \\ 30 & -42 \end{bmatrix}. \qquad \blacksquare$$

We denote $(-1)\mathbf{A}$ by $-\mathbf{A}$ and define **subtraction** of matrices as follows:

$$\mathbf{A} - \mathbf{B} = \mathbf{A} + (-\mathbf{B}). \tag{5}$$

The matrix operations just defined have the following properties, each of which is analogous to a familiar algebraic property of the real number system:

$$\mathbf{A} + \mathbf{0} = \mathbf{0} + \mathbf{A} = \mathbf{A}, \qquad \mathbf{A} - \mathbf{A} = \mathbf{0}; \tag{6}$$

$$\mathbf{A} + \mathbf{B} = \mathbf{B} + \mathbf{A} \qquad \text{(commutativity)}; \tag{7}$$

$$\mathbf{A} + (\mathbf{B} + \mathbf{C}) = (\mathbf{A} + \mathbf{B}) + \mathbf{C} \qquad \text{(associativity)}; \tag{8}$$

$$c(\mathbf{A} + \mathbf{B}) = c\mathbf{A} + c\mathbf{B}, \qquad \text{(distributivity)} \tag{9}$$

$$(c + d)\mathbf{A} = c\mathbf{A} + d\mathbf{A}.$$

Each of these properties is readily verified by elementwise application of a corresponding property of the real numbers. For example, $a_{ij} + b_{ij} = b_{ij} + a_{ij}$ for all i and j because addition of real numbers is commutative. Consequently,

$$\mathbf{A} + \mathbf{B} = [a_{ij} + b_{ij}] + [b_{ij} + a_{ij}] = \mathbf{B} + \mathbf{A}$$

The **transpose** $\mathbf{A}^T$ of the $m \times n$ matrix $\mathbf{A} = [a_{ij}]$ is the $n \times m$ (note!) matrix whose jth column is the jth row of $\mathbf{A}$ (and consequently, whose ith row is the ith column of $\mathbf{A}$). Thus $\mathbf{A}^T = [a_{ji}]$, although this is not notationally perfect; you must remember that $\mathbf{A}^T$ will not have the same shape as $\mathbf{A}$ unless $\mathbf{A}$ is a **square** matrix—that is, unless $m = n$.

An $m \times 1$ matrix—one having only a single column—is called a **column vector,** or simply a **vector.** We often denote column vectors by **boldface** lowercase letters, as in

$$\mathbf{b} = \begin{bmatrix} 3 \\ -7 \\ 0 \end{bmatrix} \quad \text{or} \quad \mathbf{x} = \begin{bmatrix} x_1 \\ x_2 \\ \vdots \\ x_m \end{bmatrix}.$$

Similarly, a **row vector** is a $1 \times n$ matrix—one having only a single row, such as $\mathbf{c} = [5\ 17\ 0\ -3]$. For aesthetic and typographical reasons, we will frequently write a column vector as the transpose of a row vector; for example, the two column vectors above may be written in the forms

$$\mathbf{b} = [3 \quad -7 \quad 0]^T \qquad \text{and} \qquad \mathbf{x} = [x_1 \quad x_2 \quad \cdots \quad x_m]^T.$$

Sometimes it is convenient to describe an $m \times n$ matrix in terms of either its m row vectors or its n column vectors. Thus if we write

$$\mathbf{A} = \begin{bmatrix} \mathbf{a}_1 \\ \mathbf{a}_2 \\ \vdots \\ \mathbf{a}_m \end{bmatrix} \qquad \text{and} \qquad \mathbf{B} = [\mathbf{b}_1 \quad \mathbf{b}_2 \quad \cdots \quad \mathbf{b}_n],$$

it is understood that $\mathbf{a}_1, \mathbf{a}_2, \ldots, \mathbf{a}_m$ are the *row* vectors of the matrix $\mathbf{A}$ and $\mathbf{b}_1, \mathbf{b}_2, \ldots, \mathbf{b}_n$ are the *column* vectors of the matrix $\mathbf{B}$.

Matrix Multiplication

The properties listed in Eqs. (6) through (9) are quite natural and expected. The first surprises in the realm of matrix arithmetic come with multiplication. We define first the **scalar product a · b** of a row vector **a** and a column vector **b**, each having the same number p of elements. If

$$\mathbf{a} = [a_1 \quad a_2 \quad \cdots \quad a_p] \quad \text{and} \quad \mathbf{b} = [b_1 \quad b_2 \quad \cdots \quad b_p]^T,$$

then **a · b** is defined as follows:

$$\mathbf{a} \cdot \mathbf{b} = \sum_{k=1}^{p} a_k b_k = a_1 b_1 + a_2 b_2 + \cdots + a_p b_p, \tag{10}$$

exactly as in the scalar or *dot* product of two vectors—a familiar topic from elementary calculus.

The product **AB** of two matrices is defined only if the number of columns of **A** is equal to the number of rows of **B**. If **A** is an $m \times p$ matrix and **B** is a $p \times n$ matrix, then their product **AB** is the $m \times n$ matrix $\mathbf{C} = [c_{ij}]$, where c_{ij} is the scalar product of the ith row vector $\mathbf{a}_i$ of **A** and the jth column vector $\mathbf{b}_j$ of **B**. Thus

$$\mathbf{AB} = [\mathbf{a}_i \cdot \mathbf{b}_j]. \tag{11}$$

In terms of the individual entries of $\mathbf{A} = [a_{ij}]$ and $\mathbf{B} = [b_{ij}]$, Eq. (11) can be recast in the form

$$c_{ij} = \sum_{k=1}^{p} a_{ik} b_{kj}. \tag{12}$$

For purposes of hand computation, the definition in (11) and (12) is easy to remember by visualizing the picture

$$\mathbf{a}_i \longrightarrow \begin{bmatrix} a_{11} & a_{12} & \cdots & a_{1p} \\ a_{21} & a_{22} & \cdots & a_{2p} \\ \vdots & \vdots & & \vdots \\ a_{i1} & a_{i2} & \cdots & a_{ip} \\ \vdots & \vdots & & \vdots \\ a_{m1} & a_{m2} & \cdots & a_{mp} \end{bmatrix} \begin{bmatrix} b_{11} & b_{12} & \cdots & b_{1j} & \cdots & b_{1n} \\ b_{21} & b_{22} & \cdots & b_{2j} & \cdots & b_{2n} \\ \vdots & \vdots & & \vdots & & \vdots \\ b_{p1} & b_{p2} & \cdots & b_{pj} & \cdots & b_{pn} \end{bmatrix},$$

$$\underset{\mathbf{b}_j}{\uparrow}$$

in which the row vector $\mathbf{a}_i$ and the column vector $\mathbf{b}_j$ are spotlighted; c_{ij} is simply their scalar product. It may help to think of "pouring the rows of **A** down the columns of **B**." This also reminds us that the number of columns of **A** must be equal to the number of rows of **B**.

EXAMPLE 2   Check your understanding of the definition of matrix multiplication by verifying that if

$$\mathbf{A} = \begin{bmatrix} 2 & -3 \\ -1 & 5 \end{bmatrix} \quad \text{and} \quad \mathbf{B} = \begin{bmatrix} 13 & 9 \\ 4 & 0 \end{bmatrix},$$

then

$$\mathbf{AB} = \begin{bmatrix} 2 & -3 \\ -1 & 5 \end{bmatrix} \begin{bmatrix} 13 & 9 \\ 4 & 0 \end{bmatrix} = \begin{bmatrix} 14 & 18 \\ 7 & -9 \end{bmatrix}.$$

Similarly, verify that

$$\begin{bmatrix} 2 & -3 & 1 \\ 4 & 5 & -2 \\ 6 & -7 & 0 \end{bmatrix} \begin{bmatrix} x \\ y \\ z \end{bmatrix} = \begin{bmatrix} 2x - 3y + z \\ 4x + 5y - 2z \\ 6x - 7y \end{bmatrix}$$

and that

$$\begin{bmatrix} 1 & 2 \\ 3 & 4 \\ 5 & 6 \\ 7 & 8 \end{bmatrix} \begin{bmatrix} 2 & 1 & 3 \\ -1 & 3 & -2 \end{bmatrix} = \begin{bmatrix} 0 & 7 & -1 \\ 2 & 15 & 1 \\ 4 & 23 & 3 \\ 6 & 31 & 5 \end{bmatrix}. \qquad ■$$

It can be shown by direct (though lengthy) computation based on its definition that matrix multiplication is associative and is also distributive with respect to matrix addition; that is,

$$\mathbf{A(BC)} = \mathbf{(AB)C} \qquad (13)$$

and

$$\mathbf{A(B + C)} = \mathbf{AB} + \mathbf{AC}, \qquad (14)$$

provided that the matrices are of such sizes that the indicated multiplications and additions are possible.

But matrix multiplication is not commutative. That is, if **A** and **B** are both $n \times n$ matrices (so that both the products **AB** and **BA** are defined and have the same dimensions—$n \times n$), then, in general,

$$\mathbf{AB} \neq \mathbf{BA}. \qquad (15)$$

Moreover, it can happen that

$$\mathbf{AB} = \mathbf{0} \quad \text{even though} \quad \mathbf{A} \neq \mathbf{0} \quad \text{and} \quad \mathbf{B} \neq \mathbf{0}. \qquad (16)$$

Examples illustrating the phenomena in (15) and (16) may be found in the problems, although you can easily construct your own examples using 2×2 matrices with small integral elements.

Inverse Matrices

A square $n \times n$ matrix is said to have **order** n. The **identity** matrix of order n is the square matrix

$$\mathbf{I} = \begin{bmatrix} 1 & 0 & 0 & 0 & \cdots & 0 \\ 0 & 1 & 0 & 0 & \cdots & 0 \\ 0 & 0 & 1 & 0 & \cdots & 0 \\ 0 & 0 & 0 & 1 & \cdots & 0 \\ \cdot & \cdot & \cdot & \cdot & & \cdot \\ \cdot & \cdot & \cdot & \cdot & & \cdot \\ \cdot & \cdot & \cdot & \cdot & & \cdot \\ 0 & 0 & 0 & 0 & \cdots & 1 \end{bmatrix} \qquad (17)$$

for which each entry on the **principal diagonal** is 1 and all off-diagonal entries are zero. It is quite easy to verify that

$$\mathbf{AI} = \mathbf{A} = \mathbf{IA} \tag{18}$$

for every square matrix **A** of the same order as **I**.

If **A** is a square matrix, then an **inverse** of **A** is a square matrix **B** of the same order as **A** such that *both*

$$\mathbf{AB} = \mathbf{I} \quad \text{and} \quad \mathbf{BA} = \mathbf{I}.$$

It is not difficult to show that if the matrix **A** has an inverse, then this inverse is unique. Consequently, we may speak of *the* inverse of **A**, and we will denote it by $\mathbf{A}^{-1}$. Thus

$$\mathbf{AA}^{-1} = \mathbf{I} = \mathbf{A}^{-1}\mathbf{A}, \tag{19}$$

given the existence of $\mathbf{A}^{-1}$. It is clear that some square matrices do not have inverses—consider any square zero matrix. It is also easy to show that if $\mathbf{A}^{-1}$ exists, then $(\mathbf{A}^{-1})^{-1}$ exists and $(\mathbf{A}^{-1})^{-1} = \mathbf{A}$.

In linear algebra it is proved that $\mathbf{A}^{-1}$ exists if and only if the determinant $\det(\mathbf{A})$ of the square matrix **A** is nonzero. If so, the matrix **A** is said to be **nonsingular;** if $\det(\mathbf{A}) = 0$, then **A** is called a **singular** matrix.

Determinants

We assume that the student has computed 2×2 and 3×3 determinants in earlier courses. If $\mathbf{A} = [a_{ij}]$ is a 2×2 matrix, then its **determinant** $\det(\mathbf{A}) = |\mathbf{A}|$ is defined as

$$|\mathbf{A}| = \begin{vmatrix} a_{11} & a_{12} \\ a_{21} & a_{22} \end{vmatrix} = a_{11}a_{22} - a_{12}a_{21}.$$

Determinants of higher order may be defined by induction, as follows. If $\mathbf{A} = [a_{ij}]$ is an $n \times n$ matrix, let $\mathbf{A}_{ij}$ denote the $(n - 1) \times (n - 1)$ matrix obtained from **A** by deleting its *i*th row and its *j*th column. The *expansion* of the determinant $|\mathbf{A}|$ along its *i*th row is given by

$$|\mathbf{A}| = \sum_{j=1}^{n} (-1)^{i+j} a_{ij} |\mathbf{A}_{ij}| \quad (i \text{ fixed}), \tag{20a}$$

and its expansion along its *j*th column is given by

$$|\mathbf{A}| = \sum_{i=1}^{n} (-1)^{i+j} a_{ij} |\mathbf{A}_{ij}| \quad (j \text{ fixed}). \tag{20b}$$

It is shown in linear algebra that whichever row we use in Eq. (20a) and whichever column we use in Eq. (20b), the results are the same in all $2n$ cases. Hence $|\mathbf{A}|$ is well-defined by these formulas.

EXAMPLE 3 If

$$\mathbf{A} = \begin{bmatrix} 3 & 1 & -2 \\ 4 & 2 & 1 \\ -2 & 3 & 5 \end{bmatrix},$$

then the expansion of **A** along its second row is

$$|\mathbf{A}| = -4 \cdot \begin{vmatrix} 1 & -2 \\ 3 & 5 \end{vmatrix} + 2 \cdot \begin{vmatrix} 3 & -2 \\ -2 & 5 \end{vmatrix} - 1 \cdot \begin{vmatrix} 3 & 1 \\ -2 & 3 \end{vmatrix}$$

$$= -4 \cdot 11 + 2 \cdot 11 - 1 \cdot 11 = -33.$$

And the expansion of $|\mathbf{A}|$ along its third column is

$$|\mathbf{A}| = -2 \cdot \begin{vmatrix} 4 & 2 \\ -2 & 3 \end{vmatrix} - 1 \cdot \begin{vmatrix} 3 & 1 \\ -2 & 3 \end{vmatrix} + 5 \cdot \begin{vmatrix} 3 & 1 \\ 4 & 2 \end{vmatrix}$$

$$= -2 \cdot 16 - 1 \cdot 11 + 5 \cdot 2 = -33. \qquad \blacksquare$$

Calculators and computers are convenient for the calculation of higher-dimensional determinants and inverse matrices, but determinants and inverses of 2×2 matrices are easy to compute by hand. For instance, if the 2×2 matrix

$$\mathbf{A} = \begin{bmatrix} a & b \\ c & d \end{bmatrix}$$

has nonzero determinant $|\mathbf{A}| = ad - bc \neq 0$, then its inverse matrix is

$$\mathbf{A}^{-1} = \frac{1}{|\mathbf{A}|} \begin{bmatrix} d & -b \\ -c & a \end{bmatrix}. \tag{21}$$

Note that the matrix on the right-hand side of Eq. (21) is obtained from **A** by interchanging the diagonal elements and changing the signs of the off-diagonal elements.

EXAMPLE 4   If

$$A = \begin{bmatrix} 6 & 8 \\ 5 & 7 \end{bmatrix},$$

then $|\mathbf{A}| = 6 \cdot 7 - 5 \cdot 8 = 2$. Hence Eq. (21) gives

$$\mathbf{A}^{-1} = \frac{1}{2} \begin{bmatrix} 7 & -8 \\ -5 & 6 \end{bmatrix} = \begin{bmatrix} \frac{7}{2} & -4 \\ -\frac{5}{2} & 3 \end{bmatrix}.$$

You should pause to verify that

$$\mathbf{A}^{-1}\mathbf{A} = \begin{bmatrix} \frac{7}{2} & -4 \\ -\frac{5}{2} & 3 \end{bmatrix} \begin{bmatrix} 6 & 8 \\ 5 & 7 \end{bmatrix} = \begin{bmatrix} 1 & 0 \\ 0 & 1 \end{bmatrix}.$$

Matrix-Valued Functions

A **matrix-valued function,** or simply **matrix function,** is a matrix such as

$$\mathbf{x}(t) = \begin{bmatrix} x_1(t) \\ x_2(t) \\ \cdot \\ \cdot \\ \cdot \\ x_n(t) \end{bmatrix} \tag{22a}$$

or

$$\mathbf{A}(t) = \begin{bmatrix} a_{11}(t) & a_{12}(t) & \cdots & a_{1n}(t) \\ a_{21}(t) & a_{22}(t) & \cdots & a_{2n}(t) \\ \cdot & \cdot & & \cdot \\ \cdot & \cdot & & \cdot \\ \cdot & \cdot & & \cdot \\ a_{m1}(t) & a_{m2}(t) & \cdots & a_{mn}(t) \end{bmatrix}, \tag{22b}$$

in which each entry is a function of t. We say that the matrix function $\mathbf{A}(t)$ is **continuous** (or **differentiable**) at a point (or on an interval) if each of its elements has the same property. The **derivative** of a differentiable matrix function is defined by elementwise differentiation; that is,

$$\mathbf{A}'(t) = \frac{d\mathbf{A}}{dt} = \left[\frac{da_{ij}}{dt} \right]. \tag{23}$$

EXAMPLE 5 If

$$x(t) = \begin{bmatrix} t \\ t^2 \\ e^{-t} \end{bmatrix} \quad \text{and} \quad \mathbf{A}(t) = \begin{bmatrix} \sin t & 1 \\ t & \cos t \end{bmatrix},$$

then

$$\frac{d\mathbf{x}}{dt} = \begin{bmatrix} 1 \\ 2t \\ -e^{-t} \end{bmatrix} \quad \text{and} \quad \mathbf{A}'(t) = \begin{bmatrix} \cos t & 0 \\ 1 & -\sin t \end{bmatrix}. \qquad \blacksquare$$

The differentiation rules

$$\frac{d}{dt}(\mathbf{A} + \mathbf{B}) = \frac{d\mathbf{A}}{dt} + \frac{d\mathbf{B}}{dt} \tag{24}$$

and

$$\frac{d}{dt}(\mathbf{AB}) = \mathbf{A}\frac{d\mathbf{B}}{dt} + \frac{d\mathbf{A}}{dt}\mathbf{B} \tag{25}$$

follow readily by elementwise application of the analogous differentiation rules of elementary calculus for real-valued functions. If c is a (constant) real number and $\mathbf{C}$ is a constant matrix, then

$$\frac{d}{dt}(c\mathbf{A}) = c\frac{d\mathbf{A}}{dt}, \quad \frac{d}{dt}(\mathbf{CA}) = \mathbf{C}\frac{d\mathbf{A}}{dt}, \quad \text{and} \quad \frac{d}{dt}(\mathbf{AC}) = \frac{d\mathbf{A}}{dt}\mathbf{C}. \tag{26}$$

Because of the noncommutativity of matrix multiplication, it is important not to reverse the order of the factors in (25) and (26).

First-Order Linear Systems

The notation and terminology of matrices and vectors may seem rather elaborate when first encountered, but it is readily assimilated with practice. Our main use for matrix notation will be the simplification of computations with systems of differential equations, especially those computations that would be burdensome in scalar notation.

We discuss here the general system of n first-order linear equations

$$
\begin{aligned}
x_1' &= p_{11}(t)x_1 + p_{12}(t)x_2 + \cdots + p_{1n}(t)x_n + f_1(t) \\
x_2' &= p_{21}(t)x_1 + p_{22}(t)x_2 + \cdots + p_{2n}(t)x_n + f_2(t) \\
x_3' &= p_{31}(t)x_1 + p_{32}(t)x_2 + \cdots + p_{3n}(t)x_n + f_3(t) \\
&\ \ \vdots \\
x_n' &= p_{n1}(t)x_1 + p_{n2}(t)x_2 + \cdots + p_{nn}(t)x_n + f_n(t).
\end{aligned}
\tag{27}
$$

If we introduce the *coefficient matrix*

$$
\mathbf{P}(t) = [p_{ij}(t)]
$$

and the column vectors

$$
\mathbf{x} = [x_i] \qquad \text{and} \qquad \mathbf{f}(t) = [f_i(t)],
$$

then the system in (27) takes the form of a single matrix equation

$$
\frac{d\mathbf{x}}{dt} = \mathbf{P}(t)\mathbf{x} + \mathbf{f}(t).
\tag{28}
$$

We will see that the general theory of the linear system in (27) closely parallels that of a single nth-order equation. The matrix notation used in Eq. (28) not only emphasizes this analogy, but also saves a great deal of space.

A **solution** of Eq. (28) on the open interval I is a column vector function $\mathbf{x}(t) = [x_i(t)]$ such that the component functions of $\mathbf{x}$ satisfy the system in (27) identically on I. If the functions $p_{ij}(t)$ and $f_i(t)$ are all continuous on I, then Theorem 1 of Section 4.1 guarantees the existence on I of a unique solution $\mathbf{x}(t)$ satisfying preassigned initial conditions $\mathbf{x}(a) = \mathbf{b}$.

EXAMPLE 6   The first-order system

$$
\begin{aligned}
x_1' &= 4x_1 - 3x_2 \\
x_2' &= 6x_1 - 7x_2
\end{aligned}
$$

can be written as the single matrix equation

$$
\frac{d\mathbf{x}}{dt} = \begin{bmatrix} 4 & -3 \\ 6 & -7 \end{bmatrix} \mathbf{x} = \mathbf{Px}.
$$

To verify that the vector functions

$$
\mathbf{x}_1(t) = \begin{bmatrix} 3e^{2t} \\ 2e^{2t} \end{bmatrix} \qquad \text{and} \qquad \mathbf{x}_2(t) = \begin{bmatrix} e^{-5t} \\ 3e^{-5t} \end{bmatrix}
$$

are both solutions of the matrix differential equation with coefficient matrix $\mathbf{P}$, we need only calculate

$$
\mathbf{Px}_1 = \begin{bmatrix} 4 & -3 \\ 6 & -7 \end{bmatrix} \begin{bmatrix} 3e^{2t} \\ 2e^{2t} \end{bmatrix} = \begin{bmatrix} 6e^{2t} \\ 4e^{2t} \end{bmatrix} = \mathbf{x}_1'.
$$

and

$$\mathbf{Px}_2 = \begin{bmatrix} 4 & -3 \\ 6 & -7 \end{bmatrix} \begin{bmatrix} e^{-5t} \\ 3e^{-5t} \end{bmatrix} = \begin{bmatrix} -5e^{-5t} \\ -15e^{-5t} \end{bmatrix} = \mathbf{x}_2'. \qquad\blacksquare$$

To investigate the general nature of the solutions of Eq. (28), we consider first the **associated homogeneous equation**

$$\blacktriangleright \qquad\qquad\qquad \frac{d\mathbf{x}}{dt} = \mathbf{P}(t)\mathbf{x}, \qquad\qquad\qquad (29)$$

which has the form shown in Eq. (28), but with $\mathbf{f}(t) \equiv \mathbf{0}$. We expect it to have n solutions $\mathbf{x}_1, \mathbf{x}_2, \ldots, \mathbf{x}_n$ that are independent in some appropriate sense, and such that every solution of Eq. (29) is a linear combination of these n particular solutions. Given n solutions $\mathbf{x}_1, \mathbf{x}_2, \ldots, \mathbf{x}_n$ of Eq. (29), let us write

$$\mathbf{x}_j(t) = \begin{bmatrix} x_{1j}(t) \\ \cdot \\ \cdot \\ \cdot \\ x_{ij}(t) \\ \cdot \\ \cdot \\ \cdot \\ x_{nj}(t) \end{bmatrix}. \qquad\qquad (30)$$

Thus $x_{ij}(t)$ denotes the ith component of the vector $\mathbf{x}_j(t)$, so the second subscript refers to the vector function $\mathbf{x}_j(t)$, whereas the first subscript refers to a component of this function. Theorem 1 is analogous to Theorem 1 of Section 3.2.

THEOREM 1: Principle of Superposition

Let $\mathbf{x}_1, \mathbf{x}_2, \ldots, \mathbf{x}_n$ be n solutions of the homogeneous linear equation in (29) on the open interval I. If $c_1, c_2, \ldots, c_n$ are constants, then the linear combination

$$\mathbf{x}(t) = c_1\mathbf{x}_1(t) + c_2\mathbf{x}_2(t) + \cdots + c_n\mathbf{x}_n(t) \qquad\qquad (31)$$

is also a solution of Eq. (29) on I.

Proof: We know that $\mathbf{x}_i' = \mathbf{P}(t)\mathbf{x}_i$ for each i ($1 \leqq i \leqq n$), so it follows immediately that

$$\begin{aligned}
\mathbf{x}' &= c_1\mathbf{x}_1' + c_2\mathbf{x}_2' + \cdots + c_n\mathbf{x}_n' \\
&= c_1\mathbf{P}(t)\mathbf{x}_1 + c_2\mathbf{P}(t)\mathbf{x}_2 + \cdots + c_n\mathbf{P}(t)\mathbf{x}_n \\
&= \mathbf{P}(t)(c_1\mathbf{x}_1 + c_2\mathbf{x}_2 + \cdots + c_n\mathbf{x}_n).
\end{aligned}$$

That is, $\mathbf{x}' = \mathbf{P}(t)\mathbf{x}$, as desired. The remarkable simplicity of this proof demonstrates clearly one advantage of matrix notation. $\blacksquare$

EXAMPLE 6
Continued

If $\mathbf{x}_1$ and $\mathbf{x}_2$ are the two solutions of

$$\frac{d\mathbf{x}}{dt} = \begin{bmatrix} 4 & -3 \\ 6 & -7 \end{bmatrix} \mathbf{x}$$

discussed in Example 6, then the linear combination

$$\mathbf{x}(t) = c_1\mathbf{x}_1(t) + c_2\mathbf{x}_2(t) = c_1\begin{bmatrix} 3e^{2t} \\ 2e^{2t} \end{bmatrix} + c_2\begin{bmatrix} e^{-5t} \\ 3e^{-5t} \end{bmatrix}$$

is also a solution. In scalar form with $\mathbf{x} = [x_1, \ x_2]^T$, this gives the solution

$$x_1(t) = 3c_1e^{2t} + c_2e^{-5t}$$
$$x_2(t) = 2c_1e^{2t} + 3c_2e^{-5t},$$

which is equivalent to the general solution we found by the method of elimination in Example 2 of Section 4.2. ∎

Independence and General Solutions

Linear independence is defined in the same way for vector-valued functions as for real-valued functions (Section 3.2). The vector-valued functions $\mathbf{x}_1, \mathbf{x}_2, \ldots, \mathbf{x}_n$ are **linearly dependent** on the interval I provided that there exist constants $c_1, c_2, \ldots, c_n$ *not all zero* such that

$$c_1\mathbf{x}_1(t) + c_2\mathbf{x}_2(t) + \cdots + c_n\mathbf{x}_n(t) = \mathbf{0} \tag{32}$$

for all t in I. Otherwise, they are **linearly independent.** Equivalently, they are linearly independent provided that no one of them is a linear combination of the others. For instance, the two solutions $\mathbf{x}_1$ and $\mathbf{x}_2$ of Example 6 are linearly independent because neither is a scalar multiple of the other—this is clear.

Just as in the case of a single nth-order equation, there is a Wronskian determinant that tells us whether or not n given solutions of the homogeneous equation in (29) are linearly dependent. If $\mathbf{x}_1, \mathbf{x}_2, \ldots, \mathbf{x}_n$ are such solutions, then their **Wronskian** is the $n \times n$ determinant

$$W = \begin{vmatrix} x_{11}(t) & x_{12}(t) & \cdots & x_{1n}(t) \\ x_{21}(t) & x_{22}(t) & \cdots & x_{2n}(t) \\ \cdot & \cdot & & \cdot \\ \cdot & \cdot & & \cdot \\ \cdot & \cdot & & \cdot \\ x_{n1}(t) & x_{n2}(t) & \cdots & x_{nn}(t) \end{vmatrix}, \tag{33}$$

using the notation in (30) for the components of the solutions. We may write either $W(t)$ or $W(\mathbf{x}_1, \mathbf{x}_2, \ldots, \mathbf{x}_n)$. Note that W is the determinant of the matrix that has as its *column* vectors the solutions $\mathbf{x}_1, \mathbf{x}_2, \ldots, \mathbf{x}_n$. Theorem 2 is analogous to Theorem 3 of Section 3.2. Moreover, its proof is essentially the same, with the definition of $W(\mathbf{x}_1, \mathbf{x}_2, \ldots, \mathbf{x}_n)$ in Eq. (33) substituted for the definition of the Wronskian of n solutions of a single nth-order equation (see Problems 42 through 44).

THEOREM 2: Wronskians of Solutions

Suppose that $\mathbf{x}_1, \mathbf{x}_2, \ldots, \mathbf{x}_n$ are n solutions of the homogeneous linear equation $\mathbf{x}' = \mathbf{P}(t)\mathbf{x}$ on an open interval I. Suppose also that $\mathbf{P}(t)$ is continuous on I. Let

$$W = W(\mathbf{x}_1, \mathbf{x}_2, \ldots, \mathbf{x}_n).$$

Then:

- If $\mathbf{x}_1, \mathbf{x}_2, \ldots, \mathbf{x}_n$ are linearly dependent on I, then $W \equiv 0$ on I.
- If $\mathbf{x}_1, \mathbf{x}_2, \ldots, \mathbf{x}_n$ are linearly independent on I, then $W \neq 0$ at each point of I.

Thus there are only two possibilities for solutions of homogeneous systems: Either $W \equiv 0$ on I, or $W = 0$ for *no* point of I. ∎

EXAMPLE 7   It is readily verified directly (as in Example 6) that

$$\mathbf{x}_1(t) = \begin{bmatrix} 2e^t \\ 2e^t \\ e^t \end{bmatrix}, \qquad \mathbf{x}_2(t) = \begin{bmatrix} 2e^{3t} \\ 0 \\ -e^{3t} \end{bmatrix}, \quad \text{and} \quad \mathbf{x}_3(t) = \begin{bmatrix} 2e^{5t} \\ -2e^{5t} \\ e^{5t} \end{bmatrix}$$

are solutions of the equation

$$\frac{d\mathbf{x}}{dt} = \begin{bmatrix} 3 & -2 & 0 \\ -1 & 3 & -2 \\ 0 & -1 & 3 \end{bmatrix}\mathbf{x}. \tag{34}$$

The Wronskian of these solutions is

$$W = \begin{vmatrix} 2e^t & 2e^{3t} & 2e^{5t} \\ 2e^t & 0 & -2e^{5t} \\ e^t & -e^{3t} & e^{5t} \end{vmatrix} = e^{9t}\begin{vmatrix} 2 & 2 & 2 \\ 2 & 0 & -2 \\ 1 & -1 & 1 \end{vmatrix} = -16e^{9t},$$

which is never zero. Hence Theorem 2 implies that the solutions $\mathbf{x}_1$, $\mathbf{x}_2$, and $\mathbf{x}_3$ are linearly independent (on any open interval). ∎

Theorem 3 is analogous to Theorem 4 of Section 3.2. It says that the **general solution** of the *homogeneous $n \times n$ system* $\mathbf{x}' = \mathbf{P}(t)\mathbf{x}$ is a linear combination

$$\mathbf{x} = c_1\mathbf{x}_1 + c_2\mathbf{x}_2 + \cdots + c_n\mathbf{x}_n \tag{35}$$

of any n given linearly independent solutions $\mathbf{x}_1, \mathbf{x}_2, \ldots, \mathbf{x}_n$.

THEOREM 3: General Solutions of Homogeneous Systems

Let $\mathbf{x}_1, \mathbf{x}_2, \ldots, \mathbf{x}_n$ be n linearly independent solutions of the homogeneous linear equation $\mathbf{x}' = \mathbf{P}(t)\mathbf{x}$ on an open interval I where $\mathbf{P}(t)$ is continuous. If $\mathbf{x}(t)$ is any solution whatsoever of the equation $\mathbf{x}' = \mathbf{P}(t)\mathbf{x}$ on I, then there exist numbers c_1,

$c_2, \ldots, c_n$ such that

$$\mathbf{x}(t) = c_1\mathbf{x}_1(t) + c_2\mathbf{x}_2(t) + \cdots + c_n\mathbf{x}_n(t) \tag{35}$$

for all t in I.

Proof: Let a be a fixed point of I. We show first that there exist numbers c_1, $c_2, \ldots, c_n$ such that the solution

$$\mathbf{y}(t) = c_1\mathbf{x}_1(t) + c_2\mathbf{x}_1(t) + \cdots + c_n\mathbf{x}_n(t) \tag{36}$$

has the same initial values at $t = a$ as does the given solution $\mathbf{x}(t)$; that is, such that

$$c_1\mathbf{x}_1(a) + c_2\mathbf{x}_2(a) + \cdots + c_n\mathbf{x}_n(a) = \mathbf{x}(a). \tag{37}$$

Let $\mathbf{X}(t)$ be the $n \times n$ matrix with column vectors $\mathbf{x}_1(t), \mathbf{x}_2(t), \ldots, \mathbf{x}_n(t)$, and let $\mathbf{c}$ be the column vector with components $c_1, c_2, \ldots, c_n$. Then Eq.(37) may be written in the form

$$\mathbf{X}(a)\mathbf{c} = \mathbf{x}(a). \tag{38}$$

The Wronskian determinant $W(a) = |\mathbf{X}(a)|$ is nonzero because the solutions $\mathbf{x}_1$, $\mathbf{x}_2, \ldots, \mathbf{x}_n$ are linearly independent. Hence the matrix $\mathbf{X}(a)$ has an inverse matrix $\mathbf{X}(a)^{-1}$. Therefore the vector $\mathbf{c} = \mathbf{X}(a)^{-1}\mathbf{x}(a)$ satisfies Eq. (38), as desired.

Finally, note that the given solution $\mathbf{x}(t)$ and the solution $\mathbf{y}(t)$ of Eq. (36)—with the values of c_i determined by the equation $\mathbf{c} = \mathbf{X}(a)^{-1}\mathbf{x}(a)$—have the same initial values (at $t = a$). It follows from the existence-uniqueness theorem of Section 4.1 that $\mathbf{x}(t) = \mathbf{y}(t)$ for all t in I. This establishes Eq. (35).　∎

Remark: Every $n \times n$ system $\mathbf{x}' = \mathbf{P}(t)\mathbf{x}$ with continuous coefficient matrix does have a set of n linearly independent solutions $\mathbf{x}_1, \mathbf{x}_2, \ldots, \mathbf{x}_n$ as in the hypotheses of Theorem 3. It suffices to choose for $\mathbf{x}_j(t)$ the unique solution such that

$$\mathbf{x}_j(a) = \begin{bmatrix} 0 \\ 0 \\ 0 \\ \cdot \\ \cdot \\ 0 \\ 1 \\ 0 \\ \cdot \\ \cdot \\ 0 \end{bmatrix} \longleftarrow \text{position } j$$

—that is, the column vector with all elements zero except for a 1 in row j. (In other words, $\mathbf{x}_j(a)$ is merely the jth column of the identity matrix.) Then

$$W(\mathbf{x}_1, \mathbf{x}_2, \ldots, \mathbf{x}_n)\big|_{t=a} = |\mathbf{I}| = 1 \neq 0,$$

so the solutions $\mathbf{x}_1, \mathbf{x}_2, \ldots, \mathbf{x}_n$ are linearly independent by Theorem 2. How actually to find these solutions explicitly is another matter—one that we address in Section 5.2 (for the case of constant coefficient matrices).

Initial Value Problems and Elementary Row Operations

The general solution in Eq. (35) of the homogeneous linear system $\mathbf{x}' = \mathbf{P}(t)\mathbf{x}$ can be written in the form

$$\mathbf{x}(t) = \mathbf{X}(t)\mathbf{c}, \tag{39}$$

where

$$\mathbf{X}(t) = [\mathbf{x}_1(t) \quad \mathbf{x}_2(t) \quad \cdots \quad \mathbf{x}_n(t)] \tag{40}$$

is the $n \times n$ matrix whose *column vectors* are the linearly independent solutions $\mathbf{x}_1$, $\mathbf{x}_2, \ldots, \mathbf{x}_n$, and $\mathbf{c} = [c_1 \ c_2 \ \cdots \ c_n]^T$ is the vector of coefficients in the linear combination

$$\mathbf{x}(t) = c_1\mathbf{x}_1(t) + c_2\mathbf{x}_2(t) + \cdots + c_n\mathbf{x}_n(t). \tag{35}$$

Suppose now that we wish to solve the *initial value problem*

$$\blacktriangleright \qquad \frac{d\mathbf{x}}{dt} = \mathbf{P}\mathbf{x}, \qquad \mathbf{x}(a) = \mathbf{b}, \tag{41}$$

where the initial vector $\mathbf{b} = [b_1 \ b_2 \ \cdots \ b_n]^T$ is given. Then, according to Eq. (39), it suffices to solve the system

$$\mathbf{X}(a)\mathbf{c} = \mathbf{b} \tag{42}$$

to find the coefficients $c_1, c_2, \ldots, c_n$ in (35).

We therefore review briefly the elementary technique of *row reduction* to solve an $n \times n$ *algebraic* linear system

$$
\begin{aligned}
a_{11}x_1 + a_{12}x_2 + \cdots + a_{1n}x_n &= b_1 \\
a_{21}x_1 + a_{22}x_2 + \cdots + a_{2n}x_n &= b_2 \\
&\ \ \vdots \\
a_{n1}x_1 + a_{n2}x_2 + \cdots + a_{nn}x_n &= b_n
\end{aligned}
\tag{43}
$$

with nonsingular coefficient matrix $\mathbf{A} = [a_{ij}]$, constant vector $\mathbf{b} = [b_i]$, and unknowns $x_1, x_2, \ldots, x_n$. The basic idea is to transform the system in (43) into the simpler *upper triangular form*

$$
\begin{aligned}
\overline{a}_{11}x_1 + \overline{a}_{12}x_2 + \cdots + \overline{a}_{1n}x_n &= \overline{b}_1 \\
\overline{a}_{22}x_2 + \cdots + \overline{a}_{2n}x_n &= \overline{b}_2 \\
&\ \ \vdots \\
\overline{a}_{nn}x_n &= \overline{b}_n
\end{aligned}
\tag{44}
$$

in which only the unknowns $x_j, x_{j+1}, \ldots, x_n$ appear explicitly in the *j*th equation ($j = 1, 2, \ldots, n$). The transformed system is then easily solved by the process of *back substitution*. First the last equation in (44) is solved for x_n, then the next-to-last is solved for x_{n-1}, and so forth, until the first equation is finally solved for x_1.

The transformation of (43) into upper triangular form is most easily described in terms of elementary row operations on the *augmented coefficient matrix*

$$[\mathbf{A} \;\vdots\; \mathbf{b}] = \begin{bmatrix} a_{11} & a_{12} & \cdots & a_{1n} & \vdots & b_1 \\ a_{21} & a_{22} & \cdots & a_{2n} & \vdots & b_2 \\ . & . & & . & \vdots & . \\ . & . & & . & \vdots & . \\ . & . & & . & \vdots & . \\ a_{n1} & a_{n2} & \cdots & a_{nn} & \vdots & b_n \end{bmatrix} \tag{45}$$

that is obtained by adjoining the vector **b** to the matrix **A** as an additional column. The admissible **elementary row operations** are of the following three types:

1. Multiply any (single) row of the matrix by a nonzero constant.
2. Interchange any two rows of the matrix.
3. Subtract a constant multiple of one row from any other row.

The goal is to use a sequence of such operations (one by one, in turn) to transform $[\mathbf{A} \;\vdots\; \mathbf{b}]$ into an upper triangular matrix, one that has only zeros beneath its principal diagonal. This upper triangular augmented coefficient matrix then corresponds to an upper triangular system as in (44). The process of transforming $[\mathbf{A} \;\vdots\; \mathbf{b}]$ is carried out one column at a time, from left to right, as in the next example.

EXAMPLE 8   Use the solution vectors given in Example 7 to solve the initial value problem

$$\frac{d\mathbf{x}}{dt} = \begin{bmatrix} 3 & -2 & 0 \\ -1 & 3 & -2 \\ 0 & -1 & 3 \end{bmatrix} \mathbf{x}, \qquad \mathbf{x}(0) = \begin{bmatrix} 0 \\ 2 \\ 6 \end{bmatrix}. \tag{46}$$

Solution: It follows from Theorem 3 that the linear combination

$$\mathbf{x}(t) = c_1 \mathbf{x}_1(t) + c_2 \mathbf{x}_2(t) + c_3 \mathbf{x}_3(t)$$

$$= c_1 \begin{bmatrix} 2e^t \\ 2e^t \\ e^t \end{bmatrix} + c_2 \begin{bmatrix} 2e^{3t} \\ 0 \\ -e^{3t} \end{bmatrix} + c_3 \begin{bmatrix} 2e^{5t} \\ -2e^{5t} \\ e^{5t} \end{bmatrix}$$

is a general solution of the 3×3 linear system in (46). In scalar form, this gives the general solution

$$x_1(t) = 2c_1 e^t + 2c_2 e^{3t} + 2c_3 e^{5t}$$
$$x_2(t) = 2c_1 e^t \qquad\qquad - 2c_3 e^{5t}$$
$$x_3(t) = \;\; c_1 e^t - \;\; c_2 e^{3t} + \;\; c_3 e^{5t}.$$

We seek the particular solution satisfying the initial conditions

$$x_1(0) = 0, \qquad x_2(0) = 2, \qquad x_3(0) = 6.$$

When we substitute these values in the three scalar equations above, we get the algebraic linear system

$$2c_1 + 2c_2 + 2c_3 = 0$$
$$2c_2 \qquad - 2c_3 = 2$$
$$c_1 - \;\; c_2 + \;\; c_3 = 6$$

with augmented coefficient matrix

$$\left[\begin{array}{ccc|c} 2 & 2 & 2 & 0 \\ 2 & 0 & -2 & 2 \\ 1 & -1 & 1 & 6 \end{array}\right].$$

Multiplication of each of the first two rows by $\frac{1}{2}$ gives

$$\left[\begin{array}{ccc|c} 1 & 1 & 1 & 0 \\ 1 & 0 & -1 & 1 \\ 1 & -1 & 1 & 6 \end{array}\right],$$

then subtraction of the first row both from the second row and from the third row gives the matrix

$$\left[\begin{array}{ccc|c} 1 & 1 & 1 & 0 \\ 0 & -1 & -2 & 1 \\ 0 & -2 & 0 & 6 \end{array}\right].$$

The first column of this matrix now has the desired form.

Now we multiply the second row by -1, then add twice the result to the third row. Thereby we get the upper triangular augmented coefficient matrix

$$\left[\begin{array}{ccc|c} 1 & 1 & 1 & 0 \\ 0 & 1 & 2 & -1 \\ 0 & 0 & 4 & 4 \end{array}\right]$$

that corresponds to the transformed system

$$
\begin{aligned}
c_1 + c_2 + c_3 &= 0 \\
c_2 + 2c_3 &= -1 \\
4c_3 &= 4.
\end{aligned}
$$

We finally solve in turn for $c_3 = 1$, $c_2 = -3$, and $c_1 = 2$. Thus the desired particular solution is given by

$$\mathbf{x}(t) = 2\mathbf{x}_1(t) - 3\mathbf{x}_2(t) + \mathbf{x}_3(t) = \begin{array}{l} 4e^t - 6e^{3t} + 2e^{5t} \\ 4e^t \qquad\;\; - 2e^{5t} \\ 2e^t + 3e^{3t} + e^{5t} \end{array}.$$

Nonhomogeneous Solutions

We finally turn our attention to a *nonhomogeneous* linear system of the form

$$\blacktriangleright \qquad\qquad \frac{d\mathbf{x}}{dt} = \mathbf{P}(t)\mathbf{x} + \mathbf{f}(t). \tag{47}$$

The following theorem is analogous to Theorem 5 of Section 3.2 and is proved in precisely the same way, substituting the preceding theorems in this section for the analogous theorems of Section 3.2. In brief, Theorem 4 means that the general solution of Eq. (47) has the form

$$\blacktriangleright \qquad \mathbf{x}(t) = \mathbf{x}_c(t) + \mathbf{x}_p(t), \qquad (48)$$

where $\mathbf{x}_p(t)$ is a single particular solution of Eq. (47) and the **complementary function $\mathbf{x}_c(t)$** is a general solution of the associated homogeneous equation $\mathbf{x}' = \mathbf{P}(t)\mathbf{x}$.

THEOREM 4: Solutions of Nonhomogeneous Systems

Let $\mathbf{x}_p$ be a particular solution of the nonhomogeneous linear equation in (47) on an open interval I on which the functions $\mathbf{P}(t)$ and $\mathbf{f}(t)$ are continuous. Let $\mathbf{x}_1$, $\mathbf{x}_2$, ... , $\mathbf{x}_n$ be linearly independent solutions of the associated homogeneous equation on I. If $\mathbf{x}(t)$ is any solution whatsoever of Eq. (47) on I, then there exist numbers $c_1, c_2, \ldots$, c_n such that

$$\blacktriangleright \qquad \mathbf{x}(t) = c_1\mathbf{x}_1(t) + c_2\mathbf{x}_2(t) + \cdots + c_n\mathbf{x}_n(t) + \mathbf{x}_p(t) \qquad (49)$$

for all t in I. ∎

Thus finding a general solution of a nonhomogeneous linear system involves two separate steps:

1. Finding the general solution $\mathbf{x}_c(t)$ of the associated homogeneous system;
2. Finding a single particular solution $\mathbf{x}_p(t)$ of the nonhomogeneous system.

The sum $\mathbf{x}(t) = \mathbf{x}_c(t) + \mathbf{x}_p(t)$ will then be a general solution of the nonhomogeneous system.

EXAMPLE 9 The nonhomogeneous linear system

$$
\begin{aligned}
x_1' &= 3x_1 - 2x_2 - 9t + 13 \\
x_2' &= -x_1 + 3x_2 - 2x_3 + 7t - 15 \\
x_3' &= - x_2 + 3x_3 - 6t + 7
\end{aligned}
$$

is of the form in (47) with

$$
\mathbf{P}(t) = \begin{bmatrix} 3 & -2 & 0 \\ -1 & 3 & -2 \\ 0 & -1 & 3 \end{bmatrix}, \qquad \mathbf{f}(t) = \begin{bmatrix} -9t + 13 \\ 7t - 15 \\ -6t + 7 \end{bmatrix}.
$$

In Example 7 we saw that a general solution of the associated homogeneous linear system

$$
\frac{d\mathbf{x}}{dt} = \begin{bmatrix} 3 & -2 & 0 \\ -1 & 3 & -2 \\ 0 & -1 & 3 \end{bmatrix} \mathbf{x}
$$

is given by

$$\mathbf{x}_c(t) = \begin{bmatrix} 2c_1e^t + 2c_2e^{3t} + 2c_3e^{5t} \\ 2c_1e^t \qquad\qquad - 2c_3e^{5t} \\ c_1e^t - c_2e^{3t} + c_3e^{5t} \end{bmatrix},$$

and we can verify by substitution that the function

$$\mathbf{x}_p(t) = \begin{bmatrix} 3t \\ 5 \\ 2t \end{bmatrix}$$

(found using a computer algebra system) is a particular solution of the original nonhomogeneous system. Consequently, Theorem 4 implies that a general solution of the nonhomogeneous system is given by

$$\mathbf{x}(t) = \mathbf{x}_c(t) + \mathbf{x}_p(t);$$

that is, by

$$x_1(t) = 2c_1e^t + 2c_2e^{3t} + 2c_3e^{5t} + 3t$$
$$x_2(t) = 2c_1e^t \qquad\qquad - 2c_3e^{5t} + 5$$
$$x_3(t) = c_1e^t - c_2e^{3t} + c_3e^{5t} + 2t.$$

5.1 Problems

1. Let

$$\mathbf{A} = \begin{bmatrix} 2 & -3 \\ 4 & 7 \end{bmatrix} \quad \text{and} \quad \mathbf{B} = \begin{bmatrix} 3 & -4 \\ 5 & 1 \end{bmatrix}.$$

Find   (a) $2\mathbf{A} + 3\mathbf{B}$;   (b) $3\mathbf{A} - 2\mathbf{B}$;   (c) $\mathbf{AB}$;   (d) $\mathbf{BA}$.

2. Verify that (a) $\mathbf{A}(\mathbf{BC}) = (\mathbf{AB})\mathbf{C}$ and that (b) $\mathbf{A}(\mathbf{B} + \mathbf{C}) = \mathbf{AB} + \mathbf{AC}$, where $\mathbf{A}$ and $\mathbf{B}$ are the matrices given in Problem 1 and

$$\mathbf{C} = \begin{bmatrix} 0 & 2 \\ 3 & -1 \end{bmatrix}.$$

3. Find $\mathbf{AB}$ and $\mathbf{BA}$ given

$$\mathbf{A} = \begin{bmatrix} 2 & 0 & -1 \\ 3 & -4 & 5 \end{bmatrix} \quad \text{and} \quad \mathbf{B} = \begin{bmatrix} 1 & 3 \\ -7 & 0 \\ 3 & -2 \end{bmatrix}.$$

4. Let $\mathbf{A}$ and $\mathbf{B}$ be the matrices given in Problem 3 and let

$$\mathbf{x} = \begin{bmatrix} 2t \\ e^{-t} \end{bmatrix} \quad \text{and} \quad \mathbf{y} = \begin{bmatrix} t^2 \\ \sin t \\ \cos t \end{bmatrix}.$$

Find $\mathbf{Ay}$ and $\mathbf{Bx}$. Are the products $\mathbf{Ax}$ and $\mathbf{By}$ defined? Explain your answer.

5. Let

$$\mathbf{A} = \begin{bmatrix} 3 & 2 & -1 \\ 0 & 4 & 3 \\ -5 & 2 & 7 \end{bmatrix} \quad \text{and} \quad \mathbf{B} = \begin{bmatrix} 0 & -3 & 2 \\ 1 & 4 & -3 \\ 2 & 5 & -1 \end{bmatrix}.$$

Find   (a) $7\mathbf{A} + 4\mathbf{B}$;   (b) $3\mathbf{A} - 5\mathbf{B}$;   (c) $\mathbf{AB}$;   (d) $\mathbf{BA}$; (e) $\mathbf{A} - t\mathbf{I}$.

6. Let

$$\mathbf{A}_1 = \begin{bmatrix} 2 & 1 \\ -3 & 2 \end{bmatrix}, \quad \mathbf{A}_2 = \begin{bmatrix} 1 & 3 \\ -1 & -2 \end{bmatrix}, \quad \mathbf{B} = \begin{bmatrix} 2 & 4 \\ 1 & 2 \end{bmatrix}.$$

(a) Show that $\mathbf{A}_1\mathbf{B} = \mathbf{A}_2\mathbf{B}$ and note that $\mathbf{A}_1 \neq \mathbf{A}_2$. Thus the cancellation law does not hold for matrices; that is, if $\mathbf{A}_1\mathbf{B} = \mathbf{A}_2\mathbf{B}$ and $\mathbf{B} \neq \mathbf{0}$, it does not follow that $\mathbf{A}_1 = \mathbf{A}_2$.
(b) Let $\mathbf{A} = \mathbf{A}_1 - \mathbf{A}_2$ and show that $\mathbf{AB} = \mathbf{0}$. Thus the product of two nonzero matrices may be the zero matrix.

7. Compute the determinants of the matrices $\mathbf{A}$ and $\mathbf{B}$ in Problem 6. Are your results consistent with the theorem to the effect that

$$\det(\mathbf{AB}) = [\det(\mathbf{A})] \cdot [\det(\mathbf{B})]$$

for any two square matrices $\mathbf{A}$ and $\mathbf{B}$ of the same order?

8. Suppose that $\mathbf{A}$ and $\mathbf{B}$ are the matrices of Problem 5. Verify that $\det(\mathbf{AB}) = \det(\mathbf{BA})$.

In Problems 9 and 10, verify the product law for differentiation, $(\mathbf{AB})' = \mathbf{A}'\mathbf{B} + \mathbf{AB}'$.

9. $\mathbf{A}(t) = \begin{bmatrix} t & 2t-1 \\ t^3 & \dfrac{1}{t} \end{bmatrix}$ and $\mathbf{B}(t) = \begin{bmatrix} 1-t & 1+t \\ 3t^2 & 4t^3 \end{bmatrix}$

10. $\mathbf{A}(t) = \begin{bmatrix} e^t & t & t^2 \\ -t & 0 & 2 \\ 8t & -1 & t^3 \end{bmatrix}$ and $\mathbf{B}(t) = \begin{bmatrix} 3 \\ 2e^{-t} \\ 3t \end{bmatrix}$

In Problems 11 through 20, write the given system in the form $\mathbf{x}' = \mathbf{P}(t)\mathbf{x} + \mathbf{f}(t)$.

11. $x' = -3y$
$y' = 3x$

12. $x' = 3x - 2y$
$y' = 2x + y$

13. $x' = 2x + 4y + 3e^t$
$y' = 5x - y - t^2$

14. $x' = tx - e^t y + \cos t$
$y' = e^{-t}x + t^2 y - \sin t$

15. $x' = y + z$
$y' = z + x$
$z' = x + y$

16. $x' = 2x - 3y$
$y' = x + y + 2z$
$z' = 5y - 7z$

17. $x' = 3x - 4y + z + t$
$y' = x \quad\quad - 3z + t^2$
$z' = \quad\quad 6y - 7z + t^3$

18. $x' = tx - y + e^t z$
$y' = 2x + t^2 y - z$
$z' = e^{-t}x + 3ty + t^3 z$

19. $x_1' = x_2$
$x_2' = 2x_3$
$x_3' = 3x_4$
$x_4' = 4x_1$

20. $x_1' = x_2 + x_3 + 1$
$x_2' = x_3 + x_4 + t$
$x_3' = x_1 + x_4 + t^2$
$x_4' = x_1 + x_2 + t^3$

In Problems 21 through 30, first verify that the given vectors are solutions of the given system. Then use the Wronskian to show that they are linearly independent. Finally, write the general solution of the system.

21. $\mathbf{x}' = \begin{bmatrix} 4 & 2 \\ -3 & -1 \end{bmatrix}\mathbf{x}$; $\mathbf{x}_1 = \begin{bmatrix} 2e^t \\ -3e^t \end{bmatrix}$, $\mathbf{x}_2 = \begin{bmatrix} e^{2t} \\ -e^{2t} \end{bmatrix}$

22. $\mathbf{x}' = \begin{bmatrix} -3 & 2 \\ -3 & 4 \end{bmatrix}\mathbf{x}$; $\mathbf{x}_1 = \begin{bmatrix} e^{3t} \\ 3e^{3t} \end{bmatrix}$, $\mathbf{x}_2 = \begin{bmatrix} 2e^{-2t} \\ e^{-2t} \end{bmatrix}$

23. $\mathbf{x}' = \begin{bmatrix} 3 & -1 \\ 5 & -3 \end{bmatrix}\mathbf{x}$; $\mathbf{x}_1 = e^{2t}\begin{bmatrix} 1 \\ 1 \end{bmatrix}$, $\mathbf{x}_2 = e^{-2t}\begin{bmatrix} 1 \\ 5 \end{bmatrix}$

24. $\mathbf{x}' = \begin{bmatrix} 4 & 1 \\ -2 & 1 \end{bmatrix}\mathbf{x}$; $\mathbf{x}_1 = e^{3t}\begin{bmatrix} 1 \\ -1 \end{bmatrix}$, $\mathbf{x}_2 = e^{2t}\begin{bmatrix} 2 \\ -1 \end{bmatrix}$

25. $\mathbf{x}' = \begin{bmatrix} 4 & -3 \\ 6 & -7 \end{bmatrix}\mathbf{x}$; $\mathbf{x}_1 = \begin{bmatrix} 3e^{2t} \\ 2e^{2t} \end{bmatrix}$, $\mathbf{x}_2 = \begin{bmatrix} e^{-5t} \\ 3e^{-5t} \end{bmatrix}$

26. $\mathbf{x}' = \begin{bmatrix} 3 & -2 & 0 \\ -1 & 3 & -2 \\ 0 & -1 & 3 \end{bmatrix}\mathbf{x}$; $\mathbf{x}_1 = e^t\begin{bmatrix} 2 \\ 2 \\ 1 \end{bmatrix}$,

$\mathbf{x}_2 = e^{3t}\begin{bmatrix} -2 \\ 0 \\ 1 \end{bmatrix}$, $\mathbf{x}_3 = e^{5t}\begin{bmatrix} 2 \\ -2 \\ 1 \end{bmatrix}$

27. $\mathbf{x}' = \begin{bmatrix} 0 & 1 & 1 \\ 1 & 0 & 1 \\ 1 & 1 & 0 \end{bmatrix}\mathbf{x}$; $\mathbf{x}_1 = e^{2t}\begin{bmatrix} 1 \\ 1 \\ 1 \end{bmatrix}$,

$\mathbf{x}_2 = e^{-t}\begin{bmatrix} 1 \\ 0 \\ -1 \end{bmatrix}$, $\mathbf{x}_3 = e^{-t}\begin{bmatrix} 0 \\ 1 \\ -1 \end{bmatrix}$

28. $\mathbf{x}' = \begin{bmatrix} 1 & 2 & 1 \\ 6 & -1 & 0 \\ -1 & -2 & -1 \end{bmatrix}\mathbf{x}$; $\mathbf{x}_1 = \begin{bmatrix} 1 \\ 6 \\ -13 \end{bmatrix}$,

$\mathbf{x}_2 = e^{3t}\begin{bmatrix} 2 \\ 3 \\ -2 \end{bmatrix}$, $\mathbf{x}_3 = e^{-4t}\begin{bmatrix} -1 \\ 2 \\ 1 \end{bmatrix}$

29. $\mathbf{x}' = \begin{bmatrix} -8 & -11 & -2 \\ 6 & 9 & 2 \\ -6 & -6 & 1 \end{bmatrix} \mathbf{x}; \quad \mathbf{x}_1 = e^{-2t} \begin{bmatrix} 3 \\ -2 \\ 2 \end{bmatrix},$

$$\mathbf{x}_2 = e^t \begin{bmatrix} 1 \\ -1 \\ 1 \end{bmatrix}, \quad \mathbf{x}_3 = e^{3t} \begin{bmatrix} 1 \\ -1 \\ 0 \end{bmatrix}$$

30. $\mathbf{x}' = \begin{bmatrix} 1 & -4 & 0 & -2 \\ 0 & 1 & 0 & 0 \\ 6 & -12 & -1 & -6 \\ 0 & -4 & 0 & -1 \end{bmatrix} \mathbf{x}; \quad \mathbf{x}_1 = e^{-t} \begin{bmatrix} 1 \\ 0 \\ 0 \\ 1 \end{bmatrix},$

$$\mathbf{x}_2 = e^{-t} \begin{bmatrix} 0 \\ 0 \\ 1 \\ 0 \end{bmatrix}, \quad \mathbf{x}_3 = e^t \begin{bmatrix} 0 \\ 1 \\ 0 \\ -2 \end{bmatrix}, \quad \mathbf{x}_4 = e^t \begin{bmatrix} 1 \\ 0 \\ 3 \\ 0 \end{bmatrix}$$

In Problems 31 through 40, find a particular solution of the indicated linear system that satisfies the given initial conditions.

31. The system of Problem 22: $x_1(0) = 0, \quad x_2(0) = 5$

32. The system of Problem 23: $x_1(0) = 5, \quad x_2(0) = -3$

33. The system of Problem 24: $x_1(0) = 11, \quad x_2(0) = -7$

34. The system of Problem 25: $x_1(0) = 8, \quad x_2(0) = 0$

35. The system of Problem 26: $x_1(0) = 0, \quad x_2(0) = 0,$ $x_3(0) = 4$

36. The system of Problem 27: $x_1(0) = 10, \quad x_2(0) = 12,$ $x_3(0) = -1$

37. The system of Problem 29: $x_1(0) = 1, \quad x_2(0) = 2,$ $x_3(0) = 3$

38. The system of Problem 29: $x_1(0) = 5, \quad x_2(0) = -7,$ $x_3(0) = 11$

39. The system of Problem 30: $x_1(0) = x_2(0) = x_3(0) = x_4(0) = 1$

40. The system of Problem 30: $x_1(0) = 1, \quad x_2(0) = 3,$ $x_3(0) = 5, \quad x_4(0) = 7$

41. (a) Show that the vector functions

$$\mathbf{x}_1(t) = \begin{bmatrix} t \\ t^2 \end{bmatrix} \quad \text{and} \quad \mathbf{x}_2 = \begin{bmatrix} t^2 \\ t^3 \end{bmatrix}$$

are linearly independent on the real line. (b) Why does it follow from Theorem 2 that there is *no* continuous matrix $\mathbf{P}(t)$ such that $\mathbf{x}_1$ and $\mathbf{x}_2$ are both solutions of $\mathbf{x}' = \mathbf{P}(t)\mathbf{x}$?

42. Suppose that one of the vector functions

$$\mathbf{x}_1(t) = \begin{bmatrix} x_{11}(t) \\ x_{21}(t) \end{bmatrix} \quad \text{and} \quad \mathbf{x}_2(t) = \begin{bmatrix} x_{12}(t) \\ x_{22}(t) \end{bmatrix}$$

is a constant multiple of the other on the open interval I. Show that their Wronskian $W(t) = |[x_{ij}(t)]|$ must vanish identically on I. This proves part (a) of Theorem 2 in the case $n = 2$.

43. Suppose that the vectors $\mathbf{x}_1(t)$ and $\mathbf{x}_2(t)$ of Problem 42 are solutions of the equation $\mathbf{x}' = \mathbf{P}(t)\mathbf{x}$, where the 2×2 matrix $\mathbf{P}(t)$ is continuous on the open interval I. Show that if there exists a point a of I at which their Wronskian $W(a)$ is zero, then there exist numbers c_1 and c_2 not both zero such that $c_1\mathbf{x}_1(a) + c_2\mathbf{x}_2(a) = \mathbf{0}$. Then conclude from the uniqueness of solutions of the equation $\mathbf{x}' = \mathbf{P}(t)\mathbf{x}$ that

$$c_1\mathbf{x}_1(t) + c_2\mathbf{x}_2(t) = \mathbf{0}$$

for all t in I; that is, that $\mathbf{x}_1$ and $\mathbf{x}_2$ are linearly dependent. This proves part (b) of Theorem 2 in the case $n = 2$.

44. Generalize Problems 42 and 43 to prove Theorem 2 for n an arbitrary positive integer.

45. Let $\mathbf{x}_1(t), \mathbf{x}_2(t), \ldots, \mathbf{x}_n(t)$ be vector functions whose ith components (for some fixed i) $x_{i1}(t), x_{i2}(t), \ldots, x_{in}(t)$ are linearly independent real-valued functions. Conclude that the vector functions are themselves linearly independent.

5.1 Computing Projects

Calculations with numerical matrices of order greater than 3 are most frequently done with the aid of calculators or computers. For instance, recall that in Example 8 we needed to solve the linear system

$$2c_1 + 2c_2 + 2c_3 = 0$$
$$2c_1 \qquad - 2c_3 = 2$$
$$c_1 - c_2 + c_3 = 6.$$

Writing this system in matrix notation $\mathbf{Ac} = \mathbf{b}$ and working with a TI-85 calculator, for instance, we would store the 3×3 coefficient matrix $\mathbf{A}$ and the column vector $\mathbf{b}$ with the commands

```
[[2,2,2] [2,0,-2] [1,-1,1]] → A
[[0] [2] [6]] → b
```

in which each matrix and each of its successive rows in enclosed within square brackets. Then we calculate and store the solution $\mathbf{c} = \mathbf{A}^{-1}\mathbf{b}$ with the command

```
A⁻¹*b → c
```

which yields the result

```
[[2 ]
[-3]
[1 ]]
```

Thus $c_1 = 2$, $c_2 = -3$, and $c_3 = 1$, as we found using elementary row operations in Example 8.

Matrix notation in a computational system such as *Maple, Mathematica,* or MATLAB is similar. To carry out the same computation using *Mathematica,* for instance, we would enter the commands

```
A = { {2, 2, 2}, {2, 0, -2}, {1, -1, 1} };
b = { {0}, {2}, {6} };
c = Inverse[A] . b
{{2},{-3},{1}}
```

Project A

To practice simple matrix algebra with whatever calculator or computer system is available, you might begin by defining a square matrix $\mathbf{A}$. Then calculate its inverse matrix $\mathbf{B}$ and check that the matrix product $\mathbf{AB}$ is the identity matrix. Do this with several square matrices of different dimensions. Most calculators and computer algebra systems will produce an error message if you request the inverse of a singular matrix. In this case *Mathematica* reports

```
LinearSolve::nosol: Linear equation encountered
which has no solution.
```

And the TI-85 reports

```
ERROR 03 SINGULAR MAT
```

Project B

Use matrix algebra as indicated above (for the computations of Example 8) to solve Problems 31 through 40 of this section.

5.2 The Eigenvalue Method for Homogeneous Systems

We now introduce a powerful alternative to the method of elimination for constructing the general solution of a *homogeneous* first-order linear system with *constant* coefficients,

$$
\begin{aligned}
x'_1 &= a_{11}x_1 + a_{12}x_2 + \cdots + a_{1n}x_n \\
x'_2 &= a_{21}x_1 + a_{22}x_2 + \cdots + a_{2n}x_n \\
&\quad\vdots \\
x'_n &= a_{n1}x_1 + a_{n2}x_2 + \cdots + a_{nn}x_n .
\end{aligned}
\tag{1}
$$

By Theorem 3 of Section 5.1, we know that it suffices to find n linearly independent solution vectors $\mathbf{x}_1, \mathbf{x}_2, \ldots, \mathbf{x}_n$; the linear combination

$$
\blacktriangleright \qquad \mathbf{x}(t) = c_1\mathbf{x}_1(t) + c_2\mathbf{x}_2(t) + \cdots + c_n\mathbf{x}_n(t)
\tag{2}
$$

with arbitrary coefficients will then be a general solution of the system in (1).

To search for the n needed linearly independent solution vectors, we proceed by analogy with the characteristic root method for solving a single homogeneous linear equation with constant coefficients (Section 3.3). It is reasonable to anticipate solution vectors of the form

$$
\mathbf{x}(t) =
\begin{bmatrix} x_1 \\ x_2 \\ x_3 \\ \vdots \\ x_n \end{bmatrix}
=
\begin{bmatrix} v_1 e^{\lambda t} \\ v_2 e^{\lambda t} \\ v_3 e^{\lambda t} \\ \vdots \\ v_n e^{\lambda t} \end{bmatrix}
=
\begin{bmatrix} v_1 \\ v_2 \\ v_3 \\ \vdots \\ v_n \end{bmatrix} e^{\lambda t} = \mathbf{v}e^{\lambda t}
\tag{3}
$$

where $\lambda, v_1, v_2, \ldots, v_n$ are appropriate scalar constants. For if we substitute

$$
x_i = v_i e^{\lambda t}, \qquad x'_i = \lambda v_i e^{\lambda t}
$$

($i = 1, 2, \ldots, n$) in (1), then the factor $e^{\lambda t}$ will cancel throughout. This will leave us with n linear equations which—for appropriate values of λ—we can hope to solve for values of the coefficients $v_1, v_2, \ldots, v_n$ in (3) so that $\mathbf{x}(t) = \mathbf{v}e^{\lambda t}$ is, indeed, a solution of the system in (1).

To investigate this possibility, it is more efficient to write the system in (1) in the matrix form

$$
\blacktriangleright \qquad\qquad \mathbf{x}' = \mathbf{Ax}
\tag{4}
$$

where $\mathbf{A} = [a_{ij}]$. When we substitute the trial solution $\mathbf{x} = \mathbf{v}e^{\lambda t}$ with derivative $\mathbf{x}' = \lambda\mathbf{v}e^{\lambda t}$ in Eq. (4), the result is

$$
\lambda\mathbf{v}e^{\lambda t} = \mathbf{Av}e^{\lambda t}.
$$

We cancel the nonzero scalar factor $e^{\lambda t}$ to get

$$
\blacktriangleright \qquad\qquad \mathbf{Av} = \lambda\mathbf{v}.
\tag{5}
$$

This means that $\mathbf{x} = \mathbf{v}e^{\lambda t}$ will be a nontrivial solution of Eq. (4) provided that $\mathbf{v}$ is a *nonzero* vector and λ is a constant such that Eq. (5) holds; that is, the *matrix product* **Av** *is a scalar multiple of the vector* **v**. The question now is this: How do we find **v** and λ?

To answer this question, we rewrite Eq. (5) in the form

$$\blacktriangleright \qquad (\mathbf{A} - \lambda\mathbf{I})\mathbf{v} = \mathbf{0}. \qquad (6)$$

Given λ, this is a system of n nonhomogeneous linear equations in the unknowns v_1, v_2, . . . , v_n. By a standard theorem of linear algebra, it has a nontrivial solution if and only if the determinant of its coefficient matrix vanishes; that is, if and only if

$$|\mathbf{A} - \lambda\mathbf{I}| = \det(\mathbf{A} - \lambda\mathbf{I}) = 0. \qquad (7)$$

In its simplest formulation, the **eigenvalue method** for solving the system $\mathbf{x}' = \mathbf{Ax}$ consists of finding λ so that Eq. (7) holds and next solving Eq. (6) with this value of λ to obtain v_1, v_2, . . . , v_n. Then $\mathbf{x} = \mathbf{v}e^{\lambda t}$ will be a solution vector. The name of the method comes from the following definition.

DEFINITION: Eigenvalues and Eigenvectors

The number λ (either zero or nonzero) is called an **eigenvalue** of the $n \times n$ matrix **A** provided that

$$|\mathbf{A} - \lambda\mathbf{I}| = 0. \qquad (7)$$

An **eigenvector** associated with the eigenvalue λ is a *nonzero* vector **v** such that $\mathbf{Av} = \lambda\mathbf{v}$, so that

$$(\mathbf{A} - \lambda\mathbf{I})\mathbf{v} = \mathbf{0}. \qquad (6) \quad \blacksquare$$

Note that if **v** is an eigenvector associated with the eigenvalue λ, then so is any nonzero constant scalar multiple of $c\mathbf{v}$ of **v**—this follows upon multiplication of each side in Eq. (6) by $c \neq 0$.

The prefix *eigen* is a German word with the approximate translation *characteristic* in this context; the terms *characteristic value* and *characteristic vector* are in common use. For this reason, the equation

$$|\mathbf{A} - \lambda\mathbf{I}| = \begin{vmatrix} a_{11} - \lambda & a_{12} & \cdots & a_{1n} \\ a_{21} & a_{22} - \lambda & \cdots & a_{2n} \\ \cdot & \cdot & & \cdot \\ \cdot & \cdot & & \cdot \\ \cdot & \cdot & & \cdot \\ a_{n1} & a_{n2} & \cdots & a_{nn} - \lambda \end{vmatrix} = 0 \qquad (8)$$

is called the **characteristic equation** of the matrix **A**; its roots are the eigenvalues of **A**. Upon expanding the determinant in (8), we evidently get an nth-degree polynomial of the form

$$(-1)^n\lambda^n + b_{n-1}\lambda^{n-1} + \cdots + b_1\lambda + b_0 = 0. \qquad (9)$$

By the fundamental theorem of algebra, this equation has n roots—possibly some are complex, possibly some are repeated—and thus an $n \times n$ matrix has n eigenvalues (counting repetitions, if any). Although we assume that the elements of **A** are real numbers, we allow the possibility of complex eigenvalues and complex-valued eigenvectors.

Our discussion of Eqs. (4) through (7) provides a proof of the following theorem, which is the basis for the eigenvalue method of solving a first-order linear system with constant coefficients.

▉ *THEOREM:* Eigenvalue Solutions of x′ = Ax

Let λ be an eigenvalue of the [constant] coefficient matrix **A** of the first-order linear system

$$\frac{d\mathbf{x}}{dt} = \mathbf{A}\mathbf{x}.$$

If **v** is an eigenvector associated with λ, then

$$\mathbf{x}(t) = \mathbf{v}e^{\lambda t}$$

is a nontrivial solution of the system.   ▉

In outline, the eigenvalue method for solving the $n \times n$ system $\mathbf{x}' = \mathbf{A}\mathbf{x}$ proceeds as follows.

1. We first solve the characteristic equation in (8) for the eigenvalues λ_1, $\lambda_2, \ldots, \lambda_n$ of the matrix **A**.
2. Next we attempt to find n *linearly independent* eigenvectors $\mathbf{v}_1, \mathbf{v}_2, \ldots, \mathbf{v}_n$ associated with these eigenvalues.
3. Step 2 is not always possible, but when it is, we get n linearly independent solutions

$$\mathbf{x}_1(t) = \mathbf{v}_1 e^{\lambda_1 t}, \qquad \mathbf{x}_2(t) = \mathbf{v}_2 e^{\lambda_2 t}, \quad \ldots, \quad \mathbf{x}_n(t) = \mathbf{v}_n e^{\lambda_n t}. \tag{10}$$

In this case the general solution of $\mathbf{x}' = \mathbf{A}\mathbf{x}$ is a linear combination

$$\mathbf{x}(t) = c_1 \mathbf{x}_1(t) + c_2 \mathbf{x}_2(t) + \cdots + c_n \mathbf{x}_n(t)$$

of these n solutions.

We will discuss separately the various cases that can occur, depending upon whether the eigenvalues are distinct or repeated, real or complex. The case of repeated eigenvalues—multiple roots of the characteristic equation—will be deferred to Section 5.4.

Distinct Real Eigenvalues

If the eigenvalues $\lambda_1, \lambda_2, \ldots, \lambda_n$ are real and distinct, then we substitute each of them in turn in Eq. (6) and solve for the associated eigenvectors $\mathbf{v}_1, \mathbf{v}_2, \ldots, \mathbf{v}_n$. In this case it can be proved that the particular solution vectors given in (10) are always linearly independent. (For instance, see Section 6.2 of Edwards and Penney, *Elementary Linear Algebra* (Englewood Cliffs, N.J.: Prentice Hall, 1988).) In any particular example such linear independence can always be verified by using the Wronskian determinant of Section 5.1. The following example illustrates the procedure.

EXAMPLE 1 Find a general solution of the system

$$x'_1 = 4x_1 + 2x_2$$
$$x'_2 = 3x_1 - x_2. \tag{11}$$

Solution: The matrix form of the system in (11) is

$$\mathbf{x}' = \begin{bmatrix} 4 & 2 \\ 3 & -1 \end{bmatrix} \mathbf{x}. \tag{12}$$

The characteristic equation of the coefficient matrix is

$$\begin{vmatrix} 4 - \lambda & 2 \\ 3 & -1 - \lambda \end{vmatrix} = (4 - \lambda)(-1 - \lambda) - 6$$

$$= \lambda^2 - 3\lambda - 10 = (\lambda + 2)(\lambda - 5) = 0,$$

so we have the distinct real eigenvalues $\lambda_1 = -2$ and $\lambda_2 = 5$.

For the coefficient matrix $\mathbf{A}$ in (12) the eigenvector equation $(\mathbf{A} - \lambda\mathbf{I})\mathbf{v} = \mathbf{0}$ takes the form

$$\begin{bmatrix} 4 - \lambda & 2 \\ 3 & -1 - \lambda \end{bmatrix} \begin{bmatrix} a \\ b \end{bmatrix} = \begin{bmatrix} 0 \\ 0 \end{bmatrix} \tag{13}$$

for the associated eigenvector $\mathbf{v} = [a \ b]^T$.

With $\lambda_1 = -2$:
Substitution of the first eigenvalue $\lambda_1 = -2$ in Eq. (13) yields the system

$$\begin{bmatrix} 6 & 2 \\ 3 & 1 \end{bmatrix} \begin{bmatrix} a \\ b \end{bmatrix} = \begin{bmatrix} 0 \\ 0 \end{bmatrix};$$

that is, the two scalar equations

$$6a + 2b = 0$$
$$3a + b = 0. \tag{14}$$

In contrast with the nonsingular (algebraic) linear systems whose solutions we discussed in Section 5.1, the homogeneous linear system in (14) is *singular*—the two scalar equations obviously are equivalent (each being a multiple of the other). Therefore Eq. (14) has infinitely many nonzero solutions—we can choose a arbitrary (but nonzero) and then solve for b.

Substitution of an eigenvalue λ in the eigenvector equation $(\mathbf{A} - \lambda\mathbf{I})\mathbf{v} = \mathbf{0}$ always yields a singular homogeneous linear system, and among its infinity of solutions we generally seek a "simple" solution with small integer values (if possible). Looking at the second equation in (14), the choice $a = 1$ yields $b = -3$, and thus

$$\mathbf{v}_1 = \begin{bmatrix} 1 \\ -3 \end{bmatrix}$$

is an eigenvector associated with $\lambda_1 = -2$ (as is any nonzero constant multiple of $\mathbf{v}_1$).

Remark: If instead of the "simplest" choice $a = 1$, $b = -3$, we had made another choice, $a = c$, $b = -3c$, we would have obtained the eigenvector

$$\mathbf{v}_1 = \begin{bmatrix} c \\ -3c \end{bmatrix} = c \begin{bmatrix} 1 \\ -3 \end{bmatrix}.$$

Because this is a constant multiple of our previous result, any choice we make leads to [a constant multiple of] the same solution

$$\mathbf{x}_1(t) = \begin{bmatrix} 1 \\ -3 \end{bmatrix} e^{-2t}.$$

With $\lambda_2 = 5$;
    Substitution of the second eigenvalue $\lambda = 5$ in (13) yields the pair

$$-a + 2b = 0$$
$$3a - 6b = 0$$
(15)

of equivalent scalar equations. With $b = 1$ in the first equation we get $a = 2$, so

$$\mathbf{v}_2 = \begin{bmatrix} 2 \\ 1 \end{bmatrix}$$

is an eigenvector associated with $\lambda_2 = 5$. A different choice $a = 2c$, $b = c$ would merely give a [constant] multiple of $\mathbf{v}_2$.

These two eigenvalues and associated eigenvectors yield the two solutions

$$\mathbf{x}_1(t) = \begin{bmatrix} 1 \\ -3 \end{bmatrix} e^{-2t} \quad \text{and} \quad \mathbf{x}_2(t) = \begin{bmatrix} 2 \\ 1 \end{bmatrix} e^{5t}.$$

They are linearly independent because their Wronskian

$$\begin{vmatrix} e^{-2t} & 2e^{5t} \\ -3e^{-2t} & e^{5t} \end{vmatrix} = 7e^{3t}$$

is nonzero. Hence a general solution of the system in (11) is

$$\mathbf{x}(t) = c_1\mathbf{x}_1(t) + c_2\mathbf{x}_2(t) = c_1 \begin{bmatrix} 1 \\ -3 \end{bmatrix} e^{-2t} + c_2 \begin{bmatrix} 2 \\ 1 \end{bmatrix} e^{5t};$$

in scalar form,

$$x_1(t) = \quad c_1 e^{-2t} + 2c_2 e^{5t}$$
$$x_2(t) = -3c_1 e^{-2t} + \quad c_2 e^{5t}.$$ ∎

Remark: As in Example 1, it is convenient when discussing a linear system $\mathbf{x}' = \mathbf{A}\mathbf{x}$ to use vectors $\mathbf{x}_1, \mathbf{x}_2, \ldots, \mathbf{x}_n$ to denote different vector-valued solutions of the system, whereas the *scalars* $x_1, x_2, \ldots, x_n$ denote the components of a single vector-valued solution $\mathbf{x}$.

Compartmental Analysis

Frequently a complex process or system can be broken down into simpler subsystems of "compartments" that can be analyzed separately. The whole system can then be modeled by describing the interactions between the various compartments. Thus a chemical plant may consist of a succession of separate stages (or even physical compartments) in which various reactants and products combine or are mixed. It may happen that a single differential equation describes each compartment of the system, and then the whole physical system is modeled by a system of differential equations.

As a simple example of a three-stage system, Fig. 5.2.1 shows three brine tanks containing V_1, V_2, and V_3 gallons of brine, respectively. Fresh water flows into tank 1, while mixed brine flows from tank 1 into tank 2, from tank 2 into tank 3, and out of tank 3. Let $x_i(t)$ denote the amount (in pounds) of salt in tank i at time t ($i = 1, 2, 3$). If each flow rate is r gallons per minute, then a simple accounting of salt concentrations, as in Example 2 of Section 4.1, yields the first-order system

r (gal/min)

$$\begin{aligned} x_1' &= -k_1 x_1 \\ x_2' &= k_1 x_1 - k_2 x_2 \\ x_3' &= k_2 x_2 - k_3 x_3 \end{aligned} \tag{16}$$

where

FIGURE 5.2.1. The three brine tanks of Example 2

$$k_i = \frac{r}{V_i}, \qquad i = 1, 2, 3. \tag{17}$$

EXAMPLE 2   If $V_1 = 20$, $V_2 = 40$, $V_3 = 50$, $r = 10$ (gal/min), and the initial amounts of salt in the three brine tanks, in pounds, are

$$x_1(0) = 15, \qquad x_2(0) = x_3(0) = 0,$$

find the amount of salt in each tank at time $t \geqq 0$.

Solution Substituting the given numerical values in (16) and (17), we get the initial value problem

$$\mathbf{x}'(t) = \begin{bmatrix} -0.5 & 0 & 0 \\ 0.5 & -0.25 & 0 \\ 0 & 0.25 & -0.2 \end{bmatrix} \mathbf{x}, \qquad \mathbf{x}(0) = \begin{bmatrix} 15 \\ 0 \\ 0 \end{bmatrix} \tag{18}$$

for the vector $\mathbf{x}(t) = [x_1(t) \ x_2(t) \ x_3(t)]^T$. The simple form of the matrix

$$\mathbf{A} - \lambda \mathbf{I} = \begin{bmatrix} -0.5 - \lambda & 0 & 0 \\ 0.5 & -0.25 - \lambda & 0 \\ 0 & 0.25 & -0.2 - \lambda \end{bmatrix} \tag{19}$$

leads readily to the characteristic equation

$$|\mathbf{A} - \lambda \mathbf{I}| = (-0.5 - \lambda)(-0.25 - \lambda)(-0.2 - \lambda) = 0.$$

Thus the coefficient matrix $\mathbf{A}$ in (18) has the distinct eigenvalues $\lambda_1 = -0.5$, $\lambda_2 = -0.25$, and $\lambda_3 = -0.2$.

With $\lambda_1 = -0.5$:

Substituting $\lambda = -0.5$ in (19), we get the equation

$$[A + (0.5) \cdot I]v = \begin{bmatrix} 0 & 0 & 0 \\ 0.5 & 0.25 & 0 \\ 0 & 0.25 & 0.3 \end{bmatrix} \begin{bmatrix} a \\ b \\ c \end{bmatrix} = \begin{bmatrix} 0 \\ 0 \\ 0 \end{bmatrix}$$

for the associated eigenvector $v = [a \ b \ c]^T$. The last two rows, upon division by 0.25 and 0.05, respectively, yield the scalar equations

$$2a + b \qquad = 0$$
$$5b + 6c = 0.$$

The second equation is satisfied by $b = -6$ and $c = 5$, and then the first equation gives $a = 3$. Thus the eigenvector

$$v_1 = [3 \ -6 \ 5]^T$$

is associated with the eigenvalue $\lambda_1 = -0.5$.

With $\lambda_2 = -0.25$:

Substituting $\lambda = -0.25$ in (19), we get the equation

$$[A + (0.25) \cdot I]v = \begin{bmatrix} -0.25 & 0 & 0 \\ 0.50 & 0 & 0 \\ 0 & 0.25 & 0.05 \end{bmatrix} \begin{bmatrix} a \\ b \\ c \end{bmatrix} = \begin{bmatrix} 0 \\ 0 \\ 0 \end{bmatrix}$$

for the associated eigenvector $v = [a \ b \ c]^T$. Each of the first two rows implies that $a = 0$, and division of the third row by 0.05 gives the equation

$$5b + c = 0,$$

which is satisfied by $b = 1, c = -5$. Thus the eigenvector

$$v_2 = [0 \ 1 \ -5]^T$$

is associated with the eigenvalue $\lambda_2 = -0.25$.

With $\lambda_3 = -0.2$:

Substituting $\lambda = -0.2$ in (19), we get the equation

$$[A + (0.2) \cdot I]v = \begin{bmatrix} -0.3 & 0 & 0 \\ 0.5 & -0.05 & 0 \\ 0 & 0.25 & 0 \end{bmatrix} \begin{bmatrix} a \\ b \\ c \end{bmatrix} = \begin{bmatrix} 0 \\ 0 \\ 0 \end{bmatrix}$$

for the eigenvector v. The first and third rows imply that $a = 0$ and $b = 0$, respectively, but the all-zero third column leaves c arbitrary (but nonzero). Thus

$$v_3 = [0 \ 0 \ 1]^T$$

is an eigenvector associated with $\lambda_3 = -0.2$.

The general solution

$$\mathbf{x}(t) = c_1\mathbf{v}_1 e^{\lambda_1 t} + c_2\mathbf{v}_2 e^{\lambda_2 t} + c_3\mathbf{v}_3 e^{\lambda_3 t}$$

therefore takes the form

$$\mathbf{x}(t) = c_1 \begin{bmatrix} 3 \\ -6 \\ 5 \end{bmatrix} e^{(-0.5)t} + c_2 \begin{bmatrix} 0 \\ 1 \\ -5 \end{bmatrix} e^{(-0.25)t} + c_3 \begin{bmatrix} 0 \\ 0 \\ 1 \end{bmatrix} e^{(-0.2)t}.$$

The resulting scalar equations are

$$x_1(t) = 3c_1 e^{(-0.5)t}$$
$$x_2(t) = -6c_1 e^{(-0.5)t} + c_2 e^{(-0.25)t}$$
$$x_3(t) = 5c_1 e^{(-0.5)t} - 5c_2 e^{(-0.25)t} + c_3 e^{(-0.2)t}.$$

When we impose the initial conditions $x_1(0) = 15$, $x_2(0) = x_3(0) = 0$, we get the equations

$$3c_1 = 15$$
$$-6c_1 + c_2 = 0$$
$$5c_1 - 5c_2 + c_3 = 0$$

that are readily solved (in turn) for $c_1 = 5$, $c_2 = 30$, and $c_3 = 125$. Thus, finally, the amounts of salt at time t in the three brine tanks are given by

$$x_1(t) = 15 e^{(-0.5)t}$$
$$x_2(t) = -30 e^{(-0.5)t} + 30 e^{(-0.25)t}$$
$$x_3(t) = 25 e^{(-0.5)t} - 150 e^{(-0.25)t} + 125 e^{(-0.2)t}.$$

Figure 5.2.2 shows the graphs of $x_1(t)$, $x_2(t)$, and $x_3(t)$. As one would expect, tank 1 is rapidly "flushed" by the incoming fresh water, and $x_1(t) \rightarrow 0$ as $t \rightarrow +\infty$. The amounts $x_2(t)$ and $x_3(t)$ of salt in tanks 2 and 3 peak in turn and then approach zero as the whole three-tank system is purged of salt as $t \rightarrow +\infty$. ∎

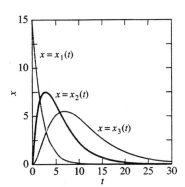

FIGURE 5.2.2. The salt content functions of Example 2

Complex Eigenvalues

Even if some of the eigenvalues are complex, so long as they are distinct the method described above still yields n linearly independent solutions. The only complication is that the eigenvectors associated with complex eigenvalues are ordinarily complex-valued, so we will have complex-valued solutions.

To obtain real-valued solutions, we note that—because we are assuming that the matrix **A** has only real entries—the coefficients in the characteristic equation in (8) will all be real. Consequently any complex eigenvalues must appear in complex conjugate pairs. Suppose then that $\lambda = p + qi$ and $\bar{\lambda} = p - qi$ are such a pair of eigenvalues. If **v** is an eigenvector associated with λ, so that

$$(\mathbf{A} - \lambda\mathbf{I})\mathbf{v} = \mathbf{0},$$

then taking complex conjugates in this equation yields

$$(\mathbf{A} - \overline{\lambda}\mathbf{I})\overline{\mathbf{v}} = \mathbf{0}.$$

Thus the conjugate $\overline{\mathbf{v}}$ of $\mathbf{v}$ is an eigenvector associated with $\overline{\lambda}$. Of course the conjugate of a vector is defined componentwise; if

$$\mathbf{v} = \begin{bmatrix} a_1 + b_1 i \\ a_2 + b_2 i \\ \vdots \\ a_n + b_n i \end{bmatrix} = \begin{bmatrix} a_1 \\ a_2 \\ \vdots \\ a_n \end{bmatrix} + \begin{bmatrix} b_1 \\ b_2 \\ \vdots \\ b_n \end{bmatrix} i = \mathbf{a} + \mathbf{b}i, \tag{20}$$

then $\overline{\mathbf{v}} = \mathbf{a} - \mathbf{b}i$. The complex-valued solution associated with λ and $\mathbf{v}$ is then

$$\mathbf{x}(t) = \mathbf{v}e^{\lambda t} = \mathbf{v}e^{(p + qi)t}$$

$$= (\mathbf{a} + \mathbf{b}i)e^{pt}(\cos qt + i \sin qt);$$

that is,

$$\mathbf{x}(t) = e^{pt}(\mathbf{a} \cos qt - \mathbf{b} \sin qt)$$

$$+ ie^{pt}(\mathbf{b} \cos qt + \mathbf{a} \sin qt). \tag{21}$$

Because the real and imaginary parts of a complex-valued solution are also solutions, we thus get the two *real-valued* solutions

$$\mathbf{x}_1(t) = \mathrm{Re}(\mathbf{x}(t)) = e^{pt}(\mathbf{a} \cos qt - \mathbf{b} \sin qt),$$
$$\mathbf{x}_2(t) = \mathrm{Im}(\mathbf{x}(t)) = e^{pt}(\mathbf{b} \cos qt + \mathbf{a} \sin qt) \tag{22}$$

associated with the complex conjugate eigenvalues $p \pm qi$. It is easy to check that the same two real-valued solutions result from taking real and imaginary parts of $\overline{v}e^{\overline{\lambda}t}$. Rather than memorizing the formulas in (22), it is preferable in a specific example to:

- First find explicitly a single complex-valued solution $\mathbf{x}(t)$ associated with the complex eigenvalue l;
- Then find the real and imaginary parts $\mathbf{x}_1(t)$ and $\mathbf{x}_2(t)$ of $\mathbf{x}(t)$ to get two independent real-valued solutions corresponding to the two complex conjugate eigenvalues λ and $\overline{\lambda}$.

EXAMPLE 3   Find a general solution of the system

$$\frac{dx_1}{dt} = 4x_1 - 3x_2$$
$$\frac{dx_2}{dt} = 3x_1 + 4x_2. \tag{23}$$

Solution The coefficient matrix

$$\mathbf{A} = \begin{bmatrix} 4 & -3 \\ 3 & 4 \end{bmatrix}$$

has characteristic equation

$$|\mathbf{A} - \lambda \mathbf{I}| = \begin{vmatrix} 4 - \lambda & -3 \\ 3 & 4 - \lambda \end{vmatrix} = (4 - \lambda)^2 + 9 = 0,$$

and hence has the complex conjugate eigenvalues $\lambda = 4 - 3i$ and $\overline{\lambda} = 4 + 3i$. Substituting $\lambda = 4 - 3i$ in the eigenvector equation $(\mathbf{A} - \lambda \mathbf{I})\mathbf{v} = \mathbf{0}$, we get the equation

$$[\mathbf{A} - (4 - 3i) \cdot \mathbf{I}]\mathbf{v} = \begin{bmatrix} 3i & -3 \\ 3 & 3i \end{bmatrix} \begin{bmatrix} a \\ b \end{bmatrix} = \begin{bmatrix} 0 \\ 0 \end{bmatrix}$$

for an associated eigenvalue $\mathbf{v} = [a \; b]^T$. Division of each row by 3 yields the two scalar equations

$$ia - b = 0$$
$$a + ib = 0,$$

each of which is satisfied by $a = 1$ and $b = i$. Thus $\mathbf{v} = [1 \; i]^T$ is a complex eigenvector associated with the complex eigenvalue $\lambda = 4 - 3i$.

The corresponding complex-valued solution $\mathbf{x}(t) = \mathbf{v}e^{\lambda t}$ of $\mathbf{x}' = \mathbf{A}\mathbf{x}$ is then

$$\mathbf{x}(t) = \begin{bmatrix} 1 \\ i \end{bmatrix} e^{(4 - 3i)t} = \begin{bmatrix} 1 \\ i \end{bmatrix} e^{4t}(\cos 3t - i \sin 3t) = e^{4t} \begin{bmatrix} \cos 3t - i \sin 3t \\ i \cos 3t + \sin 3t \end{bmatrix}.$$

The real and imaginary parts of $\mathbf{x}(t)$ are the real-valued solutions

$$\mathbf{x}_1(t) = e^{4t} \begin{bmatrix} \cos 3t \\ \sin 3t \end{bmatrix} \quad \text{and} \quad \mathbf{x}_2(t) = e^{4t} \begin{bmatrix} -\sin 3t \\ \cos 3t \end{bmatrix}.$$

A real-valued general solution of $\mathbf{x}' = \mathbf{A}\mathbf{x}$ is then given by

$$\mathbf{x}(t) = c_1 \mathbf{x}_1(t) + c_2 \mathbf{x}_2(t) = e^{4t} \begin{bmatrix} c_1 \cos 3t - c_2 \sin 3t \\ c_1 \sin 3t + c_2 \cos 3t \end{bmatrix}.$$

Finally, a general solution of (23) in scalar form is

$$x_1(t) = e^{4t}(c_1 \cos 3t - c_2 \sin 3t)$$
$$x_2(t) = e^{4t}(c_1 \sin 3t + c_2 \cos 3t). \qquad \blacksquare$$

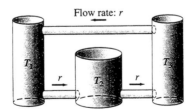

FIGURE 5.2.3. The three brine tanks of Example 4

Figure 5.2.3 shows a "closed" system of three brine tanks with volumes V_1, V_2, and V_3. The difference between this system and the "open" system of Fig. 5.2.1 is that now the inflow to tank 1 is the outflow from tank 3. With the same notation as in Example 2, the appropriate modification of Eq. (16) is

$$\frac{dx_1}{dt} = -k_1 x_1 + k_3 x_3$$

$$\frac{dx_2}{dt} = k_1 x_1 - k_2 x_2 \qquad (24)$$

$$\frac{dx_3}{dt} = k_2 x_2 - k_3 x_3,$$

where $k_i = r/V_i$ as in (17).

EXAMPLE 4   Find the amounts $x_1(t)$, $x_2(t)$, and $x_3(t)$ of salt in the three brine tanks at time t if $V_1 = 50$ gal, $V_2 = 25$ gal, $V_3 = 50$ gal, and $r = 10$ gal/min.

Solution With the given numerical values, (24) takes the form

$$\frac{d\mathbf{x}}{dt} = \begin{bmatrix} -0.2 & 0 & 0.2 \\ 0.2 & -0.4 & 0 \\ 0 & 0.4 & -0.2 \end{bmatrix} \mathbf{x} \tag{25}$$

with $\mathbf{x} = [x_1 \ x_2 \ x_3]^T$ as usual. When we expand the determinant of the matrix

$$\mathbf{A} - \lambda\mathbf{I} = \begin{bmatrix} -0.2 - \lambda & 0 & 0.2 \\ 0.2 & -0.4 - \lambda & 0 \\ 0 & 0.4 & -0.2 - \lambda \end{bmatrix} \tag{26}$$

along its first row, we find that the characteristic equation of $\mathbf{A}$ is

$$(-0.2 - \lambda)(-0.4 - \lambda)(-0.2 - \lambda) + (0.2)(0.2)(0.4)$$

$$= -\lambda^3 - (0.8) \cdot \lambda^2 - (0.2) \cdot \lambda$$

$$= -\lambda[(\lambda + 0.4)^2 + (0.2)^2] = 0.$$

Thus $\mathbf{A}$ has the zero eigenvalue $\lambda_0 = 0$ and the complex conjugate eigenvalues $\lambda, \overline{\lambda} = -0.4 \pm (0.2)i$.

With $\lambda_0 = 0$:

Substitution of $\lambda = 0$ in Eq. (26) gives the eigenvector equation

$$(\mathbf{A} - 0 \cdot \mathbf{I})\mathbf{v} = \begin{bmatrix} -0.2 & 0 & 0.2 \\ 0.2 & -0.4 & 0 \\ 0 & 0.4 & -0.2 \end{bmatrix} \begin{bmatrix} a \\ b \\ c \end{bmatrix} = \begin{bmatrix} 0 \\ 0 \\ 0 \end{bmatrix} \tag{26}$$

for $\mathbf{v} = [a \ b \ c]^T$. The first row gives $a = c$ and the second row gives $a = 2b$, so $\mathbf{v}_0 = [2 \ 1 \ 2]^T$ is an eigenvector associated with the eigenvalue $\lambda_0 = 0$. The corresponding solution $\mathbf{x}_0(t) = \mathbf{v}_0 e^{\lambda_0 t}$ of Eq. (25) is the constant solution

$$\mathbf{x}_0(t) = \begin{bmatrix} 2 \\ 1 \\ 2 \end{bmatrix}. \tag{27}$$

With $\lambda = -0.4 - 0.2i$:

Substitution of $\lambda = -0.4 - 0.2i$ in (26) gives the eigenvector equation

$$[\mathbf{A} - (-0.4 - 0.2i)\mathbf{I}]\mathbf{v} = \begin{bmatrix} 0.2 + 0.2i & 0 & 0.2 \\ 0.2 & 0.2i & 0 \\ 0 & 0.4 & 0.2 + 0.2i \end{bmatrix} \begin{bmatrix} a \\ b \\ c \end{bmatrix} = \begin{bmatrix} 0 \\ 0 \\ 0 \end{bmatrix}.$$

The second equation $(0.2)a + (0.2)ib = 0$ is satisfied by $a = 1$ and $b = i$. Then the first equation

$$(0.2 + 0.2i)a + (0.2)c = 0$$

gives $c = -1 - i$. Thus $\mathbf{v} = [1 \quad i \quad (-1 - i)]^T$ is a complex eigenvector associated with the complex eigenvalue $\lambda = -0.4 - 0.2i$.

The corresponding complex-valued solution $\mathbf{x}(t) = \mathbf{v}e^{\lambda t}$ of (25) is

$$\mathbf{x}(t) = \begin{bmatrix} 1 \\ i \\ -1 - i \end{bmatrix} e^{(-0.4 - 0.2i)t}$$

$$= \begin{bmatrix} 1 \\ i \\ -1 - i \end{bmatrix} e^{(-0.4)t}(\cos 0.2t - i \sin 0.2t)$$

$$= e^{(-0.4)t} \begin{bmatrix} \cos 0.2t - i \sin 0.2t \\ \sin 0.2t + i \cos 0.2t \\ -\cos 0.2t - \sin 0.2t - i \cos 0.2t + i \sin 0.2t \end{bmatrix}.$$

The real and imaginary parts of $\mathbf{x}(t)$ are the real-valued solutions

$$\mathbf{x}_1(t) = e^{(-0.4)t} \begin{bmatrix} \cos 0.2t \\ \sin 0.2t \\ -\cos 0.2t - \sin 0.2t \end{bmatrix},$$

$$\mathbf{x}_2(t) = e^{(-0.4)t} \begin{bmatrix} -\sin 0.2t \\ \cos 0.2t \\ -\cos 0.2t + \sin 0.2t \end{bmatrix}. \tag{28}$$

The general solution

$$\mathbf{x}(t) = c_0\mathbf{x}_0(t) + c_1\mathbf{x}_1(t) + c_2\mathbf{x}_2(t)$$

has scalar components

$$x_1(t) = 2c_0 + e^{(-0.4)t}(c_1 \cos 0.2t - c_2 \sin 0.2t)$$
$$x_2(t) = c_0 + e^{(-0.4)t}(c_1 \sin 0.2t + c_2 \cos 0.2t) \tag{29}$$
$$x_3(t) = 2c_0 + e^{(-0.4)t}[(-c_1 - c_2)\cos 0.2t + (-c_1 + c_2)\sin 0.2t]$$

giving the amounts of salt in the three tanks at time t.

Observe that

$$x_1(t) + x_2(t) + x_3(t) \equiv 5c_0. \tag{30}$$

Of course the total amount of salt in the closed system is constant; the constant c_0 in

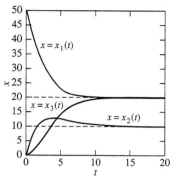

FIGURE 5.2.4. The salt content functions of Example 4

(29) is one-fifth of the total initial amount of salt. Because of the factors of $e^{(-0.4)t}$ in (29), we see that

$$\lim_{t \to \infty} x_1(t) = 2c_0, \qquad \lim_{x \to \infty} x_2(t) = c_0, \qquad \text{and} \qquad \lim_{t \to \infty} x_3(t) = 2c_0.$$

Thus as $t \to +\infty$ the salt in the system approaches a *steady-state* distribution with 40% of the salt in each of the two 50-gallon tanks and 20% in the 25-gallon tank. So, whatever the initial distribution of salt among the three tanks, the limiting distribution is one of uniform concentration throughout the system. Figure 5.2.4 shows the graphs of the three solution functions with $c_0 = 10$, $c_1 = 30$, and $c_2 = -10$, so

$$x_1(0) = 50 \quad \text{and} \quad x_2(0) = x_3(0) = 0.$$

5.2 Problems

In Problems 1 through 16, apply the eigenvalue method of this section to find a general solution of the given system. If initial values are given, find also the corresponding particular solution.

1. $x_1' = x_1 + 2x_2$
$x_2' = 2x_1 + x_2$

2. $x_1' = 2x_1 + 3x_2$
$x_2' = 2x_1 + x_2$

3. $x_1' = 3x_1 + 4x_2$
$x_2' = 3x_1 + 2x_2$
$x_1(0) = x_2(0) = 1$

4. $x_1' = 4x_1 + x_2$
$x_2' = 6x_1 - x_2$

5. $x_1' = 6x_1 - 7x_2$
$x_2' = x_1 - 2x_2$

6. $x_1' = 9x_1 + 5x_2$
$x_2' = -6x_1 - 2x_2$
$x_1(0) = 1, \quad x_2(0) = 0$

7. $x_1' = -3x_1 + 4x_2$
$x_2' = 6x_1 - 5x_2$

8. $x_1' = x_1 - 5x_2$
$x_2' = x_1 - x_2$

9. $x_1' = 2x_1 - 5x_2$
$x_2' = 4x_1 - 2x_2$
$x_1(0) = 2, \quad x_2(0) = 3$

10. $x_1' = -3x_1 - 2x_2$
$x_2' = 9x_1 + 3x_2$

11. $x_1' = x_1 - 2x_2$
$x_2' = 2x_1 + x_2$
$x_1(0) = 0, \quad x_2(0) = 4$

12. $x_1' = x_1 - 5x_2$
$x_2' = x_1 + 3x_2$

13. $x_1' = 5x_1 - 9x_2$
$x_2' = 2x_1 - x_2$

14. $x_1' = 3x_1 - 4x_2$
$x_2' = 4x_1 + 3x_2$

15. $x_1' = 7x_1 - 5x_2$
$x_2' = 4x_1 + 3x_2$

16. $x_1' = -50x_1 + 20x_2$
$x_2' = 100x_1 - 60x_2$

In Problems 17 through 25, the eigenvalues of the coefficient matrix can be found by inspection and factoring. Apply the eigenvalue method to find a general solution of each system.

17. $x_1' = 4x_1 + x_2 + 4x_3$
$x_2' = x_1 + 7x_2 + x_3$
$x_3' = 4x_1 + x_2 + 4x_3$

18. $x_1' = x_1 + 2x_2 + 2x_3$
$x_2' = 2x_1 + 7x_2 + x_3$
$x_3' = 2x_1 + x_2 + 7x_3$

19. $x_1' = 4x_1 + x_2 + x_3$
$x_2' = x_1 + 4x_2 + x_3$
$x_3' = x_1 + x_2 + 4x_3$

20. $x_1' = 5x_1 + x_2 + 3x_3$
$x_2' = x_1 + 7x_2 + x_3$
$x_3' = 3x_1 + x_2 + 5x_3$

21. $x_1' = 5x_1 - 6x_3$
$x_2' = 2x_1 - x_2 - 2x_3$
$x_3' = 4x_1 - 2x_2 - 4x_3$

22. $x_1' = 3x_1 + 2x_2 + 2x_3$
$x_2' = -5x_1 - 4x_2 - 2x_3$
$x_3' = 5x_1 + 5x_2 + 3x_3$

23. $x_1' = 3x_1 + x_2 + x_3$
$x_2' = -5x_1 - 3x_2 - x_3$
$x_3' = 5x_1 + 5x_2 + 3x_3$

24. $x_1' = 2x_1 + x_2 - x_3$
$x_2' = -4x_1 - 3x_2 - x_3$
$x_3' = 4x_1 + 4x_2 + 2x_3$

25. $x_1' = 5x_1 + 5x_2 + 2x_3$
$x_2' = -6x_1 - 6x_2 - 5x_3$
$x_3' = 6x_1 + 6x_2 + 5x_3$

26. Find the particular solution of the system

$$\frac{dx_1}{dt} = 3x_1 + x_3$$

$$\frac{dx_2}{dt} = 9x_1 - x_2 + 2x_3$$

$$\frac{dx_3}{dt} = -9x_1 + 4x_2 - x_3$$

that satisfies the initial conditions $x_1(0) = 0$, $x_2(0) = 0$, $x_3(0) = 17$.

The amounts $x_1(t)$ and $x_2(t)$ of salt in the two brine tanks of Fig. 5.2.5 satisfy the differential equations

$$\frac{dx_1}{dt} = -k_1 x_1, \qquad \frac{dx_2}{dt} = k_1 x_1 - k_2 x_2,$$

where $k_i = r/V_i$ for $i = 1, 2$. In Problems 27 and 28 the volumes V_1 and V_2 are given. First solve for $x_1(t)$ and $x_2(t)$, assuming that

$r = 10$ (gal/min), $x_1(0) = 15$ (gal), and $x_2(0) = 0$. Then find the maximum amount of salt ever in tank 2.

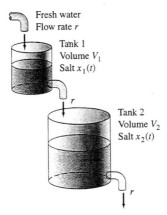

FIGURE 5.2.5. The two brine tanks of Problems 27 and 28

27. $V_1 = 50$ (gal), $V_2 = 25$ (gal)

28. $V_1 = 25$ (gal), $V_2 = 40$ (gal)

The amounts $x_1(t)$ and $x_2(t)$ of salt in the two brine tanks of Fig. 5.2.6 satisfy the differential equations

$$\frac{dx_1}{dt} = -k_1 x_1 + k_2 x_2, \qquad \frac{dx_2}{dt} = k_1 x_1 - k_2 x_2,$$

where $k_i = r/V_i$ as usual. In Problems 29 and 30, solve for $x_1(t)$ and $x_2(t)$, assuming that $r = 10$ (gal/min), $x_1(0) = 15$ (gal), and $x_2(0) = 0$.

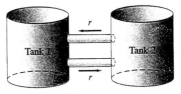

FIGURE 5.2.6. The two brine tanks of Problems 29 and 30

29. $V_1 = 50$ (gal), $V_2 = 25$ (gal)

30. $V_1 = 25$ (gal), $V_2 = 40$ (gal)

Problems 31 and 32 deal with the open three-tank system of Fig. 5.2.1. Find the general solution of the system in (16) with $r = 10$ (gal/min) and the given volumes.

31. $V_1 = 20$ (gal), $V_2 = 50$ (gal), $V_3 = 40$ (gal)

32. $V_1 = 50$ (gal), $V_2 = 25$ (gal), $V_3 = 20$ (gal)

33. Find the general solution of the system in (24) describing the closed three-tank system of Fig. 5.2.3, given that $r = 10$ (gal/min), $V_1 = 20$ (gal), $V_2 = 50$ (gal), and $V_3 = 20$ (gal).

For each matrix **A** given in Problems 34 through 36, the zeros in the matrix make its characteristic polynomial easy to calculate. Find the general solution of $\mathbf{x}' = \mathbf{Ax}$.

34. $\mathbf{A} = \begin{bmatrix} 1 & 0 & 0 & 0 \\ 2 & 2 & 0 & 0 \\ 0 & 3 & 3 & 0 \\ 0 & 0 & 4 & 4 \end{bmatrix}$ **35.** $\mathbf{A} = \begin{bmatrix} -2 & 0 & 0 & 9 \\ 4 & 2 & 0 & -10 \\ 0 & 0 & -1 & 8 \\ 0 & 0 & 0 & 1 \end{bmatrix}$

36. $\mathbf{A} = \begin{bmatrix} 2 & 0 & 0 & 0 \\ -21 & -5 & -27 & -9 \\ 0 & 0 & 5 & 0 \\ 0 & 0 & -21 & -2 \end{bmatrix}$

37. The coefficient matrix **A** of the 4×4 system

$$\begin{aligned} x_1' &= 4x_1 + x_2 + x_3 + 7x_4 \\ x_2' &= x_1 + 4x_2 + 10x_3 + x_4 \\ x_3' &= x_1 + 10x_2 + 4x_3 + x_4 \\ x_4' &= 7x_1 + x_2 + x_3 + 4x_4 \end{aligned}$$

has eigenvalues $\lambda_1 = -3$, $\lambda_2 = -6$, $\lambda_3 = 10$, and $\lambda_4 = 15$. Find the particular solution of this system that satisfies the initial conditions

$$x_1(0) = 3, \quad x_2(0) = x_3(0) = 1, \quad x_4(0) = 3.$$

5.2 Computing Project

Most computational systems offer the capability to find eigenvalues and eigenvectors readily. For instance, for the matrix

$$\mathbf{A} = \begin{bmatrix} -0.5 & 0 & 0 \\ 0.5 & -0.25 & 0 \\ 0 & 0.25 & -0.2 \end{bmatrix}$$

of Example 2, the TI-85 commands

```
[[-0.5,0,0][0.5,-0.25,0][0,0.25,-0.2]] → A
eigVl A
    {-.2, -.25, -.5}
eigVc A
[[0.00    0.00    1.00]
 [0.00    1.00   -2.00]
 [1.00   -5.00    1.67]]
```

produce the three eigenvalues of **A** and display beneath each its (column) eigenvector. Note that with results presented in decimal form, it is up to us to guess (and verify by matrix multiplication) that the exact eigenvector associated with the eigenvalue $\lambda = -\frac{1}{2}$ is $\mathbf{v} = [1 \; -2 \; \frac{5}{3}]^T$. The *Maple* commands

```
with(linalg):
A := matrix(3,3,[-0.5,0,0,0.5,-0.25,0,0,0.25,-0.2]);
eigenvects(A);
```

the *Mathematica* commands

```
A = {{-0.5,0,0}, {0.5,-0.25,0}, {0,0.25,-0.2}}
Eigensystem[A]
```

and the MATLAB commands

```
A = [-0.5,0,0; 0.5,-0.25,0; 0,0.25,-0.2]
[V,D] = eig(A)
```

(where **D** will be a diagonal matrix displaying the eigenvalues of **A** and the column vectors of **V** are the corresponding eigenvectors) produce similar results. You can use these commands to find the eigenvalues and eigenvectors needed for any of the problems in this section.

For a more substantial project, choose a positive integer $n < 10$ ($n = 5$, for example) and let $V_1, V_2, \ldots, V_n$ denote the first n nonzero digits of your student ID number. Now consider an open system of brine tanks as in Fig. 5.2.1, except with n (rather than three) successive tanks having volumes $V_1, V_2, \ldots, V_n$ (in gallons). If each flow rate is r gal/min, then the salt amounts $x_1(t), x_2(t), \ldots, x_n(t)$ satisfy the linear system

$$x_1' = -k_1 x_1$$
$$x_i' = k_{i-1} x_{i-1} - k_i x_i \qquad (i = 2, 3, \ldots, n)$$

where $k_i = r/V_i$. If $r = 1$ gal/min, apply the eigenvalue method to solve this system with initial conditions

$$x_1(0) = 10, \quad x_2(0) = \cdots = x_n(0) = 0.$$

Graph the solution functions, and estimate graphically the maximum amount of salt that each tank ever contains.

6 Nonlinear Systems and Phenomena

6.1 Stability and the Phase Plane

A wide variety of natural phenomena are modeled by two-dimensional first-order systems of the form

$$\frac{dx}{dt} = F(x, y)$$

$$\frac{dy}{dt} = G(x, y)$$

(1)

in which the independent variable t does *not* appear explicitly. Such a system is called an **autonomous system.** The absence of t on the right-hand sides in (1) makes the system easier to analyze and its solutions easier to visualize. We assume that the functions F and G are continuously differentiable in some region R in the xy-plane, which is called the **phase plane** for the system in (1). Then, according to the existence and uniqueness theorems of the Appendix, given t_0 and any point (x_0, y_0) of R, there is a *unique* solution $x = x(t)$, $y = y(t)$ of (1) that is defined on some open interval (a, b) containing t_0 and satisfies the initial conditions

$$x(t_0) = x_0, \qquad y(t_0) = y_0.$$

(2)

The equations $x = x(t)$, $y = y(t)$ then describe a parametrized solution curve in the phase plane. Any such solution curve is called a **trajectory** of the system in (1), and precisely one trajectory passes through each point of the region R (Problem 29). A **critical point** of the system in (1) is a point (x_*, y_*) such that

▶
$$F(x_*, y_*) = G(x_*, y_*) = 0. \tag{3}$$

If (x_*, y_*) is a critical point of the system, then the constant-valued functions

$$x(t) \equiv x_*, \qquad y(t) \equiv y_* \tag{4}$$

satisfy the equations in (1). Such a constant-valued solution is called an **equilibrium solution** of the system. Note that the trajectory of the equilibrium solution in (4) consists of the single point (x_*, y_*).

In some practical situations these very simple solutions and trajectories are the ones of most interest. For example, suppose that the system $x' = F(x, y)$, $y' = G(x, y)$ models two populations $x(t)$ and $y(t)$ of animals that cohabit the same environment, and perhaps compete for the same food or prey on one another; $x(t)$ might denote the number of foxes and $y(t)$ the number of rabbits present at time t. Then a critical point (x_*, y_*) of the system specifies a *constant* population x_* of foxes and a *constant* population y_* of rabbits that can coexist with one another in the environment. If (x_0, y_0) is *not* a critical point of the system, then it is *not* possible for constant populations of x_0 foxes and y_0 rabbits to coexist; one or both must change with time.

EXAMPLE 1   Find the critical points of the system

$$\frac{dx}{dt} = 60x - 3x^2 - 4xy,$$

$$\frac{dy}{dt} = 42y - 3y^2 - 2xy. \tag{5}$$

Solution   When we look at the equations

$$60x - 3x^2 - 4xy = x(60 - 3x - 4y) = 0,$$

$$42y - 3y^2 - 2xy = y(42 - 3y - 2x) = 0$$

that a critical point (x, y) must satisfy, we see that either

$$x = 0 \qquad \text{or} \qquad 60 - 3x - 4y = 0, \tag{6a}$$

and either

$$y = 0 \qquad \text{or} \qquad 42 - 3y - 2x = 0. \tag{6b}$$

If $x = 0$ and $y \neq 0$, then the second equation in (6b) gives $y = 14$. If $y = 0$ and $x \neq 0$, then the second equation in (6a) gives $x = 20$. If x and y are each nonzero, then we solve the simultaneous equations

$$3x + 4y = 60, \qquad 2x + 3y = 42$$

for $x = 12$, $y = 6$. Thus the system in (5) has the four critical points $(0, 0)$, $(0, 14)$, $(20, 0)$, and $(12, 6)$. If $x(t)$ and $y(t)$ denote the number of foxes and the number of rabbits, respectively, and if both populations are *constant*, it follows that the equations in (5) allow only three nontrivial possibilities: either no foxes and 14 rabbits, or 20 foxes and no rabbits, or 12 foxes and 6 rabbits. In particular, the critical point $(12, 6)$ describes the *only* possibility for the coexistence of constant nonzero populations of both species. ■

Phase Portraits

If the initial point (x_0, y_0) is not a critical point, the corresponding trajectory is a curve in the *xy*-plane along which the point $(x(t), y(t))$ moves as *t* increases. It turns out that any trajectory not consisting of a single point is a nondegenerate curve with no self-intersections (Problem 30). We can demonstrate qualitatively the behavior of solutions of the system in (1) by constructing its **phase portrait**—a phase plane picture of its critical points and typical nondegenerate trajectories. We may construct a **slope field** by drawing typical line segments having slope

$$\frac{dy}{dx} = \frac{y'}{x'} = \frac{G(x, y)}{F(x, y)},$$

or a **direction field** by drawing typical vectors pointing in the same direction at each point as the vector $(F(x, y), G(x, y))$. Such a vector field then indicates which direction along a trajectory to travel in order to "go with the flow" described by the system.

EXAMPLE 2   For the system

$$\begin{aligned} x' &= x - y \\ y' &= 1 - x^2 \end{aligned} \tag{7}$$

we see from the first equation that $x = y$ and from the second that $x = \pm 1$ at each critical point. Thus this system has the two critical points $(-1, -1)$ and $(1, 1)$. The direction field in Fig. 6.1.1 suggests that trajectories somehow "circulate" counterclockwise around the critical point $(-1, -1)$, whereas it appears that some trajectories may approach, while others recede from, the critical point $(1, 1)$. These observations are corroborated by the phase portrait in Fig. 6.1.2 for the system in (7). ■

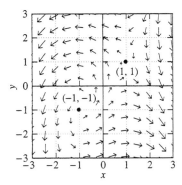

FIGURE 6.1.1. Direction field for the system in (7)

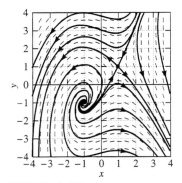

FIGURE 6.1.2. Phase portrait for the system in (7)

Critical Point Behavior

The behavior of the trajectories near an isolated critical point of an autonomous system is of particular interest. In the remainder of this section we illustrate with some simple examples some of the most common possibilities.

EXAMPLE 3 Consider the autonomous linear system

$$\frac{dx}{dt} = -x$$

$$\frac{dy}{dt} = -ky \quad (k \text{ constant}),$$

(8)

which has the origin $(0, 0)$ as its only critical point. The solution with initial point (x_0, y_0) is

$$x(t) = x_0 e^{-t}, \qquad y(t) = y_0 e^{-kt}.$$

(9)

If $x_0 \neq 0$, we can write

$$y = y_0 e^{-kt} = \frac{y_0}{x_0^k} (x_0 e^{-t})^k = bx^k,$$

(10)

where $b = y_0/x_0^k$.

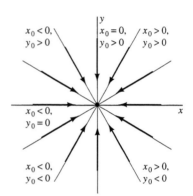

$x_0 < 0,\ y_0 > 0$ $x_0 = 0,\ y_0 > 0$ $x_0 > 0,\ y_0 > 0$

$x_0 < 0,\ y_0 = 0$

$x_0 < 0,\ y_0 < 0$ $x_0 > 0,\ y_0 < 0$

FIGURE 6.1.3. A stable proper node

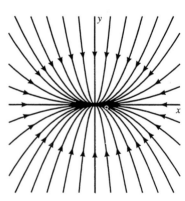

FIGURE 6.1.4. A stable improper node

If $k = 1$, then each curve in Eq. (10) is a straight line through the origin. Each trajectory is an open ray along which the point

$$(x(t), y(t)) = (x_0 e^{-t}, y_0 e^{-t})$$

approaches the origin as $t \to +\infty$. This type of critical point, shown in Fig. 6.1.3, is called a **proper node.** Note the arrows that indicate the orientations of the trajectories; they indicate the direction of motion of $(x(t), y(t))$ with increasing t.

In general, the critical point (x_0, y_0) of the autonomous system in (1) is called a **node** provided that *either* every trajectory approaches (x_0, y_0) as $t \to +\infty$ *or* every trajectory recedes from (x_0, y_0) as $t \to +\infty$, *and* every trajectory is tangent at (x_0, y_0) to some straight line through the critical point. Note that the critical point $(0, 0)$ in Fig. 6.1.3—where the trajectories *are* straight lines, not merely tangents to straight lines— would remain a node if all the arrows were reversed to make the trajectories recede from the critical point rather than approach it. This node is said to be **proper** because no two different pairs of "opposite" trajectories are tangent to the same straight line. In the next paragraph we consider a case in which the critical point is a node that is not proper.

If $k = 2$ and neither x_0 nor y_0 is zero in Eq. (10), then each curve is a parabola $y = bx^2$ tangent to the x-axis at the origin. The solution curve in (9) is half of the x-axis if $y_0 = 0$, and half of the y-axis if $x_0 = 0$. The trajectories are the semiaxes and the right and left halves of the parabolas shown in Fig. 6.1.4. Along each trajectory the point $(x(t), y(t))$ approaches the origin as $t \to +\infty$. Thus all trajectories except for a single pair approach the origin tangent to the same line—the x-axis. This sort of critical point is called an **improper node.**

If $k = -1$, then $x(t) = x_0 e^{-t}$ and $y(t) = y_0 e^t$, so $xy = x_0 y_0 = b$. If neither x_0 nor y_0 is zero, then the trajectory is one branch of the rectangular hyperbola $xy = b$, and $y \to \pm\infty$ as $t \to +\infty$. If $x_0 = 0$ or $y_0 = 0$, the trajectory is a semiaxis of the hyperbola. The point $(x(t), y(t))$ approaches the origin along the x-axis, but recedes from it along the y-axis as $t \to +\infty$. Thus there are two trajectories that approach the critical point

(0, 0) and all others are unbounded as $t \rightarrow +\infty$. This type of critical point, shown in Fig. 6.1.5, is called a **saddle point.**

Stability

A critical point (x_*, y_*) of the autonomous system in (1) is said to be *stable* provided that if the initial point (x_0, y_0) is sufficiently close to (x_*, y_*), then $(x(t), y(t))$ remains close to (x_*, y_*) for all $t > 0$. In vector notation, with $\mathbf{x}(t) = (x(t), y(t))$, the distance between the initial point $\mathbf{x}_0 = (x_0, y_0)$ and the critical point $\mathbf{x}_* = (x_*, y_*)$ is

$$|\mathbf{x}_0 - \mathbf{x}_*| = \sqrt{(x_0 - x_*)^2 + (y_0 - y_*)^2}.$$

Thus the critical point $\mathbf{x}_*$ is **stable** provided that, for each $\epsilon > 0$, there exists $\delta > 0$ such that

$$\blacktriangleright \qquad |\mathbf{x}_0 - \mathbf{x}_*| < \delta \quad \text{implies that} \quad |\mathbf{x}(t) - \mathbf{x}_*| < \epsilon \qquad (11)$$

for all $t > 0$. The critical point (x_*, y_*) is called **unstable** if it is not stable. In each of Figs. 6.1.3 and 6.1.4, the origin (0, 0) is a stable critical point. The saddle point at (0, 0) shown in Fig. 6.1.5 is an unstable critical point.

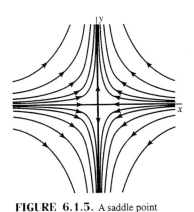

FIGURE 6.1.5. A saddle point

EXAMPLE 3
Continued

If the signs on the right-hand side in (8) are changed to obtain the system

$$\frac{dx}{dt} = x$$

$$\frac{dy}{dt} = ky, \qquad (12)$$

the solution is $x(t) = x_0 e^t$, $y(t) = y_0 e^{kt}$. Then with $k = 1$ and $k = 2$, the trajectories are the same as those shown in Figs. 6.1.3 and 6.1.4, respectively, but with the arrows reversed. In Fig. 6.1.3 with the arrows reversed, the origin is an unstable proper node; in Fig. 6.1.4 with the arrows reversed, the origin is an unstable improper node. ∎

If (x_*, y_*) is a critical point, the equilibrium solution $x(t) \equiv x_*$, $y(t) \equiv y_*$ is called **stable** or **unstable** depending upon the nature of the critical point. In applications the stability of an equilibrium solution is often a crucial matter. For instance, suppose in Example 1 that $x(t)$ and $y(t)$ denote the fox and rabbit populations, respectively, *in hundreds*. We will see in Section 6.3 that the critical point (12, 6) is stable. It follows that if we begin with *close to* 1200 foxes and 600 rabbits—rather than exactly these equilibrium values—then for all future time there will remain close to 1200 foxes and close to 600 rabbits. Thus the practical consequence of stability is that slight changes (perhaps due to random births and deaths) in the equilibrium populations will not so upset the equilibrium as to result in large deviations from the equilibrium solution.

It is possible for trajectories to remain near a stable critical point without approaching it, as Example 4 shows.

EXAMPLE 4

Consider a mass m that oscillates without damping on a spring with Hooke's constant k, so that its position function $x(t)$ satisfies the differential equation $x'' + \omega^2 x = 0$

(where $\omega^2 = k/m$). If we introduce the velocity $y = dx/dt$ of the mass, we get the system

$$\frac{dx}{dt} = y$$

$$\frac{dy}{dt} = -\omega^2 x$$

$$(13)$$

with general solution

$$x(t) = A \cos \omega t + B \sin \omega t, \tag{14a}$$

$$y(t) = -A\omega \sin \omega t + B\omega \cos \omega t. \tag{14b}$$

With $C = \sqrt{A^2 + B^2}$ and $\alpha = \tan^{-1}(B/A)$, we can rewrite the solution in (14) in the form

$$x(t) = C \cos(\omega t - \alpha), \tag{15a}$$

$$y(t) = -\omega C \sin(\omega t - \alpha), \tag{15b}$$

so it becomes clear that each trajectory other than the critical point $(0, 0)$ is an ellipse with equation of the form

$$\frac{x^2}{C^2} + \frac{y^2}{\omega^2 C^2} = 1. \tag{16}$$

Each point $(x_0, y_0) \neq (0, 0)$ in the xy-plane lies on exactly one of these ellipses, and a solution $(x(t), y(t))$ with initial point (x_0, y_0) traverses the ellipse containing (x_0, y_0) in the clockwise direction with *period* $T = 2\pi/\omega$. (It is clear from (15) that $x(t + T) = x(t)$ and $y(t + T) = y(t)$ for all t.) Thus each nontrivial solution of the system in (13) is periodic and its trajectory is a simple closed curve. ∎

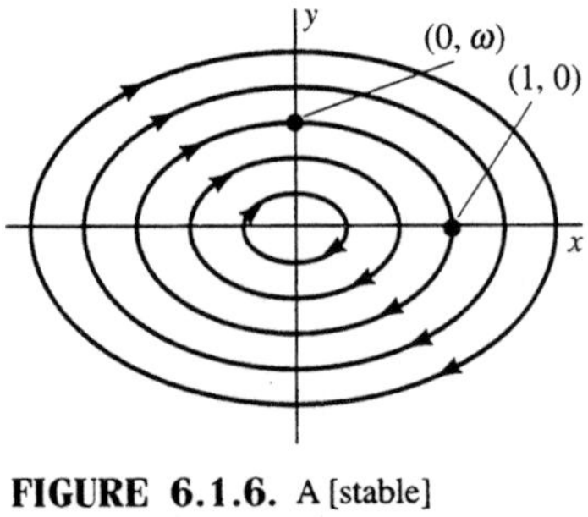

FIGURE 6.1.6. A [stable] center surrounded by closed trajectories

It is clear in Fig. 6.1.6, in which $\omega < 1$, that if the distance from (x_0, y_0) to $(0, 0)$ is less than $\delta = \omega \epsilon$, then for all t the distance from $(x(t), y(t))$ is less than ϵ. Hence $(0, 0)$ is a stable critical point of the system $x' = y$, $y' = -\omega^2 x$. Unlike the situation shown in Figs. 6.1.3 and 6.1.4, though, no single trajectory approaches $(0, 0)$. A critical point surrounded by simple closed trajectories representing periodic solutions is called a **[stable] center.**

Asymptotic Stability

The critical point (x_*, y_*) is called **asymptotically stable** if it is stable and, moreover, every trajectory that begins sufficiently close to (x_*, y_*) also approaches (x_*, y_*) as $t \to +\infty$. That is, there exists $\delta > 0$ such that

▶ $$|x_0 - x_*| < \delta \quad \text{implies that} \quad \lim_{t \to \infty} \mathbf{x}(t) = \mathbf{x}_*, \tag{17}$$

where $\mathbf{x}_0 = (x_0, y_0)$, $\mathbf{x}_* = (x_*, y_*)$, and $\mathbf{x}(t) = (x(t), y(t))$ is a solution with $\mathbf{x}(0) = \mathbf{x}_0$.

Remark The stable nodes shown in Figs. 6.1.3 and 6.1.4 are asymptotically stable because every trajectory approaches the critical point $(0, 0)$ as $t \to +\infty$. The center $(0, 0)$ in Fig. 6.1.6 is stable but not asymptotically stable, because however small an elliptical trajectory we consider, a point moving around this ellipse does not approach the origin. Thus asymptotic stability is a stronger condition than mere stability.

Now suppose that $x(t)$ and $y(t)$ denote coexisting populations for which (x_*, y_*) is an asymptotically stable critical point. Then if the initial populations x_0 and y_0 are sufficiently close to x_* and y_*, respectively, it follows that both

$$\lim_{t \to \infty} x(t) = x_* \quad \text{and} \quad \lim_{t \to \infty} y(t) = y_*. \tag{18}$$

That is, $x(t)$ and $y(t)$ actually approach the equilibrium populations x_* and y_* as $t \to +\infty$, rather than merely remaining close to those values.

For a mechanical system as in Example 4, a critical point represents an *equilibrium state* of the system—if the velocity $y = x'$ and the acceleration $y' = x''$ vanish simultaneously, then the mass remains at rest with no net force acting on it. Stability of a critical point concerns the question whether, when the mass is displaced slightly from its equilibrium, it

1. Moves back toward the equilibrium point as $t \to +\infty$,

2. Merely remains near the equilibrium point without approaching it, or

3. Moves farther away from equilibrium.

In Case 1 the critical [equilibrium] point is asymptotically stable; in Case 2 it is stable but not asymptotically so; in Case 3 it is an unstable critical point. A marble balanced on the top of a basketball is an example of an unstable critical point. A mass on a spring with damping illustrates the case of asymptotic stability of a mechanical system. The mass-and-spring without damping in Example 4 is an example of a system that is stable but not asymptotically stable.

EXAMPLE 5 Suppose that $m = 1$ and $k = 2$ for the mass and spring of Example 4 and that the mass is attached also to a dashpot with damping constant $c = 2$. Then its displacement function $x(t)$ satisfies the second-order equation

$$x''(t) + 2x'(t) + 2x(t) = 0. \tag{19}$$

With $y = x'$ we obtain the equivalent first-order system

$$\frac{dx}{dt} = y$$
$$\frac{dy}{dt} = -2x - 2y \tag{20}$$

with critical point $(0, 0)$. The characteristic equation $r^2 + 2r + 2 = 0$ of Eq. (19) has roots $-1 + i$ and $-1 - i$, so the general solution of the system in (20) is given by

$$x(t) = e^{-t}(A\cos t + B\sin t) = Ce^{-t}\cos(t - \alpha), \tag{21a}$$

$$y(t) = e^{-t}[(B - A)\cos t - (A + B)\sin t] = -C\sqrt{2}\,e^{-t}\sin\left(t - \alpha + \frac{\pi}{4}\right), \tag{21b}$$

where $C = \sqrt{A^2 + B^2}$ and $\alpha = \tan^{-1}(B/A)$. We see that $x(t)$ and $y(t)$ oscillate between positive and negative values and that each approaches zero as $t \to +\infty$. Consequently, a typical trajectory spirals toward the origin, as indicated in Fig. 6.1.7. It is clear that the critical point $(0, 0)$ is asymptotically stable; this type of critical point is called a

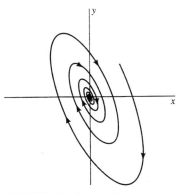

FIGURE 6.1.7. A stable spiral point and one nearby trajectory

[stable] spiral point. In the case of the mass-spring-dashpot system, a spiral point is the manifestation in the phase plane of the damped oscillations that occur because of resistance. ■

The trajectory illustrated in Fig. 6.1.7 spirals *into* the critical point as $t \to +\infty$. In Fig. 6.1.2 we see trajectories spiraling *away from* the critical point $(-1, -1)$, which is therefore an *unstable* spiral point. Example 6 shows that it is also possible for a trajectory to spiral into a closed trajectory. A **closed** trajectory is a simple closed solution curve representing a periodic solution (like the ellipses in Fig. 6.1.6).

EXAMPLE 6 Consider the system

$$\frac{dx}{dt} = -ky + x(1 - x^2 - y^2),$$

$$\frac{dy}{dt} = kx + y(1 - x^2 - y^2). \tag{22}$$

In Problem 21 we ask you to show that $(0, 0)$ is its only critical point. This system can be solved explicitly by introducing polar coordinates $x = r \cos\theta$, $y = r \sin\theta$, as follows. First note that

$$\frac{d\theta}{dt} = \frac{d}{dt}\left(\arctan\frac{y}{x}\right) = \frac{xy' - yx'}{x^2 + y^2}.$$

Then substitute the expressions given in (22) for x' and y' to obtain

$$\frac{d\theta}{dt} = \frac{k(x^2 + y^2)}{x^2 + y^2} = k.$$

It follows that

$$\theta(t) = kt + \theta_0, \qquad \text{where } \theta_0 = \theta(0). \tag{23}$$

Then differentiation of $r^2 = x^2 + y^2$ yields

$$2r\frac{dr}{dt} = 2x\frac{dx}{dt} + 2y\frac{dy}{dt}$$

$$= 2(x^2 + y^2)(1 - x^2 - y^2) = 2r^2(1 - r^2),$$

so $r = r(t)$ satisfies the differential equation

$$\frac{dr}{dt} = r(1 - r^2). \tag{24}$$

In Problem 22 we ask you to derive the solution

$$r(t) = \frac{r_0}{\sqrt{r_0^2 + (1 - r_0^2)e^{-2t}}}, \tag{25}$$

where $r_0 = r(0)$. Thus the typical solution of Eq. (22) may be expressed in the form

$$x(t) = r(t)\cos(kt + \theta_0),$$

$$y(t) = r(t)\sin(kt + \theta_0). \tag{26}$$

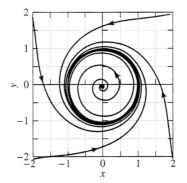

FIGURE 6.1.8. Spiral trajectories of the system in (22) with $k = 5$.

If $r_0 = 1$, then Eq. (25) gives $r(t) \equiv 1$ (the unit circle). Otherwise, if $r_0 > 0$, then Eq. (25) implies that $r(t) \to 1$ as $t \to +\infty$. Hence the trajectory defined in (26) spirals in toward the unit circle if $r_0 > 1$ and spirals out toward this closed trajectory if $0 < r_0 < 1$. Figure 6.1.8 shows a trajectory spiraling outward from the origin and four trajectories spiraling inward, all approaching the closed trajectory $r(t) \equiv 1$. ∎

Under rather general hypotheses it can be shown that there are four possibilities for a nondegenerate trajectory of the autonomous system

$$\frac{dx}{dt} = F(x, y), \qquad \frac{dy}{dt} = G(x, y).$$

The four possibilities are these:

1. $(x(t), y(t))$ approaches a critical point as $t \to +\infty$.

2. $(x(t), y(t))$ is unbounded with increasing t.

3. $(x(t), y(t))$ is a periodic solution with a closed trajectory.

4. $(x(t), y(t))$ spirals toward a closed trajectory as $t \to +\infty$.

As a consequence, the qualitative nature of the phase plane picture of the trajectories of an autonomous system is determined largely by the locations of its critical points and by the behavior of its trajectories near its critical points. We will see in Section 6.2 that, subject to mild restrictions on the functions F and G, each isolated critical point of the system $x' = F(x, y)$, $y' = G(x, y)$ resembles qualitatively one of the examples of this section—it is either a node (proper or improper), a saddle point, a center, or a spiral point.

6.1 Problems

In Problems 1 through 8, find the critical point or points of the given autonomous system, and thereby match each system with its phase portrait among Figs. 6.1.9 through 6.1.16.

1. $\dfrac{dx}{dt} = 2x - y, \quad \dfrac{dy}{dt} = x - 3y$

2. $\dfrac{dx}{dt} = x - y, \quad \dfrac{dy}{dt} = x + 3y - 4$

3. $\dfrac{dx}{dt} = x - 2y + 3, \quad \dfrac{dy}{dt} = x - y + 2$

4. $\dfrac{dx}{dt} = 2x - 2y - 4, \quad \dfrac{dy}{dt} = x + 4y + 3$

5. $\dfrac{dx}{dt} = 1 - y^2, \quad \dfrac{dy}{dt} = x + 2y$

6. $\dfrac{dx}{dt} = x^2 + 4xy + 2y^2, \quad \dfrac{dy}{dt} = 4 - x^2$

7. $\dfrac{dx}{dt} = x - 2y, \quad \dfrac{dy}{dt} = 4x - x^3$

8. $\dfrac{dx}{dt} = x - y - x^2 + xy, \quad \dfrac{dy}{dt} = -y - x^2$

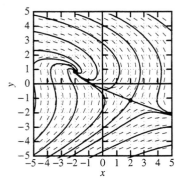

FIGURE 6.1.9. Spiral point $(-2, 1)$ and saddle point $(2, -1)$

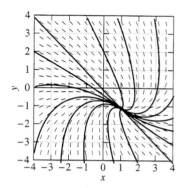

FIGURE 6.1.10. Spiral point $(1, -1)$

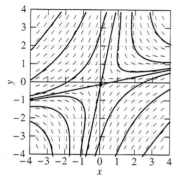

FIGURE 6.1.11. Saddle point $(0, 0)$

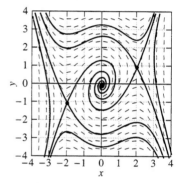

FIGURE 6.1.12. Spiral point $(0, 0)$; saddle points $(-2, -1)$ and $(2, 1)$

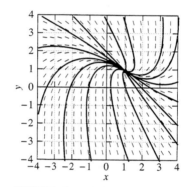

FIGURE 6.1.13. Node $(1, 1)$

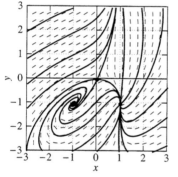

FIGURE 6.1.14. Spiral point $(-1, -1)$; saddle point $(0, 0)$ and node $(1, -1)$

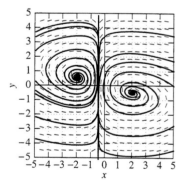

FIGURE 6.1.15. Spiral points $(-2, 2/3)$ and $(2, -2/5)$

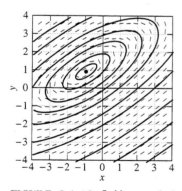

FIGURE 6.1.16. Stable center $(-1, 1)$

In Problems 9 through 12, find all equilibrium solutions (of the form $x(t) \equiv x_0$, a constant) of the given second-order differential equation.

9. $x'' + 4x - x^3 = 0$

10. $x'' + 2x' + x + 4x^3 = 0$

11. $x'' + 3x' + 4 \sin x = 0$

12. $x'' + (x^2 - 1)x' + x = 0$

Solve each of the linear systems in Problems 13 through 20 to determine whether the critical point $(0, 0)$ is stable, asymptotically stable, or unstable. Sketch typical trajectories and indicate the direction of motion with increasing t. Identify the critical point as a node, a saddle point, a center, or a spiral point.

13. $\dfrac{dx}{dt} = -2x, \quad \dfrac{dy}{dt} = -2y$

14. $\dfrac{dx}{dt} = 2x, \quad \dfrac{dy}{dt} = -2y$

15. $\dfrac{dx}{dt} = -2x, \quad \dfrac{dy}{dt} = -y$

16. $\dfrac{dx}{dt} = x, \quad \dfrac{dy}{dt} = 3y$

17. $\dfrac{dx}{dt} = y, \quad \dfrac{dy}{dt} = -x$

18. $\dfrac{dx}{dt} = -y, \quad \dfrac{dy}{dt} = 4x$

19. $\dfrac{dx}{dt} = 2y, \quad \dfrac{dy}{dt} = -2x$

20. $\dfrac{dx}{dt} = y, \quad \dfrac{dy}{dt} = -5x - 4y$

21. Verify that $(0, 0)$ is the only critical point of the system in Example 6.

22. Separate variables in (24) to derive the solution given in (25).

In Problems 23 through 26, a system $dx/dt = F(x, y)$, $dy/dt = G(x, y)$ is given. Solve the equation

$$\frac{dy}{dx} = \frac{G(x, y)}{F(x, y)}$$

to find the trajectories of the given system.

23. $\dfrac{dx}{dt} = y, \quad \dfrac{dy}{dt} = -x$

24. $\dfrac{dx}{dt} = y(1 + x^2 + y^2), \quad \dfrac{dy}{dt} = x(1 + x^2 + y^2)$

25. $\dfrac{dx}{dt} = 4y(1 + x^2 + y^2), \quad \dfrac{dy}{dt} = -x(1 + x^2 + y^2)$

26. $\dfrac{dx}{dt} = y^3 e^{x+y}, \quad \dfrac{dy}{dt} = -x^3 e^{x+y}$

27. Let $(x(t), y(t))$ be a nontrivial solution of the nonautonomous system

$$\frac{dx}{dt} = y, \qquad \frac{dy}{dt} = tx.$$

Suppose that $\phi(t) = x(t + \gamma)$ and $\psi(t) = y(t + \gamma)$, where $\gamma \neq 0$. Show that $(\phi(t), \psi(t))$ is *not* a solution of the system.

Problems 28 through 30 deal with the system

$$\frac{dx}{dt} = F(x, y), \qquad \frac{dy}{dt} = G(x, y)$$

in a region where the functions F and G are continuously differentiable, so for each number a and point (x_0, y_0), there is a unique solution with $x(a) = x_0$ and $y(a) = y_0$.

28. Suppose that $(x(t), y(t))$ is a solution of the autonomous system and that $\gamma \neq 0$. Define $\phi(t) = x(t + \gamma)$ and $\psi(t) = y(t + \gamma)$. Then show (in contrast with the situation in Problem 27) that $(\phi(t), \psi(t))$ is also a solution of the system. Thus autonomous systems have the simple but important property that a "t-translate" of a solution is again a solution.

29. Let $(x_1(t), y_1(t))$ and $(x_2(t), y_2(t))$ be two solutions having trajectories that meet at the point (x_0, y_0); thus $x_1(a) = x_2(b) = x_0$ and $y_1(a) = y_2(b) = y_0$ for some values a and b of t. Define

$$x_3(t) = x_2(t + \gamma) \qquad \text{and} \qquad y_3(t) = y_2(t + \gamma)$$

where $\gamma = b - a$, so $(x_2(t), y_2(t))$ and $(x_3(t), y_3(t))$ have the same trajectory. Apply the uniqueness theorem to show that $(x_1(t), y_1(t))$ and $(x_3(t), y_3(t))$ are identical solutions. Hence the original two trajectories are identical. Thus no two different trajectories of an autonomous system can intersect.

30. Suppose that the solution $(x_1(t), y_1(t))$ is defined for all t and that its trajectory has an apparent self-intersection:

$$x_1(a) = x_1(a + T) = x_0, \qquad y_1(a) = y_1(a + T) = y_0$$

for some $T > 0$. Introduce the solution

$$x_2(t) = x_1(t + T), \qquad y_2(t) = y_1(t + T)$$

and then apply the uniqueness theorem to show that

$$x_1(t) = x_1(t + T) \qquad \text{and} \qquad y_1(t) = y_1(t + T)$$

for *all* t. Thus the solution $(x_1(t), y_1(t))$ is periodic with period T and has a closed trajectory. Consequently a solution of an autonomous system either is periodic with a closed trajectory, or else its trajectory never passes through the same point twice.

6.1 **Computing Project**

Consider a first-order differential equation of the form

$$\frac{dy}{dx} = \frac{G(x, y)}{F(x, y)}, \tag{1}$$

which may be difficult or impossible to solve explicitly. Its solution curves can nevertheless be plotted as trajectories of the corresponding autonomous two-dimensional system

$$\frac{dx}{dt} = F(x, y), \qquad \frac{dy}{dt} = G(x, y). \tag{2}$$

Most ODE plotters can routinely generate phase portraits for autonomous systems. (Those appearing in this chapter were plotted using the program **pplane** accompanying John Polking's *MATLAB Manual for Ordinary Differential Equations*, Prentice Hall, 1995.)

For example, to plot solution curves for the differential equation

$$\frac{dy}{dx} = \frac{2xy - y^2}{x^2 - 2xy}, \tag{3}$$

we plot trajectories of the system

$$\frac{dx}{dt} = x^2 - 2xy, \qquad \frac{dy}{dt} = 2xy - y^2. \tag{4}$$

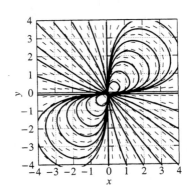

FIGURE 6.1.17. Phase portrait for the system in (4)

The result is shown in Fig. 6.1.17.

Plot similarly some solution curves for the following differential equations.

1. $\dfrac{dy}{dx} = \dfrac{4x - 5y}{2x + 3y}$

2. $\dfrac{dy}{dx} = \dfrac{4x - 5y}{2x - 3y}$

3. $\dfrac{dy}{dx} = \dfrac{4x - 3y}{2x - 5y}$

4. $\dfrac{dy}{dx} = \dfrac{2xy}{x^2 - y^2}$

5. $\dfrac{dy}{dx} = \dfrac{x^2 + 2xy}{y^2 + 2xy}$

Now construct some examples of your own. Homogeneous functions like those in Problems 1 through 5—rational functions with numerator and denominator of the same degree in x and y—work well. The differential equation

$$\frac{dy}{dx} = \frac{25x + y(1 - x^2 - y^2)(4 - x^2 - y^2)}{-25y + x(1 - x^2 - y^2)(4 - x^2 - y^2)} \tag{5}$$

of this form generalizes Example 6 in this section, but would be inconvenient to solve explicitly. Its phase portrait (Fig. 6.1.18) shows two periodic closed trajectories—the circles $r = 1$ and $r = 2$. Anyone want to try for three circles?

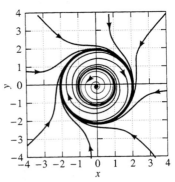

FIGURE 6.1.18. Phase portrait for the system corresponding to (5)

6.3 Ecological Models: Predators and Competitors

Some of the most interesting and important applications of stability theory involve the interactions between two or more biological populations occupying the same environment. We consider first a **predator–prey** situation involving two species. One species—the **predators**—feeds on the other species—the **prey**—which in turn feeds on some third food item readily available in the environment. A standard example is a population of foxes and rabbits in a woodland; the foxes (predators) eat rabbits (the prey), while the rabbits eat certain vegetation in the woodland. Other examples are sharks (predators) and food fish (prey), bass (predators) and sunfish (prey), ladybugs (predators) and aphids (prey), and beetles (predators) and scale insects (prey).

The classical mathematical model of a predator–prey situation was developed in the 1920s by the Italian mathematician Vito Volterra (1860–1940) in order to analyze the cyclic variations observed in the shark and food fish populations in the Adriatic Sea. To construct such a model, we denote the number of prey at time t by $x(t)$ and the number of predators by $y(t)$, and make the following simplifying assumptions.

1. In the absence of predators, the prey population would grow at a natural rate, with $dx/dt = ax, a > 0$.

2. In the absence of prey, the predator population would decline at a natural rate, with $dy/dt = -cy, c > 0$.

3. When both predator and prey are present, there occur, in combination with these natural rates of growth and decline, a decline in the prey population and a growth in the predator population, each at a rate proportional to the frequency of encounters between individuals of the two species. We assume further that the frequency of such encounters is proportional to the product xy, reasoning that doubling either population alone should double the frequency of encoun-

ters, while doubling both populations ought to quadruple the frequency of encounters. Consequently, the effect of predators eating prey is an *interaction rate* of decline $-bxy$ in the prey population x, and an interaction rate of growth dxy of the predator population y, with b and d positive constants.

When we adjoin the interaction rates described above to the natural rates, we obtain the **predator–prey equations**

$$\frac{dx}{dt} = ax - bxy = x(a - by)$$

$$\frac{dy}{dt} = -cy + dxy = y(-c + dx),$$

(1)

with the constants a, b, c, and d all positive. This is an almost linear system with two critical points, $(0, 0)$ and $(c/d, a/b)$. The point $(0, 0)$ is a saddle point, but the corresponding equilibrium solution $x(t) \equiv 0$, $y(t) \equiv 0$ merely describes simultaneous extinction of both species.

The critical point $(c/d, a/b)$ is of greater interest; $x(t) \equiv c/d$ and $y(t) \equiv a/b$ are the nonzero constant prey and predator populations, respectively, that can coexist in equilibrium. We would like to know, if the initial populations x_0 and y_0 are near these critical populations, whether $(x(t), y(t))$ remains near $(c/d, a/b)$ for all $t > 0$. That is, is the critical point $(c/d, a/b)$ stable? To attempt to answer this question, we substitute $u = x - c/d$, $v = y - a/b$ in (1). We thereby obtain the almost linear system

$$\frac{du}{dt} = -\frac{bc}{d} v - buv$$

$$\frac{dv}{dt} = \frac{ad}{b} u + duv,$$

(2)

which has $(0, 0)$ as its critical point corresponding to the critical point $(c/d, a/b)$ of the system in (1). The corresponding linear system

$$\frac{du}{dt} = -\frac{bc}{d} v$$

$$\frac{dv}{dt} = \frac{ad}{b} u$$

(3)

has characteristic equation $\lambda^2 + ac = 0$ with pure imaginary roots $\lambda_1, \lambda_2 = \pm i\sqrt{ac}$. Hence $(0, 0)$ is a stable center of (3), and the trajectories are ellipses centered at $(0, 0)$. In fact, if we divide the second equation in (3) by the first, we obtain

$$\frac{dv}{du} = -\frac{ad/b}{bc/d} \cdot \frac{u}{v} = -\frac{ad^2u}{cb^2v},$$

$$ad^2u \, du + cb^2v \, dv = 0,$$

$$ad^2u^2 + cb^2v^2 = C$$

$$\frac{u^2}{A^2} + \frac{v^2}{B^2} = 1,$$

(4)

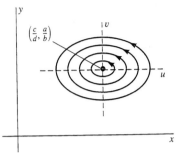

FIGURE 6.3.1. Linearized trajectories of the system in (2); the directions indicated by the arrows are determined by the signs in Eq. (3).

where C is a constant of integration, $A^2 = C/ad^2$, and $B^2 = C/cb^2$. In terms of x and y, the trajectories of the linearized system are, therefore, ellipses of the form

$$\frac{1}{A^2}\left(x - \frac{c}{d}\right)^2 + \frac{1}{B^2}\left(y - \frac{a}{b}\right)^2 = 1 \tag{5}$$

centered at the critical point $(c/d, a/b)$. Some of these ellipses are shown in Fig. 6.3.1.

Unfortunately, this analysis does not settle the question of the stability of the critical point $(c/d, a/b)$ of the original nonlinear system in (1), because a stable center represents the indeterminate case of Theorem 2 of Section 6.2, in which the critical point can (aside from a center) be either an unstable or an asymptotically stable spiral point. We can in this case, however, find the trajectories explicitly by dividing the second equation in (1) by the first to obtain

$$\frac{dy}{dx} = \frac{y(-c + dx)}{x(a - by)} \qquad (\textit{Note: } d \textit{ times } x \textit{ on the right}).$$

We separate the variables to get

$$\frac{c - dx}{x}\,dx + \frac{a - by}{y}\,dy = 0,$$

and thus

$$c\ln x - dx + a\ln y - by = C, \tag{6}$$

where C is a constant of integration (and dx in Eq. (6) is not a differential, but the product of the positive constant d with x). In any case, the trajectories of the system in (1) near the critical point $(c/d, a/b)$ are the level curves of the function $f(x, y)$ that appears on the left-hand side in Eq. (6). It can be shown that these trajectories are simple closed curves enclosing $(c/d, a/b)$, which is therefore a stable center. Figure 6.3.2 shows a phase plane portrait of these trajectories for the case $a = b = c = d = 1$. It follows from Problem 30 of Section 6.1 that $x(t)$ and $y(t)$ are both periodic functions of t; this explains the fluctuations that are experimentally observed in predator–prey populations. If we follow a single trajectory in Fig. 6.3.2, beginning at a point where the prey population x is maximal and $y = a/b$ (Why is $y = a/b$ when x is maximal?), we see that x decreases and y increases until $x = c/d$ and the predator population y is maximal. Then both decrease until x is minimal and $y = a/b$ again. And so on around the trajectory back to the initial point. In particular, we see that if both $x_0 > 0$ and $y_0 > 0$, then both $x(t) > 0$ and $y(t) > 0$ for all t, so both populations survive in coexistence with each other. Exception: If the fluctuations are so wide that $x(t)$ is nearly zero, there is a significant possibility that the last few prey will be devoured, resulting in their immediate extinction and the consequent eventual extinction of the predators.

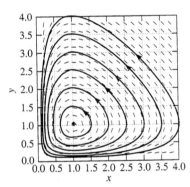

FIGURE 6.3.2. Actual trajectories of the predator-prey system $x' = x - xy, \quad y' = -y + xy$

A Predator–Prey Bifurcation

Figure 6.3.3 illustrates trajectories of the predator-prey system

$$\frac{dx}{dt} = x - xy + \epsilon x(1 - x)$$

$$\frac{dy}{dt} = -y + xy \tag{7}$$

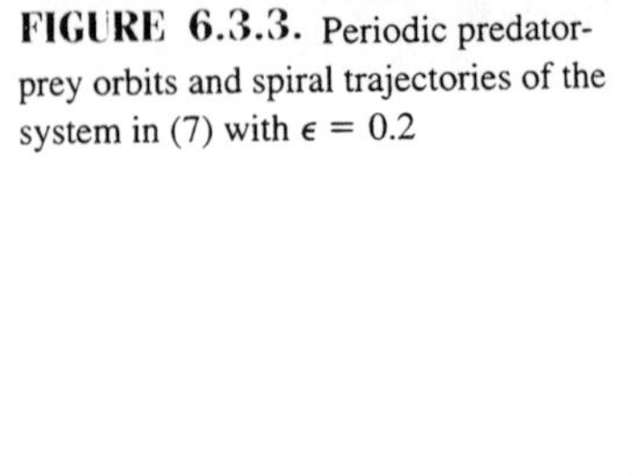

FIGURE 6.3.3. Periodic predator-prey orbits and spiral trajectories of the system in (7) with $\epsilon = 0.2$.

near the critical point $(1,1)$ for different values of the parameter ϵ. For $\epsilon = 0$ this system is of the standard form in (1), so the point $(1,1)$ is a stable center surrounded by simple closed trajectories, as in Fig. 6.3.2. But with $\epsilon > 0$ the prey population $x(t)$ would, in the absence of predators, exhibit logistic rather than natural growth. In this case a *bifurcation* occurs and $(1,1)$ becomes a stable spiral point. Figure 6.3.3 shows also some spiral trajectories with $\epsilon = 0.2$. (The figure is printed with aspect ratio 0.65, so that a unit square in the xy-plane is printed as a rectangle with base $x = 1$ and height $y = 0.65$.) Each trajectory was computed numerically with a *Mathematica* command of the form

```
NDSolve[ {x'[t]  ==  x[t](1 - y[y]) + eps x[t](1 - x[t]),
           y'[t]  ==  -y[t](1 - x[t]),
           x[0] == a,
           y[0] == b}, {x,y}, {t, 0, t1} ]
```

to solve the predator-prey system on the interval $0 \leqq t \leqq t_1$ with initial point (a, b).

Competing Species

Now we consider two species (of animals, plants, or bacteria, for instance) with populations $x(t)$ and $y(t)$ at time t and which compete with each other for the food available in their common environment. This is in marked contrast to the case in which one species preys upon the other. To construct a mathematical model that is as realistic as possible, let us assume that in the absence of either species, the other would have a bounded [logistic] population like that considered in Section 2.1. In the absence of any interaction or competition between the two species, their populations would then satisfy the differential equations

$$\frac{dx}{dt} = a_1 x - b_1 x^2$$

$$\frac{dy}{dt} = a_2 y - b_2 y^2, \tag{8}$$

each of the form of Eq. (3) of Section 2.1. But in addition, we assume that competition has the effect of a rate of decline in each population that is proportional to their product xy. We insert such terms with *negative* proportionality constants $-c_1$ and $-c_2$ in the equations in (8) to obtain the **competition equations**

$$\frac{dx}{dt} = a_1 x - b_1 x^2 - c_1 xy = x(a_1 - b_1 x - c_1 y)$$

$$\frac{dy}{dt} = a_2 y - b_2 y^2 - c_2 xy = y(a_2 - b_2 y - c_2 x), \tag{9}$$

where the coefficients a_1, a_2, b_1, b_2, c_1, and c_2 are all positive.

The almost linear system in (9) has four critical points. Upon setting the right-hand sides of the two equations equal to zero, we see that if $x = 0$, then either $y = 0$ or $y = a_2/b_2$, whereas if $y = 0$, then either $x = 0$ or $x = a_1/b_1$. This gives the three critical points $(0, 0)$, $(0, a_2/b_2)$, and $(a_1/b_1, 0)$. The fourth is at the intersection of the two lines with equations

$$b_1 x + c_1 y = a_1,$$
$$c_2 x + b_2 y = a_2. \tag{10}$$

We assume that these two lines are not parallel and that they intersect at a point in the first quadrant. (The other cases will be explored in the exercises.) Then this point (x_E, y_E) is the fourth critical point, and it represents the possibility of peaceful coexistence of the two species, with stable populations $x(t) \equiv x_E$ and $y(t) \equiv y_E$.

We are interested in the stability of the critical point (x_E, y_E). This turns out to depend upon the relative orientation of the two lines in (10). The two possibilities are shown in Fig. 6.3.4, with the first line in (10) blue and the second black. Comparing the slopes of the two lines, we see that Fig. 6.3.4(a) corresponds to the condition that

$$\frac{a_2/b_2}{a_2/c_2} < \frac{a_1/c_1}{a_1/b_1}; \quad \text{that is,} \quad c_1 c_2 < b_1 b_2. \tag{11}$$

Similarly, Fig. 6.3.4(b) corresponds to the condition that

$$\frac{a_2/b_2}{a_2/c_2} > \frac{a_1/c_1}{a_1/b_1}; \quad \text{that is,} \quad c_1 c_2 > b_1 b_2. \tag{12}$$

The conditions in (11) and (12) have a natural interpretation. In the equations in (8), we see that b_1 and b_2 represent the inhibiting effect of each population on its own growth (possibly due to limitations of food or space). On the other hand, c_1 and c_2 represent the effect of competition between the two populations. Thus $b_1 b_2$ is a measure of *inhibition* while $c_1 c_2$ is a measure of *competition*. A general analysis of the system in (9) shows the following:

1. If $c_1 c_2 < b_1 b_2$, so that competition is small in comparison with inhibition, then (x_E, y_E) is an asymptotically stable critical point that is approached by each solution as $t \to +\infty$. Thus the two species can and do coexist in this case.

2. If $c_1 c_2 > b_1 b_2$, so that competition is large in comparison with inhibition, then (x_E, y_E) is an unstable critical point, and either $x(t)$ or $y(t)$ approaches zero as $t \to +\infty$. Thus the two species cannot coexist in this case; one survives and the other becomes locally extinct.

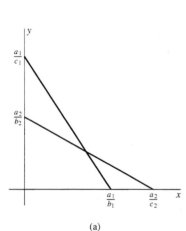

(a)

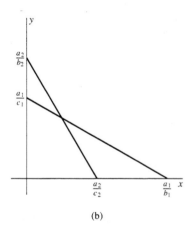

(b)

FIGURE 6.3.4. Stability of the critical point (x_E, y_E)

Rather than carrying out the general analysis that leads to the conclusions stated above, we present two examples that illustrate these two possibilities.

EXAMPLE 1   **Survival of a Single Species**

Suppose that the populations $x(t)$ and $y(t)$ satisfy the equations

$$\frac{dx}{dt} = 60x - 4x^2 - 3xy = x(60 - 4x - 3y),$$
$$\frac{dy}{dt} = 42y - 2y^2 - 3xy = y(42 - 3x - 2y). \tag{13}$$

These are the competition equations with $a_1 = 60$, $a_2 = 42$, $b_1 = 4$, $b_2 = 2$, and $c_1 = c_2 = 3$. Note that $c_1 c_2 = 9 > 8 = b_1 b_2$, so we should expect the results in Case 2. The four critical points are $(0, 0)$, $(0, 21)$, $(15, 0)$, and $(6, 12)$. We will analyze them individually.

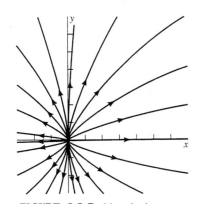

FIGURE 6.3.5. Linearized trajectories of (13) near $(0, 0)$; the common tangent is the y-axis.

The Critical Point (0, 0). We linearize the system in (13) by dropping the quadratic terms; the result is the linear system

$$\frac{dx}{dt} = 60x, \qquad \frac{dy}{dt} = 42y. \tag{14}$$

The general solution of this system is

$$x(t) = Ae^{60t}, \qquad y(t) = Be^{42t}, \tag{15}$$

so $(0, 0)$ is an unstable node for the linearized system in (14). Because the equations in (14) yield $y = Cx^{7/10}$, all the trajectories other than the x-axis are tangent to the y-axis at the origin. Figure 6.3.5 shows some of these trajectories near the critical point $(0, 0)$.

The Critical Point (0, 21). To linearize the equations in (13) near the critical point $(0, 21)$, we substitute $u = x$ and $v = y - 21$. The result is the almost linear system

$$\frac{du}{dt} = -3u - 4u^2 - 3uv$$

$$\frac{dv}{dt} = -63u - 42v - 3uv - 2v^2 \tag{16}$$

with critical point $(0, 0)$. The corresponding linear system

$$\frac{du}{dt} = -3u, \qquad \frac{dv}{dt} = -63u - 42v \tag{17}$$

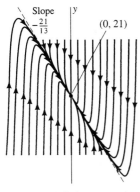

FIGURE 6.3.6. Linearized trajectories of (13) near the improper node $(0, 21)$; the trajectories are drawn accurately by computer. Although they appear to "enter" the line with slope $-21/13$, they actually are all tangent to it at the single point $(0, 21)$.

has characteristic roots $\lambda_1 = -3$ and $\lambda_2 = -42$. So $(0, 21)$ is an asymptotically stable node. The general solution of (17) has the form

$$u(t) = Ae^{-3t}, \qquad v(t) = -\frac{21}{13}Ae^{-3t} + Be^{-42t}, \tag{18}$$

where A and B are arbitrary constants. As $t \to +\infty$, (u, v) approaches $(0, 0)$, so (x, y) approaches $(0, 21)$. With $A = 0$, Eq. (18) gives the vertical line through the critical point. The slope of any trajectory with $A \neq 0$ is

$$\frac{dy}{dx} = \frac{dy/dt}{dx/dt} = \frac{dv/dt}{du/dt} = \frac{\frac{63}{13}Ae^{-3t} - 42Be^{-42t}}{-3Ae^{-3t}} = -\frac{21}{13} + \frac{14B}{A}e^{-39t}.$$

Hence $dy/dx \to -\frac{21}{13}$ as $t \to +\infty$ and (x, y) approaches $(0, 21)$. Consequently the trajectories near the critical point $(0, 21)$ resemble those shown in Fig. 6.3.6.

The Critical Point (15, 0). The substitution $u = x - 15$, $v = y$ in the equations in (13) yields

$$\frac{du}{dt} = -60u - 45v - 4u^2 - 3uv$$

$$\frac{dv}{dt} = -3v - 3uv - 2v^2. \tag{19}$$

The corresponding linear system

$$\frac{du}{dt} = -60u - 45v, \qquad \frac{dv}{dt} = -3v \tag{20}$$

has characteristic roots $\lambda_1 = -3$ and $\lambda_2 = -60$, so this critical point is also an asymptotically stable node. The general solution is of the form

$$u(t) = -\frac{15}{19} Ae^{-3t}, \qquad v(t) = Ae^{-3t}. \tag{21}$$

As $t \to +\infty$, $(u, v) \to (0, 0)$ and so $(x, y) \to (15, 0)$. With $A = 0$ we get the horizontal line through the critical point. The slope of any trajectory with $A \neq 0$ is

$$\frac{dy}{dx} = \frac{dy/dt}{dx/dt} = \frac{dv/dt}{du/dt} = \frac{-3Ae^{-3t}}{\frac{45}{19}Ae^{-3t} - 60Be^{-60t}} = \frac{-A}{\frac{15}{19}A - 20Be^{-57t}}.$$

Hence $dy/dx \to -\frac{19}{15}$ as $t \to +\infty$ and $(x, y) \to (15, 0)$. The trajectories near $(15, 0)$ therefore resemble those shown in Fig. 6.3.7.

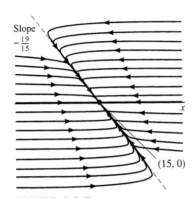

FIGURE 6.3.7. Linearized trajectories of (31) near the improper node (15, 0); the trajectories are drawn accurately by computer. Although they appear to "enter" the line with slope $-19/15$, they actually are all tangent to it at the single point (15, 0).

The Critical Point (6, 12). To linearize the equations in (13) near the critical point (6, 12) (the one representing the possibility of coexistence of the two species), we substitute $u = x - 6$ and $v = y - 12$. The result is the almost linear system

$$\frac{du}{dt} = -24u - 18v - 4u^2 - 3uv$$

$$\frac{dv}{dt} = -36u - 24v - uv - 2v^2. \tag{22}$$

The associated linear system is

$$\frac{du}{dt} = -24u - 18v, \qquad \frac{dv}{dt} = -36u - 24v. \tag{23}$$

The characteristic equation associated with Eq. (23) is

$$(-24 - \lambda)^2 - (-36) \cdot (-18) = (\lambda + 24)^2 - 2 \cdot (18)^2 = 0$$

with roots $\lambda_1 = -24 + 18\sqrt{2} > 0$ and $\lambda_2 = -24 - 18\sqrt{2} < 0$. Thus this critical point is an unstable saddle point. We find that the general solution of (23) is

$$u(t) = Ae^{\lambda_1 t} + Be^{\lambda_2 t}, \qquad v(t) = -\sqrt{2}Ae^{\lambda_1 t} + \sqrt{2}Be^{\lambda_2 t}, \tag{24}$$

where A and B are arbitrary constants. The slope of a trajectory in the linearized system is given by

$$\frac{dy}{dx} = \frac{dv/dt}{du/dt} = \sqrt{2}\left(\frac{-\lambda_1 Ae^{\lambda_1 t} + \lambda_2 Be^{\lambda_2 t}}{\lambda_1 Ae^{\lambda_1 t} + \lambda_2 Be^{\lambda_2 t}}\right). \tag{25}$$

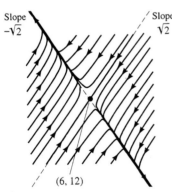

FIGURE 6.3.8. Linearized trajectories of (13) near the point (6, 12); the trajectories are drawn accurately by computer. Although they appear to "enter" the line with slope $-\sqrt{2}$, they actually have the two lines with slopes $\pm\sqrt{2}$ as asymptotes.

If $A = 0$, then $(u, v) \rightarrow (0, 0)$ and so $(x, y) \rightarrow (6, 12)$ as $t \rightarrow +\infty$ because $\lambda_2 < 0$. From (24) and (25) we see that (x, y) then approaches the critical point $(6, 12)$ along the straight line of slope $\sqrt{2}$. If $A \neq 0$ then from (25) we find that

$$\frac{dy}{dx} = \sqrt{2}\left(\frac{-\lambda_1 A + \lambda_2 B e^{-36t\sqrt{2}}}{\lambda_1 A + \lambda_2 B e^{-36t\sqrt{2}}}\right). \tag{26}$$

With $B = 0$ we have the straight line of slope $-\sqrt{2}$ along which (x, y) leaves the saddle point as t increases, and from (26) we see that $dy/dx \rightarrow -\sqrt{2}$ along any other trajectory as $t \rightarrow +\infty$. Hence the trajectories near the critical point $(6, 12)$ resemble those shown in Fig. 6.3.8.

Now that we have completed our local analysis of the four critical points of the almost linear system in (13), we want to assemble this information into a coherent whole—to construct a phase plane picture (phase portrait) of the global behavior of the trajectories in the first quadrant (where both populations are nonnegative). If we accept the facts that

1. Near each critical point the trajectories look qualitatively like the linearized trajectories shown in Figs. 6.3.5 through 6.3.8, and

2. As $t \rightarrow +\infty$, each trajectory either approaches a critical point or diverges toward infinity somewhere in the first quadrant,

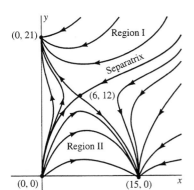

FIGURE 6.3.9. Artist's conception of trajectories consistent with the analysis in Example 1

then it follows that the phase plane picture should look qualitatively similar to the linearized trajectories shown in the schematic Fig. 6.3.9.

The two trajectories that approach the saddle point $(6, 12)$, together with that saddle point, form a **separatrix** that separates regions I and II in the figure. It plays a crucial role in determining the long-term behavior of the two populations. If the initial point (x_0, y_0) lies precisely on the separatrix, then $(x(t), y(t))$ approaches $(6, 12)$ as $t \rightarrow +\infty$. Of course, random events make it extremely unlikely that $(x(t), y(t))$ will remain on the separatrix. If not, peaceful coexistence of the two species is impossible. If (x_0, y_0) lies in Region I above the separatrix, then $(x(t), y(t))$ approaches $(0, 21)$ as $t \rightarrow +\infty$, so the population $x(t)$ decreases to zero. Alternatively, if (x_0, y_0) lies in Region II below the separatrix, then $(x(t), y(t))$ approaches $(15, 0)$ as $t \rightarrow +\infty$, so the population $y(t)$ dies out. In short, whichever population has the initial competitive advantage survives, while the other faces extinction. ∎

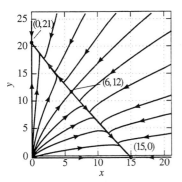

FIGURE 6.3.10. Computer-generated phase plane portrait for the system in (13)

The schematic diagram in Fig. 6.3.9 was drawn by an artist on the basis of our mathematical analysis in Example 1, before the computer-generated phase plane portrait in Fig. 6.3.10 was available. Which do you prefer—the artist's license or the computer's precision?

EXAMPLE 2 **Peaceful Coexistence**

Now suppose that the two populations satisfy the equations

$$\frac{dx}{dt} = 60x - 3x^2 - 4xy = x(60 - 3x - 4y),$$

$$\frac{dy}{dt} = 42y - 3y^2 - 2xy = y(42 - 2x - 3y). \tag{27}$$

Here $a_1 = 60$, $a_2 = 42$, $b_1 = b_2 = 3$, $c_1 = 4$, and $c_2 = 2$. So $c_1 c_1 = 8 < 9 = b_1 b_2$: Competition is smaller than inhibition. The analysis of the system in (27) follows step by step that of the system in (13) of Example 1. We will present only the results of this analysis, leaving the details to Problems 2 through 6. There are four critical points: $(0, 0)$, $(0, 14)$, $(20, 0)$, and $(12, 6)$.

The critical point $(0, 0)$ is an unstable node of the linearized system, just as in Example 1.

The critical point $(0, 14)$ is an unstable saddle point of the linearized system. The entering trajectories lie along the y-axis, while the departing trajectories lie along the line through $(0, 14)$ with slope $-\frac{14}{23}$.

The critical point $(20, 0)$ is also an unstable saddle point of the linearized system. The entering trajectories lie along the x-axis, while the departing trajectories lie along the straight lie through $(20, 0)$ with slope $-\frac{31}{40}$.

The critical point $(12, 6)$ represents the possibility of peaceful coexistence because it is an asymptotically stable node. One pair of trajectories lies along the line through $(12, 6)$ with slope $\left(-3 + \sqrt{73}\right)/16 \approx 0.35$. All other trajectories of the linearized system enter the node and are tangent to the line with slope $\left(-3 - \sqrt{73}\right)/16 \approx -0.72$. ∎

Figure 6.3.11 shows an artist-drawn schematic diagram illustrating the results outlined above, whereas Fig. 6.3.12 is a computer-generated phase plane portrait for the system in (27). One especially notable feature of this system is that for *any* positive initial values x_0 and y_0, $(x(t), y(t))$ approaches $(12, 6)$ as $t \to +\infty$, so the two species both survive in stable (peaceful) coexistence.

Examples 1 and 2 illustrate the power of elementary critical point analysis. But we must conclude with a word of caution. Ecological systems in nature are never so simple as in these examples; they normally involve far more than two species, and the rates of growth of these populations and their interactions are always more complex than those discussed in this section.

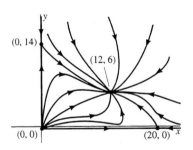

FIGURE 6.3.11. Artist's conception of trajectories consistent with the analysis in Example 2

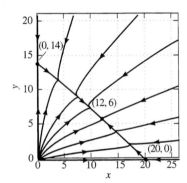

FIGURE 6.3.12. Computer-generated phase plane portrait for the system in (27)

6.3 Problems

1. Let $x(t)$ be a harmful insect population (aphids?) that under natural conditions is held somewhat in check by a benign predator insect population $y(t)$ (ladybugs?). Assume that $x(t)$ and $y(t)$ satisfy the predator–prey equations in (1), so that the stable equilibrium populations are $x_E = c/d$ and $y_E = a/b$ Now suppose that an insecticide is employed that kills (per unit time) the same fraction $f < a$ of each species of insect. Show that the harmful population x_E is increased, while the benign population y_E is decreased, so the use of the insecticide is counterproductive. This is an instance in which mathematical analysis reveals undesirable consequences of a well-intentioned interference with nature.

Problems 2 through 6 provide the details cited in Example 2 for the two competing populations $x(t)$ and $y(t)$ that satisfy the equations

$$\frac{dx}{dt} = 60x - 3x^2 - 4xy = x(60 - 3x - 4y)$$

$$\frac{dy}{dt} = 42y - 3y^2 - 2xy = y(42 - 2x - 3y). \tag{27}$$

2. Show that the critical points of the system in (27) are $(0, 0)$, $(0, 14)$, $(20, 0)$, and $(12, 6)$.

3. Show that the critical point $(0, 0)$ is an unstable node at which all but two trajectories are tangent to the y-axis.

4. (a) To investigate the critical point $(0, 14)$, substitute $u = x$, $v = y - 14$; then show that the corresponding linear system is

$$\frac{du}{dt} = 4u, \qquad \frac{dv}{dt} = -28u - 42v.$$

(b) Show that the general solution of this linear system is

$$u(t) = Ae^{4t}, \qquad v(t) = -\frac{14}{23}Ae^{4t} + Be^{-24t}.$$

(c) Then conclude that $(0, 14)$ is an unstable saddle point at which the entering and departing trajectories lie on the y-axis and on the line through $(0, 14)$ with slope $-\frac{14}{23}$.

5. (a) To investigate the critical point $(20, 0)$, substitute $u = x - 20$, $v = y$; then show that the corresponding linear system is

$$\frac{du}{dt} = -60u - 80v, \qquad \frac{dv}{dt} = 2v.$$

(b) Show that the general solution of this linear system is

$$u(t) = Ae^{-60t} - \frac{40}{31}Be^{2t}, \qquad v(t) = Be^{2t}.$$

(c) Then conclude that $(20, 0)$ is an unstable saddle point at which entering and departing trajectories lie on the x-axis and on the line through $(20, 0)$ with slope $-\frac{31}{40}$.

6. (a) To investigate the critical point $(12, 6)$, substitute $u = x - 12$, $v = y - 6$; then show that the corresponding linear system is

$$\frac{du}{dt} = -36u - 48v, \qquad \frac{dv}{dt} = -12u - 18v.$$

(b) Show that the characteristic roots of this linear system are

$$\lambda_1 = -27 + 3\sqrt{73} < 0 \quad \text{and} \quad \lambda_2 = -27 + 3\sqrt{73} < 0,$$

and that its general solution is

$$u(t) = Ae^{\lambda_1 t} + Be^{\lambda_2 t}, \qquad v(t) = Ce^{\lambda_1 t} + De^{\lambda_2 t},$$

where $C = \left(-3 + \sqrt{73}\right)A/16$ and $D = \left(-3 + \sqrt{73}\right)B/16$. (c) Hence conclude that $(12, 6)$ is an asymptotically stable node, where two trajectories lie on the line through $(12, 6)$ with slope $\left(-3 + \sqrt{73}\right)/16$ and the others are tangent to the line through $(12, 6)$ with slope $\left(-3 - \sqrt{73}\right)/16$.

Problems 7 through 11 deal with the predator–prey system that is modeled by the equations

$$\frac{dx}{dt} = 5x - x^2 - xy = x(5 - x - y)$$

$$\frac{dy}{dt} = xy - 2y = y(x - 2). \tag{28}$$

In contrast with the system in (1) discussed in the text, the prey population $x(t)$ would—in the absence of any predators—be a bounded population described by the logistic equation $dx/dt = 5x - x^2$.

7. Show that the critical points of the system in (28) are $(0, 0)$, $(5, 0)$, and $(2, 3)$.

8. Show that the critical point $(0, 0)$ is an unstable saddle point of the linearized system, with trajectories entering along the y-axis and departing along the x-axis.

9. Show that the critical point $(5, 0)$ is an unstable saddle point of the linearized system, with trajectories entering along the x-axis and departing along the line through $(5, 0)$ with slope $-\frac{8}{5}$.

10. Show that the critical point $(2, 3)$ is an asymptotically stable spiral point of the linearized system.

11. Show that the results of Problems 7 through 10 are consistent with the global phase portrait for the original nonlinear sys-

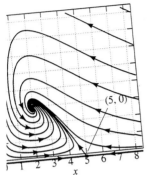

JRE 6.3.13. Phase plane portrait for the system in (28)

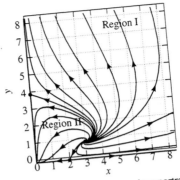

FIGURE 6.3.14. Phase plane portrait for the system in (29)

in (28) shown in Fig. 6.3.13. Conclude that the prey and
ators coexist with stable equilibrium populations $x_E = 2$ and
= 3.

Problems 12 through 17 deal with the predator–prey sys-
modeled by the equations

$$\frac{dx}{dt} = x^2 - 2x - xy = x(x - y - 2) \qquad (29)$$

$$\frac{dy}{dt} = y^2 - 4y + xy = y(x + y - 4).$$

n this system, each population—the prey population $x(t)$ and
he predator population $y(t)$—is an unsophisticated population
similar to the one considered in Problem 15 of Section 2.1) for
each of which the only alternatives (in the absence of the other)
are doomsday and extinction.

12. Show that the critical points of the system in (29) are $(0, 0)$,
$(0, 4)$, $(2, 0)$, and $(3, 1)$.

13. Show that the critical point $(0, 0)$ is an asymptotically stable
node of the linearized system, at which one pair of trajectories
lie along the y-axis and the others are tangent to the x-axis.

14. Show that the critical point $(0, 4)$ is an unstable saddle point
of the linearized system, with trajectories departing along the
y-axis and entering along the line through $(0, 4)$ with slope $-\frac{2}{5}$.

15. Show that the critical point $(2, 0)$ is an unstable saddle point
of the linearized system, with trajectories departing along the
x-axis and entering along the line through $(2, 0)$ with slope 2.

16. Show that the critical point $(3, 1)$ is an unstable spiral point
of the linearized system.

17. Verify that the results of Problems 12 through 16 are consistent with the global phase portrait for the original nonlinear system in (29) shown in Fig. 6.3.14. This is a two-dimensional version of doomsday versus extinction. If the initial point (x_0, y_0)
lies in Region I, then both populations increase without bound
(until doomsday), whereas if it lies in Region II, then both populations will decrease to zero.

The next two problems deal with the competition equations
in (9) and the associated linearized system. The discussion in the
text covered only the case in which the critical point of interest
(x_E, y_E) lay in the first quadrant. You may now explore the other
possibilities.

18. Determine the behavior of the linearized system associated
with the system in (9) in the case that (x_E, y_E) exists but does
not lie in the first quadrant. Because the populations are never
negative, there are only three critical points to examine. There
are two cases, depending upon whether (x_E, y_E) lies in the second quadrant or the fourth quadrant.

19. Determine the behavior of the linearized system associated
with the system in (9) in the case that (x_E, y_E) does not exist because the two lines having the equations in (10) are parallel.
There will be two cases, depending upon which line is above the
other. (You may take for granted that the improbable—coincidence of the two lines—does not occur.)

20. A lake is initially stocked with 100 bass and 600 redear.
There is ample food for the redear. Because bass prey on redear,
the population of bass will increase at a rate proportional to the
number of encounters between the two species; bass will also
die at a rate proportional to the bass population. The redear multiply at a rate proportional to their population and die off at a
rate proportional to the number of encounters between the two
species. This implies that the populations $B(t)$ of bass and $R(t)$
of redear satisfy a system of differential equations of the following form:

$$B'(t) = pBR - qB, \qquad R'(t) = uR - vBR.$$

Suppose it is known that $p = 0.00004$, $q = 0.02$, $u = 0.05$,
and $v = 0.0004$, with t measured in days. Then we have a
predator–prey system as in Eq. (1) of this section, and the populations of the two species oscillate periodically with the same
period. Approximate this period by solving the system numerically with the given initial conditions, using the Runge–Kutta
method of Section 4.3.

6.3 Computing Project

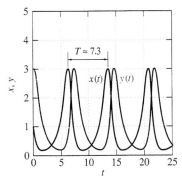

FIGURE 6.3.15. *x*- and *y*-solution curves for the predator-prey system (1) with $x(0) = 1$, $y(0) = 3$

The closed trajectories in Fig. 6.3.2 represent periodic solutions of the predator–prey system

$$\frac{dx}{dt} = x - xy, \qquad \frac{dy}{dt} = -y + xy, \qquad (1)$$

but provide no information as to the actual periods of the oscillations these solutions describe. The period of a particular solution $(x(t), y(t))$ can be gleaned from the graphs of x and y as functions of t. Figure 6.3.15 shows these graphs for the solution of (1) with initial conditions $x(0) = 1$, $y(0) = 3$. The indicated measurement on the figure indicates that the (equal) periods of oscillation of $x(t)$ and $y(t)$ are given approximately by $T \approx 7.3$.

For your own predator–prey system

$$\frac{dx}{dt} = ax - bxy, \qquad \frac{dy}{dt} = -cy + dxy, \qquad (2)$$

let a, b, c, and d be the last four nonzero digits of your student I.D. number. Use whatever software is available to plot typical $x(t)$- and $y(t)$-solution curves and measure the periods of oscillation of the two populations.

6.5 Chaos in Dynamical Systems

In preceding sections we have looked at population growth and mechanical systems from a deterministic point of view—with the expectation that the initial state of a physical system fully determines its future evolution. But many common systems exhibit behavior that sometimes appears chaotic, in the sense that future states may not seem reliably predictable from a knowledge of initial conditions. This section includes project material illustrating the phenomenon of *chaos,* which is a topic of much current interest in science and engineering.

Population Growth and Period-Doubling

In Section 2.1 we introduced the logistic differential equation

$$\frac{dP}{dt} = aP - bP^2 \qquad (a, b > 0) \tag{1}$$

that models a bounded (rather than exponentially growing) population. Indeed, if the population $P(t)$ satisfies Eq. (1), then as $t \rightarrow +\infty$, $P(t)$ approaches the [finite] limiting population $M = a/b$. We discuss here a "discrete" version of the logistic equation that has long been familiar to scientists, but only recently has been discovered to predict quite exotic and unexpected patterns of behavior for certain populations.

In order to solve Eq. (1) numerically as in Section 2.4, we first choose a fixed step size $h > 0$ and consider the sequence of discrete times

$$t_0, \quad t_1, \quad t_2, \quad \ldots, \quad t_n, \quad t_{n+1}, \quad \ldots, \tag{2}$$

where $t_{n+1} = t_n + h$ for each n. Beginning with the initial value $P_0 = P(t_0)$, we then calculate approximations

$$P_1, \quad P_2, \quad \ldots, \quad P_n, \quad P_{n+1}, \quad \ldots \tag{3}$$

to the true values $P(t_1)$, $P(t_2)$, $P(t_3)$, $\ldots$ of the actual population $P(t)$. For instance, Euler's method for the logistic equation in (1) consists of calculating the approximations in (3) iteratively by means of the formula

$$P_{n+1} = P_n + (aP_n - bP_n^2) \cdot h. \tag{4}$$

Now suppose that the population is one for which the step size h can be chosen so that the approximations calculated using Eq. (4) agree to acceptable accuracy with the actual population values. This might be the case, for instance, for an animal or insect population in which all reproduction takes place within short-duration breeding seasons that recur at regular intervals. If h is the interval between successive breeding seasons, then the population P_n during one breeding season may depend only upon the population P_{n-1} during the previous season, and P_n may completely determine the population P_{n+1} during the next breeding season.

So let us assume for the sake of discussion that the successive values $P_n = P(t_n)$ of the population are given by the equation

$$P_{n+1} = P_n + (aP_n - bP_n^2) \cdot h. \tag{4}$$

Thus we replace the original differential equation in (1) with a "discrete" *difference equation*

$$\Delta P_n = (aP_n - bP_n^2)\Delta t \tag{5}$$

that gives the population difference $\Delta P_n = P_{n+1} - P_n$ in terms of the time difference $h = \Delta t$ and the preceding population P_n.

Equation (4) can be rewritten as the *logistic difference equation*

$$P_{n+1} = rP_n - sP_n^2, \tag{6}$$

where

$$r = 1 + ah \quad \text{and} \quad s = bh. \tag{7}$$

The substitution

$$P_n = \frac{r}{s}x_n \tag{8}$$

in Eq. (6) simplifies it still further to

$$x_{n+1} = rx_n(1 - x_n). \tag{9}$$

At this point we focus our attention on the final iterative formula in Eq. (9). Beginning with given values of x_0 and r, this formula generates a sequence x_1, x_2,

$x_3, \ldots$ of values corresponding to the successive times $t_1, t_2, t_3, \ldots$. We may think of x_n, the value at time t_n, as the *fraction* of the maximum population that the environment can support. Assuming that the limiting fractional population

$$x_\infty = \lim_{n \to \infty} x_n \tag{10}$$

exists, we want to investigate the way in which x_∞ depends upon the *growth parameter* r in Eq. (9). That is, if we regard r as the *input* to the process and x_∞ as the *output*, we ask how the output depends upon the input.

	TI-85	BASIC
	`:1.5->R`	`R = 1.5`
	`:0.5->X`	`X = 0.5`
	`:For(N,1,200)`	`FOR N=1 TO 200`
	`:R*X*(1-X)->X`	`X = R*X*(1-X)`
	`:Disp X`	`PRINT X`
	`:End`	`NEXT`

FIGURE 6.5.1. TI-85 and BASIC versions of a simple iteration program

The iteration in Eq. (9) is readily implemented in any available calculator or computer language. Figure 6.5.1 shows illustrative TI-85 and BASIC code for a simple program that calculates the first couple of hundred iterates. The corresponding *Maple* or MATLAB code would be virtually identical. *Mathematica* has a convenient iteration command `NestList[g, x0, k]` that displays the list $\{x_0, x_1, x_2, \ldots, x_k\}$ obtained by beginning with x_0 and applying the iteration $x_{n+1} = g(x_n)$ the preassigned number k times in succession. [In Eq. (9) we have $g(x) = rx(1-x)$.] For instance, the commands

```
g[x_] := r x (1 - x)

r = 1.5;

NestList[g, 0.5, 200];

Partition[ Drop[ %, 195 ], 5] // TableForm

0.333333   0.333333   0.333333   0.333333   0.333333
```

carry out the iteration in (9) with $r = 1.5$ and $x_0 = 0.5$. The last command simply drops the first 195 iterates and displays the next five.

Because $r = 1 + ah$ in (7), only values of r greater than 1 are pertinent to our idealized model of discrete population growth. It turns out that, for a typical such value of the growth parameter r entered at the first line, the results do not depend materially on the starting value x_0. After a reasonable number of iterations—the number required depends on the value of r—the value of x_n generally appears to "stabilize" on a limiting value x_∞ as in (10). For example, Fig. 6.5.2 shows results of runs of our simple iteration program with the values $r = 1.5$, 2.0, and 2.5 of the growth rate parameter, yielding limiting (fractional) populations

$$x_\infty = 0.333333, \qquad 0.500000, \qquad \text{and} \qquad 0.600000,$$

respectively. Thus it appears that x_∞ exists and that its value grows moderately as r increases.

With	$r = 1.5$	$r = 2.0$	$r = 2.5$
x0	0.5	0.5	0.5
x_1	0.3750	0.5000	0.6250
x_2	0.3516	0.5000	0.5859
$\cdot$	$\cdot$	$\cdot$	$\cdot$
$\cdot$	$\cdot$	$\cdot$	$\cdot$
x_{197}	0.3333	0.5000	0.6000
x_{198}	0.3333	0.5000	0.6000
x_{199}	0.3333	0.5000	0.6000
x_{200}	0.3333	0.5000	0.6000

FIGURE 6.5.2. Iterates with growth parameters $r = 1.5, 2.0, 2.5$

Exercise 1. Try several other values of the growth rate parameter in the range $1 < r < 3$. Do your results support the conjecture that the limiting population always exists and is an increasing function of r?

The results in Fig. 6.5.3 show that the conjecture stated in Exercise 1 is false! With growth rate parameters $r = 3$ and $r = 3.25$, the [fractional] population fails to stabilize on a single limiting population. Instead, it oscillates between two different populations in alternate months (thinking of a month as our unit of time). For instance, with $r = 3.25$ we see that

$$x_{1000} = x_{1002} = x_{1004} = \cdots = 0.4953,$$

```
g[x_] := r x (1 -x)
r = 3;
NestList[g, 0.5, 1006];
Partition[Drop[%, 1000],2] // TableForm
0.6592   0.6740
0.6592   0.6740
0.6592   0.6740

r = 3.25;
NestList[g, 0.5, 1006];
Partition[Drop[%, 1000],2] // TableForm
0.4953   0.8124
0.4953   0.8124
0.4953   0.8124

r = 3.5;
NestList[g, 0.5, 1012];
Partition[Drop[%, 1000],4] // TableForm
0.5009   0.8750   0.3828   0.8269
0.5009   0.8750   0.3828   0.8269
0.5009   0.8750   0.3828   0.8269
```

FIGURE 6.5.3. Cycles with periods 2 and 4

whereas

$$x_{1001} = x_{1003} = x_{1005} = \cdots = 0.8124.$$

Thus we have not a single limiting population, but rather a "limiting cycle" consisting of two distinct populations. Furthermore, when the growth rate is increased to $r = 3.5$, the period of the cycle *doubles,* and now we have a limiting cycle with a *period* of 4—the population cycles repeatedly through the four distinct values 0.5009, 0.8750, 0.3828, and 0.8269.

Exercise 2. Try values of the growth rate parameter in the range $2.9 < r < 3.0$ to determine as closely as possible just where the single limiting population splits (as r increases) into a cycle of period 2. This should happen just a bit short of $r = 3$.

Figure 6.5.4 shows cycles with periods 8 and 16 obtained with parameter values $r = 3.55$ and $r = 3.565$, respectively. Obviously events are now changing quite rapidly. This is the phenomenon of *period doubling* for which the innocuous (in appearance) iteration $x_{n+1} = rx_n(1 - x_n)$ has become famous in recent years.

```
r = 3.55;
NestList[g, 0.5, 1025];
Partition[Drop[%, 1000],8] // TableForm
```

0.5060	0.8874	0.3548	0.8127	0.5405	0.8817	0.3703	0.8278
0.5060	0.8874	0.3548	0.8127	0.5405	0.8817	0.3703	0.8278
0.5060	0.8874	0.3548	0.8127	0.5405	0.8817	0.3703	0.8278

```
r = 3.565;
NestList[g, 0.5, 1035];
Partition[Drop[%, 1000],16] // TableForm
```

0.4860	0.8905	0.3475	0.8083	0.5523	0.8815	0.3724	0.8332
0.4954	0.8912	0.3457	0.8064	0.5565	0.8799	0.3768	0.8372
0.4860	0.8905	0.3475	0.8083	0.5523	0.8815	0.3724	0.8332
0.4954	0.8912	0.3457	0.8064	0.5565	0.8799	0.3768	0.8372

FIGURE 6.5.4. Cycles with periods 8 and 16

Exercise 3. See if you can find a cycle of period 32 somewhere between $r = 3.565$ and $r = 3.57$.

As the growth rate parameter is increased beyond $r = 3.56$, period doubling occurs so rapidly that utter chaos appears to break out somewhere near $r = 3.57$. The iterations shown in Fig. 6.5.5 indicate that, with $r = 3.57$ and with $r = 3.60$, the earlier periodicity seems to have disappeared. No periodic cycles are evident, and the population appears to be changing (from one month to the next) in some essentially random fashion. Indeed, the deterministic population growth that is observed with smaller growth parameters seems now to have degenerated into a non-deterministic process of seemingly random change.

```
r = 3.57;
NestList[g, 0.5, 1035];
Partition[Drop[%, 1000],8] // TableForm
```

0.4751	0.8903	0.3487	0.8108	0.5477	0.8844	0.3650	0.8275
0.5096	0.8922	0.3434	0.8050	0.5604	0.8795	0.3784	0.8397
0.4805	0.8911	0.3463	0.8082	0.5534	0.8823	0.3707	0.8328
0.4970	0.8925	0.3426	0.8041	0.5624	0.8786	0.3808	0.8418

```
r = 3.6;
NestList[g, 0.5, 1035];
Partition[Drop[%, 1000],8] // TableForm
```

0.4345	0.8846	0.3676	0.8369	0.4914	0.8997	0.3248	0.7895
0.5984	0.8652	0.4199	0.8769	0.3885	0.8553	0.4456	0.8893
0.3543	0.8236	0.5231	0.8981	0.3295	0.7954	0.5859	0.8734
0.3980	0.8626	0.4268	0.8807	0.3782	0.8466	0.4675	0.8962

FIGURE 6.5.5. Chaos!

The solutions and computer lab manuals accompanying this text include BASIC, *Mathematica,* and other versions of a program called PICHFORK. This program produces a visual presentation of the way in which the behavior of our iteration depends upon the value of the growth parameter r. For each value of r in the input interval $a \leqq r \leqq b$ (the horizontal axis in the resulting diagram), 1000 iterations are first carried out to achieve "stability." Then the next 250 values of x generated by the iteration are plotted on the vertical axis—that is, the screen pixel at (r, x) is "turned on." The descriptively named "pitchfork diagram" that results then shows at a glance whether a given value of r corresponds to a cycle (with finite period) or to chaos. If the resolution in the picture suffices to make it clear that only finitely many values of x are plotted above a given value of r, then we see that the iteration is "eventually periodic" for that specific value of the growth rate parameter.

Figure 6.5.6 shows the pitchfork diagram for the range $2.8 \leqq r \leqq 4.0$. Scanning from left to right, we see a single limiting population until $r \approx 3$, then a cycle with period 2 until $r \approx 3.45$, then a cycle of period 4, then one of period 8, and so forth, rapidly approaching the darkness of chaos. But note the vertical bands of "white space" that appear in the diagram between $r = 3.6$ and $r = 3.7$, between $r = 3.7$ and $r = 3.8$, and again between $r = 3.8$ and $r = 3.9$. These represent regions where [periodic] order returns from the preceding chaos.

For instance, Fig. 6.5.7 shows the interval $3.8 \leqq r \leqq 3.9$, where we observe a cycle of period 3 that emerges suddenly from the chaos near $r = 3.83$, and then splits successively into cycles of orders 6, 12, 24, . . . (Fig. 6.5.8). This period-doubling beginning with a cycle of period 3 is especially significant—a fundamental article by James Yorke and T.-Y. Li in the 1975 *American Mathematical Monthly* was entitled "Period Three Implies Chaos." According to this article, the existence of a cycle of period 3 (for an appropriate iteration) implies the existence of cycles of every other [finite] period, as well as chaotic "cycles" with no period at all.

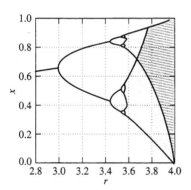

FIGURE 6.5.6. The pitchfork diagram with $2.8 \leqq r \leqq 4$, $0 \leqq x \leqq 1$

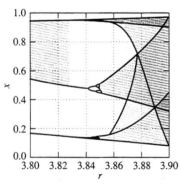

FIGURE 6.5.7. The pitchfork diagram with $3.8 \leqq r \leqq 3.9$, $0 \leqq x \leqq 1$

Project 1. Use Program PICHFORK to search for other interesting cycles, and verify their apparent periods by appropriate iterative computations. For instance, you should find a cycle with period 10 between $r = 3.60$ and $r = 3.61$, and one with pe-

```
r = 3.84;
NestList[g, 0.5, 1010];
Partition[Drop[%, 1000],3] // TableForm
```

```
0.9594   0.1494   0.4880
0.9594   0.1494   0.4880
0.9594   0.1494   0.4880
```

```
r = 3.845;
NestList[g, 0.5, 1020];
Partition[Drop[%, 1000],6] // TableForm
```

```
0.9582    0.1540   0.5009   0.9612   0.1432   0.4718
0.9582    0.1540   0.5009   0.9612   0.1432   0.4718
0.9582    0.1540   0.5009   0.9612   0.1432   0.4718
```

```
r = 3.848;
NestList[g, 0.5, 1040];
Partition[Drop[%, 1000],12] // TableForm
```

```
0.9573   0.1571   0.5096   0.9616   0.1419   0.4686
0.9582   0.1541   0.5015   0.9620   0.1407   0.4652

0.9573   0.1571   0.5096   0.9616   0.1419   0.4686
0.9582   0.1541   0.5015   0.9620   0.1407   0.4652

0.9573   0.1571   0.5096   0.9616   0.1419   0.4686
0.9582   0.1541   0.5015   0.9620   0.1407   0.4652
```

FIGURE 6.5.8. Cycles with periods 3, 6, and 12

riod 14 between $r = 3.59$ and $r = 3.60$. Can you find cycles with period 5 and 7? If so, look for subsequent period-doubling. A run of PICHFORK requires several hundred thousand iterations, so it will help if you have a fast computer (or one you can leave running overnight).

As we scan the pitchfork diagram (Fig. 6.5.6) from left to right, we spot the successive values $r_1, r_2, r_3, \ldots$ of the growth rate parameter at which a *bifurcation* or qualitative change in the iteration $x_{n+1} = rx_n(1 - x_n)$ occurs as the value of r is increased further. These are the discrete values of r at which any sufficiently small increase in the growth parameter doubles the period of the iteration. In the 1970s the Los Alamos physicist Mitchell Feigenbaum discovered that a certain order underlies this period-doubling toward chaos:

$$\lim_{k \to \infty} \frac{r_k - r_{k-1}}{r_{k+1} - r_k} = 4.6692016091 \ldots \ldots \tag{11}$$

The fraction on the left in Eq. (11) is the ratio of the lengths of successive constant-period "windows" in the pitchfork diagram. It is the fact that this ratio approaches a limit as $k \to \infty$, rather than the specific value of this limit, that demonstrates a sort of "order" underlying the period-doubling observed with the particular iteration $x_{n+1} = rx_n(1 - x_n)$. On the other hand, it is now known that precisely the same *Feigenbaum constant* 4.6692016901 . . . plays exactly the same role for a wide variety of period-doubling phenomena arising in many different areas of science.

Project 2. Feigenbaum used an HP-65 pocket calculator (rather than a powerful computer) to carry out the computations leading to the discovery of his famous constant. Perhaps you would like to use iterative computations and/or PICHFORK to isolate the first few bifurcation values $r_1, r_2, r_3, \ldots$ with sufficient accuracy to verify that the limit in (11) is approximately 4.67. You can consult pages 124–126 of T. Gray and J. Glynn, *Exploring Mathematics with Mathematica* (Addison-Wesley, 1991) for a fancier approach.

Period-Doubling in Mechanical Systems

In Section 6.4 we introduced the second-order differential equation

$$mx'' + cx' + kx + \beta x^3 = 0 \tag{12}$$

to model the free velocity-damped vibrations of a mass m on a nonlinear spring. Recall that the term kx in Eq. (12) represents the force exerted on the mass by a *linear* spring, whereas the term βx^3 represents the nonlinearity of an actual spring.

We want now to discuss the *forced vibrations* that result when an external force $F(t) = F_0 \cos \omega t$ acts on the mass. With such a force adjoined to the system in Eq. (12), we obtain the **forced Duffing equation**

▶ $$mx'' + cx' + kx + \beta x^3 = F_0 \cos \omega t \tag{13}$$

for the displacement $x(t)$ of the mass from its equilibrium position. For most values of the parameters it is impossible to solve Eq. (13) explicitly for $x(t)$. Nevertheless, its solutions can be portrayed qualitatively by means of [numerically approximated] phase plane trajectories like those we used in Section 6.4 to describe free vibrations of nonlinear mechanical systems.

The Hooke's constant k is positive for a typical spring that resists displacement from equilibrium. But there do exist simple physical systems that emulate a spring having a negative Hooke's constant. For example, Fig. 6.5.9 shows a mass m atop a vertical metal filament. We assume that the thin metal filament can oscillate only in a vertical plane, and behaves like a flexible column that "buckles" or bends when the mass is displaced to either side of the vertical position. Then there is one stable equilibrium point to the left ($x < 0$) and another to the right ($x > 0$), but the vertical equilibrium position ($x = 0$) is unstable. When the mass is displaced slightly from this unstable equilibrium position, the internal force exerted on it is *repulsive* rather than attractive; this corresponds to a *negative* value of k in Eq. (13). If a periodic force is exerted on the mass by an oscillating electromagnetic field, and air resistance damps its oscillations, then Eq. (13) with $k < 0$ but with $c, \beta > 0$ is a reasonable mathematical model for its horizontal displacement function $x(t)$.

In the absence of both damping and the external force, the phase plane trajectories of the free oscillations of the mass would resemble those shown in Fig. 6.4.13 (with Problem 12 in Section 6.4). The mass behaves as though it is repelled by the unstable critical point at $x = 0$ but is attracted by each of the two stable critical points symmetrically located on either side of the origin.

We saw in Section 3.6 that in the *linear* case a periodic external force $F(t) = F_0 \cos \omega t$ causes a steady periodic response $x(t) = C \cos(\omega t - \alpha)$ with the *same* fre-

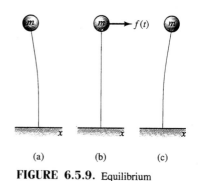

FIGURE 6.5.9. Equilibrium positions of a mass on a filament: (a) stable equilibrium with $x < 0$; (b) unstable equilibrium at $x = 0$; (c) stable equilibrium with $x > 0$.

quency ω. The amplitude C of the steady periodic response is proportional to the amplitude F_0 of the external force. For instance, if the periodic external force is doubled in amplitude, then the only change in the response is that its amplitude is doubled also.

To illustrate the quite different behavior of a nonlinear system, we take $k = -1$ and $m = c = \beta = \omega = 1$ in Eq. (13) so the differential equation is

$$x'' + x' - x + x^3 = F_0 \cos t. \qquad (14)$$

As an exercise you may verify that the two stable critical points are $(-1, 0)$ and $(1, 0)$. We want to examine the dependence of the (presumably steady periodic) response $x(t)$ upon the amplitude F_0 of the periodic external force of period $2\pi/\omega = 2\pi$.

Figures 6.5.10 through 6.5.13 show the solutions of Eq. (14) obtained with the successive values $F_0 = 0.60$, 0.70, 0.75, and 0.80 of the amplitude of the external force. In each case the equation was solved numerically with initial conditions

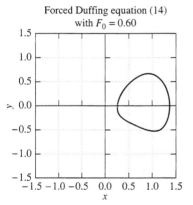

FIGURE 6.5.10(a). Period 2π response with $F_0 = 0.60$: (a) phase plane trajectory

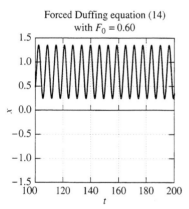

FIGURE 6.5.10(b). Period 2π response with $F_0 = 0.60$: (b) solution $x(t)$

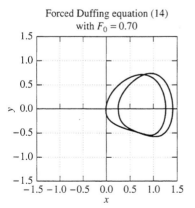

FIGURE 6.5.11(a). Period 4π response with $F_0 = 0.70$: (a) phase plane trajectory

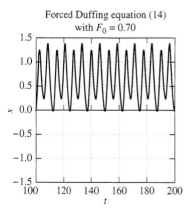

FIGURE 6.5.11(b). Period 4π response with $F_0 = 0.70$: (b) solution $x(t)$

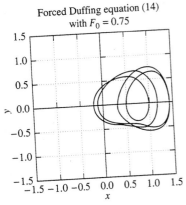

FIGURE 6.5.12(a). Period 8π response with $F_0 = 0.75$: (a) phase plane trajectory

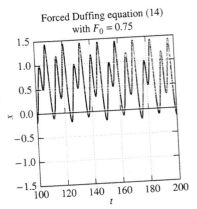

FIGURE 6.5.12(b). Period 8π response with $F_0 = 0.75$: (b) solution $x(t)$

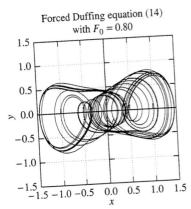

FIGURE 6.5.13(a). Chaotic response with $F_0 = 0.80$: (a) phase plane trajectory

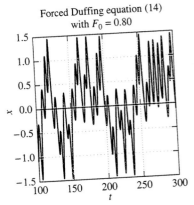

FIGURE 6.5.13(b). Chaotic response with $F_0 = 0.80$: (b) solution $x(t)$

$x(0) = 1$, $x'(0) = 0$ and the resulting solution plotted for the range $100 \leq t \leq 200$ (to show the steady periodic response remaining after the initial transient response has died out). Part (a) of each figure shows the phase plane trajectory $x = x(t)$, $y = x'(t)$, and part (b) shows the actual solution curve $x = x(t)$ in the tx-plane. Part (a) exhibits the qualitative character of the solution more vividly, but part (b) is required to determine the period and frequency of the solution.

Figure 6.5.10 shows a simple oscillation of period 2π of the mass about the right-hand critical point. In the ensuing sequence of figures we see successive *period-doubling* and finally *chaos* as the amplitude of the external force is increased in the range from $F_0 = 0.6$ to $F_0 = 0.8$. This *period-doubling toward chaos* is a common characteristic of the behavior of a *nonlinear* mechanical system as an appropriate physical parameter (such as m, c, k, β, F_0, or ω in Eq. (13)) is increased or decreased. No such phenomenon occurs in linear systems.

Project 3. Use an ODE plotting utility to see whether you can reproduce Figs. 6.5.10–6.5.13. Then investigate the parameter range $1.00 \leq F_0 \leq 1.10$ for the force constant in Eq. (14). With $F_0 = 1.00$ you should see a period 6π phase plane trajectory that encircles *both* stable critical points (as well as the unstable one). The period doubles around $F_0 = 1.07$ and chaos sets in around $F_0 = 1.10$. See whether you can spot a second period-doubling somewhere between $F_0 = 1.07$ and $F_0 = 1.10$. Produce both phase plane trajectories and *tx*-solution curves on which you can measure the periods.

The Lorenz Strange Attractor

The substitution of $x_1 = x$, $x_2 = x'$ in the forced Duffing equation (Eq. (13)) yields a two-dimensional nonlinear system of first-order differential equations, and period-doubling phenomena are characteristic of such systems. But in higher dimensions even more exotic phenomena occur, and are currently the subject of much active investigation. All this work stems ultimately from the original investigation of an extraordinary three-dimensional nonlinear system by the mathematical meteorologist E. N. Lorenz, who later described its discovery as follows.

> By the middle 1950s "numerical weather prediction;" i.e., forecasting by numerically integrating such approximations to the atmospheric equations as could feasibly be handled, was very much in vogue, despite the rather mediocre results which it was then yielding. A smaller but determined group favored statistical prediction . . . I was skeptical, and decided to test the idea by applying the statistical method to a set of artificial data, generated by solving a system of equations numerically . . . The first task was to find a suitable system of equations to solve . . . The system would have to be simple enough . . . and the general solution would have to be aperiodic, since the statistical prediction of a periodic series would be a trivial matter, once the periodicity had been detected . . . [In the course of talks with Dr. Barry Saltzman] he showed me some work on thermal convections, in which he used a system of seven ordinary differential equations. Most of his solutions soon acquired periodic behavior, but one solution refused to settle down. Moreover, in this solution four of the variables appeared to approach zero. Presumably the equations governing the remaining three variables, with the terms containing the four variables eliminated, would also possess aperiodic solutions. Upon my return I put the three equations on our computer, and confirmed the aperiodicity which Saltzman had noted. We were finally in business. [Quoted in E. Hairer, S. P. Norsett, and G. Wanner, *Solving Ordinary Differential Equations I* (New York: Springer–Verlag, 1987).]

The famous *Lorenz system* of differential equations is given by

$$\frac{dx}{dt} = -sx + sy$$

$$\frac{dy}{dt} = -xz + rx - y \tag{15}$$

$$\frac{dz}{dt} = xy - bz.$$

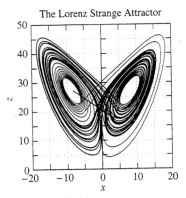

FIGURE 6.5.14. The *xz*-projection of the Lorenz trajectory with $-20 \leqq x \leqq 20, 0 \leqq z \leqq 50$

A solution curve in *xyz*-space is best visualized by looking at its projection into some *plane*, typically one of the three coordinate planes. Fig. 6.5.14 shows the projection into the *xz*-plane of the solution obtained by numerical integration with the parameter values $b = \frac{8}{3}, s = 10, r = 28$ and the initial values $x(0) = -8, y(0) = 8, z(0) = 27$.

As the projection in Fig. 6.5.14 is traced in "real time," the moving solution point $P(x(t), y(t), x(t))$ appears to undergo a random number of oscillations on the right followed by a random number of oscillations on the left, then a random number on the right followed by a random number on the left, and so on. Given the meteorological origin of the Lorenz system, one naturally thinks of a random number of clear days followed by a random number of rainy days, then a random number of clear days followed by a random number of rainy days, and so on.

A close examination of such projections of the Lorenz trajectory shows that it is *not* simply oscillating back and forth around a pair of critical points (as Fig. 6.5.14 may initially suggest). Instead, as $t \to +\infty$, the solution point $P(t)$ on the trajectory wanders back in forth in space approaching closer and closer to a certain complicated set of points whose detailed structure is not yet fully understood. This elusive set that appears somehow to "attract" the solution point is the famous *Lorenz strange attractor.*

Project 4. First use an ODE plotting utility to reproduce the *xz*-projection of the Lorenz trajectory shown in Fig. 6.5.14. Use the parameter values and initial conditions listed immediately after Eq. (15) and numerically integrate the Lorenz system on the interval $0 \leqq t \leqq 50$. Plot also the *xy*- and *yz*-projections of this same solution. Next, experiment with different parameter values and initial conditions. For instance, see if you can find a periodic solution with $r = 70$ (and $b = \frac{8}{3}, s = 10$ as before) and initial values $x_0 = -4$ and $z_0 = 64$. To get a trajectory that almost repeats itself, you will need to try different values of y_0 in the range $0 < y_0 < 10$ and look at *xz*-projections as in Fig. 6.5.14.

Project 5. Another much-studied nonlinear three-dimensional system is the Rossler system

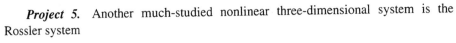

$$\frac{dx}{dt} = -y - z$$

$$\frac{dy}{dt} = x + ay \tag{16}$$

$$\frac{dz}{dt} = b + z(x - c).$$

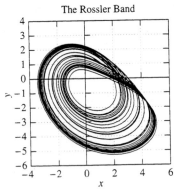

FIGURE 6.5.15. The *xy*-projection of the Rossler band

Figure 6.5.15 shows an *xy*-projection of the *Rossler band,* a chaotic attractor obtained with the values $a = 0.398, b = 2$, and $c = 4$ of the parameters in (16). In the *xy*-plane the Rossler band looks "folded," but in space it appears twisted like a Möbius strip. Investigate the period-doubling toward chaos that occurs with the Rossler system as the parameter a is increased, beginning with $a = 0.3, a = 0.35$, and $a = 0.375$ (take $b = 2$ and $c = 4$ in all cases).

In this section we have given just a taste of the ideas that are the focus of contemporary applications of nonlinear systems. To see how these ideas come full circle, consult the discussion of the Lorenz system in pages 117–123 of the book by Hairer *et al.* referenced above. There you will see a certain aspect of the Lorenz trajectory described visually by means of a picture that looks very much like the pitchfork diagram shown in Fig. 6.5.6, together with the very same Feigenbaum constant 4.6692 . . . !

For an engaging account of the historical background to this final section of Chapter 6, see James Gleick, *Chaos: Making a New Science* (New York: Viking Press, 1987). For more detailed discussions of the forced Duffing, Lorenz, and Rossler equations, see J. M. T. Thompson and H. B. Stewart, *Nonlinear Dynamics and Chaos* (New York: John Wiley, 1986).